Assault on the Worker

Occupational Health and Safety in Canada

Charles E. Reasons, Ph.D.
Professor of Sociology, University of Calgary

Lois L. Ross
Freelance Journalist, Calgary

Craig Paterson, LL.B., LL.M.
Lawyer, Vancouver

With a foreword by
Robert Sass
Associate Deputy Minister of Labour
Occupational Health and Safety Branch, Saskatchewan

BUTTERWORTHS
TORONTO

Assault on the Worker
© 1981 Butterworth & Co. (Canada) Ltd.

All rights reserved. No part of this publication may be reproduced, stored in a retrieval system, or transmitted, in any form or by any means, photocopying, electronic, mechanical, recording, or otherwise, without the prior written permission of the copyright holder.

Printed and bound in Canada

The Butterworth Group of Companies

Canada:
Butterworth & Co. (Canada) Ltd., Toronto and Vancouver

United Kingdom:
Butterworth & Co. (Publishers) Ltd., London

Australia:
Butterworths Pty. Ltd., Sydney

New Zealand:
Butterworths of New Zealand Ltd., Wellington

South Africa:
Butterworth & Co. (South Africa) Ltd., Durban

United States:
Butterworth (Publishers) Inc., Boston
Butterworth (Legal Publishers) Inc., Seattle
Mason Publishing Company, St. Paul

Canadian Cataloguing in Publication Data

Reasons, Charles E., 1945-
Assault on the worker

Bibliography: p.
Includes index.
ISBN 0-409-85776-9

1. Industrial hygiene - Canada.
2. Industrial hygiene - Canada - Case studies.
3. Industrial safety - Canada.
I. Ross, Lois L.
II. Paterson, Craig, 1946-
III. Title.

HD7658.R42 363.1'1'0971 C81-094548-7

36,745

Printed by John Deyell Company
Cover design by Julian Cleva
Photographs by Lois L. Ross, except pages 2 and 222 by Joanne Leithead and page 254 by Mike Phillips

To yesterday's, today's, and tomorrow's injured workers
and the struggle for a healthy and safe work environment.

CAMROSE LUTHERAN COLLEGE
LIBRARY

Preface

We have combined our talents in the fields of sociology, journalism, and law in an effort to provide an introduction to the health and safety hazards which face the Canadian work force. Every day, every Canadian worker, whether or not he or she is aware of it, endures a work environment which harbours the potential of causing various degrees of debilitation. It could happen to you . . . today or tomorrow. Besides outlining the dangers of work, our book also includes possible remedies. The first step toward changing an environment is recognizing its potential or harm.

While the profiles of injured workers and case histories and examples we have used throughout the book are largely taken from western Canada, it was not with the intent of creating a western slant. Workers across Canada confront the same occupational hazards and the same myths. In the past, the industrialized east and the Maritimes have always been thought to harbour the majority of occupational health and safety problems. By using western examples we have exposed that myth.

Acknowledgements

During nearly two years of reseach we have met with hundreds of individuals from numerous organizations who have helped this book become reality. Unfortunately we can't list them all. Here, however, are a few we would like to give special thanks to: Ray Sentes; Larry Katz, John Calvert, and Colin Lambert of CUPE National Office; Robert Sass; Jean Cyr; Alfred Lemieux; Professors Terence Ison and Harry Glasbeek; Janet Bertinuson; Dennis Malayko; Bill Gilbey; The Honourable Bill Diachuk, Dr. Herbert Buchwald, and Bill Gibson of Alberta Workers' Health and Safety and Compensation; Garry Cwitco, Dr. Gordon Atherley; Walter Bury; Dr. Kate Hankins; Judy Birdsell, Louise Hall; Phil Biggin; and Julyan Reid.

In preparing the final manuscript we were fortunate to be helped by Monique Canas, Janice Hillmo and Carol McPherson.

Contents

Foreword

*by Robert Sass**

It is a pleasure to have the opportunity of introducing to the Canadian public Mr. Reasons's, Ms Ross's, and Mr. Paterson's book *Assault on the Worker: Occupational Health and Safety in Canada.*

The authors contend that our workplaces not only produce commodities, goods, and services, but also affect the attitudes of workers and, more importantly, produce wounds and cause deaths. They regard with horror the fact that our workplaces present one of the most authoritarian settings in society. *Assault on the Worker* is an admirable epitome of the various forms of assault on our working population.

While it is difficult to obtain a true picture of the present state of affairs regarding working conditions in Canada, the authors argue most convincingly that those who have shaped the field of occupational health and safety in Canada have failed to take adequate care in minimizing the unacceptable levels of human suffering and dying in industry. They accuse industry, government, and company physicians of criminal negligence, since much industrial disease and injury is preventable. At the same time they demonstrate that insufficient attention is paid to looking after those damaged "in the course of employment."

Assault on the Worker is not intended to add to the technical knowledge about occupational health and safety and workers' compensation, but to generate enthusiasm for the actions necessary to change things. In this regard, the authors have written a most valuable contribution on behalf of those who desire to bring about much-needed reform in working conditions.

When one grasps the effects of workplace injury on the worker's life—his relationship to his wife, children, and the long-term effect of unemployment or being a cripple—one cannot help but be changed and desire social reconstruction. I sympathize with the authors' outrage throughout their book. I too am of the opinion that society's general insensitivity to the effects of industrial disease, injury, and fatalities on loved ones left behind is one of the blind spots of social policy in the writings of well-intentioned political scientists and sociologists.

The first part of this provocative book outlines the assault on industrial workers, farmers, and women, emanating from chemicals, stress, and sexual

* Associate Deputy Minister of Labour, Director, Occupational Health and Safety Branch, Regina, Saskatchewan.

harassment. The second part examines the deficiencies of our workers' compensation system for the victims.[1]

An extremely poignant chapter, "The 'Dumb Worker': Blaming the Victim," shows that the assault upon workers is compounded with insult, such as the widely held view that 80 per cent or more of industrial accidents are due to "worker carelessness" or the notion that a large part of these accidents are the result of "accident-prone" workers. The autors effectively expose these myths, which represent dubious knowledge at best and a retrograde approach which promotes the passivity of workers rather than reliance upon their intelligence and powers. Further, these myths are based upon the historical exclusion of any consideration of the rights of workers to alter dangerous conditions. I believe that these fanciful unexamined "worker attitude" propositions are promoted to divert attention from the real cause of damage to the worker—the conditions of work—so that the victim is blamed.[2]

For my own part, I believe it is imperative that we recognize that the present course travelled by most administrators,[3] practitioners, and the various diverse professionals and experts in occupational health and safety programs leads nowhere. Their efforts are energetic but futile, and it is therefore necessary to follow another path. In effect, it is crucial that we begin to see occupational health and safety from the point of view of the worker. If we do so, a more critical, persistent, and reforming pattern of thought will emerge.

Unfortunately, many government officials see this field from the point of view of official policy, while management sees it in behalf of production. At the same time, many social scientists and theorists tend to judge industrial life by industrial output and the quality of the product. They think of production as having a good of its own quite distinct from the good of the worker.

I have therefore come to believe that there are two elements necessary in our thinking about occupational health and safety: first, the recognition of industrial reality and its adverse effects on the well-being of the workers and, second, the will to improve existing conditions. In both instances, we have seen the limitations of industry, the professionals, and government or external agencies in cleaning up our workplaces. All too often, the judgments of those outside pro-

---

1 Earlier this year, Ed Vance, health and safety officer of the United Steelworkers of America local at Elliot Lake, Ontario, told me that one of the Elliot Lake workers had a silicotic lung removed and was immediately cut off workers' compensation because he no longer had silicosis. As a result one union had to put in another application on behalf of this worker in order to maintain a claim. In the meantime, cancer was diagnosed and an "appropriate" claim filed.

2 Dr. Reasons, in writing this book, interviewed my counterpart in Alberta, Dr. Herbert Buchwald, who supports the "unsafe act" thesis based upon his "experience" in the field of occupational health and safety. My own experience leads me to hold the exact opposite point of view from that of Dr. Buchwald. Further, I cannot imagine any good emerging from holding the view that 80 per cent or more of industrial accidents derive from an unsafe act on the part of the worker. More importantly, I do not believe there is any evidence to support this notion. I am of the opinion that it is primarily the working conditions and not "sin" which is the parent of industrial disease, and to a lesser extent industrial injury.

3 I sometimes believe that in the world of the administrator, the concerns of the worker are viewed as a nuisance.

duction or factory life are guided by what might be called the "aristocratic fallacy"—judging the experiences of the ordinary worker from the perspective of a privileged minority. This minority fails to understand industrial reality and to recognize the fact that the majority of workers merely find themselves placed in a small niche in the great machine, with little room for individual initiative and satisfaction. Can we expect the proper initiative to come from those who fit comfortably into the existing system and who are unaware of the need for fundamental reforms? I think not!

Rather, reform will emerge to the degree that *workers are in motion*. Consequently, it becomes more crucial for organized labour to make even wider sweeps with regard to workplace health and safety than it has in the past.

Assault on the Worker, with its uncompromising affirmation for healthy and safe work environments, is all the more called for today—especially in light of the growing use of cost-benefit analysis to accompany environmental and workplace health and safety standards, the growing mood of deregulation, and the entry into Canada of such management services as the "Workmen's Compensation Records Service" offered by Equifax Services Limited, which provides information to employers on a job applicant's previous workers' compensation claims. The authors examine these tendencies and, so far as I am able to judge, are wholly reliable as to the facts and have shown good judgment in selecting from an enormous mass of material.

Finally, I especially appreciate their use of profiles of workers who have been injured, diseased and then unfairly treated by workers' compensation boards. These profiles present a glimpse of the catastrophes in workers' lives that result from our failure to be a more caring society.

The experiences of these profiled workers represent important information about the way we do business in our country. This information cannot be computerized. Computers cannot tell us what our experiences are, or appreciate self-concept. They cannot tell us that human dignity matters greatly. Regrettably, there are many who hold respectable positions in the community who believe that it is only the well-to-do or well-educated who experience soiled identities. They refuse to believe that working people have identities, let alone ones worth preserving.

It takes no special expertise to know that the work of a keypunch operator is boring, monotonous and noisy, or to recognize that sexual harassment is practically a steady diet for working women, with all the damaging consequences that follow.

These vignettes or brief interviews scattered throughout the book demonstrate that the assault on workers' bodies and minds also pierces the soul.[4] Our workplaces in general are devoid of a feeling of at-homeness, while the structure of command and intrinsic nature of work humiliate and degrade. In

4 In an article by Alice Hamilton entitled "Occupational Diseases and Industrial Surgery" in *Industrial Medicine*, Vol. 7, No. 1 (1938), the heroine of occupational health in North America states that one of the effects of poor working conditions is "fatigue of mind, body and soul."

today's factory, the machine demands mindless obedience, producing human resignation and hemorrhaging morale. This process results in the numbing of consciousness through the suppression of feelings, and creates a deadening effect on spontaneity of activity, vigour, and vitality, so that much of our productive human activity becomes heartless and corrupt. This is the affliction of our time.

It is lamentable that at our present level of civilization we are unable to flatter ourselves by declaring that Canada, or any of its provinces, is exempt from this accusation. While it is a temptation to abandon hope when the undoing of such oppression seems distant and difficult, the authors do not despair but passionately counsel workers to demand greater control over their work processes[5] in order to minimize the senseless damage to their bodies and minds. Let me add that *Assault on the Worker* does not harbour subversive opinions. Rather, it boldly outlines the evils of our system, which has failed to put the health and safety of our workers before profits. The authors, in their attempt to dispel complacency, clearly long for the socialization of production and a time when men and women labour not simply for wages, but also because work is what we can do for one another. Only then shall we end the harsh discipline and the existing techniques of production which kill, wound, and humiliate, making happiness impossible. I confess to a temperamental sympathy with this point of view.

---

[5] Even attempts at piecemeal democratization of industry at this time would, I believe, retard the growing disillusionment with democracy and the rapid rate of centralization and authoritarianism in industry.

Part I

Introduction

THOS. JAS.

Chapter 1

Your Money and Your Life

I'm only a broken down mucker
My life in the mines I have spent
I've been fooled and played for a sucker
My back's all broken and bent

. . .

But I realize now that I'm older
I used my back where he used his brains.
The drifting machine done for my hearing,
The mine glasses dimmed my sight.
I know my last days are nearing,
But I'll rally for one last fight.[1]

"Industry Kills." "Job Accidents Nearing a Crisis." "Serious Ailments Found in Workers." "Occupational Health Official Warns of Reproductive Injuries." "Crushed Miners Had Little Warning." "Asbestos Cases Showing Up." "Government May Be Failing to Keep Cancer Out of Work Place." "On-Job Death Rate Has Labor Upset." The titles of these recent newspaper articles suggest that working may be dangerous to our health. We are just beginning to realize that our job brings us not only a periodic paycheque, but often death, injury and disability due to disease or accident. Between 1973 and 1976 one work injury occurred every seven seconds. In 1978 there were over one million work injuries and illnesses among the 8.5 million workers employed in Canada. Between 1969 and 1978 overall injuries increased 35 per cent while disabling injuries increased 69 per cent. A Canadian worker dies on the job every six hours. What this all means is that as Canadian workers we are much more likely to meet violence through injury or illness in the workplace than in the streets.

On The Nature of Violence In Canada

Most people think of violence as something bad and illegal which is perpetrated by a person or persons against another person or persons. Therefore, when someone sprays mace in our face it is violence, while when one is forced to inhale asbestos dust at work it is uncomfortable, but not violent. According to the *Concise Oxford Dictionary* violence is the "unlawful exercise of force." To "violate" is to disregard, fail to comply with, act against the dictates or requirements of such things as an oath, treaty, law, terms, or conscience. While the inhalation of asbestos dust may not be unlawful, it *violates* the health of the worker. A recent book, *Violence in Canada*, points out the difficulty of defining violence:

> The problem has perhaps been that while violence is a word we hear every day, it is rarely clearly defined, and the listener quickly learns to associate the word violence with the word bad. While cultural and socioeconomic class differences tell us something about the nature of crime, what is perceived as violence is frequently a matter of interpretation. From this perspective violence is in the eye of the beholder.[2]

Many more Canadians die yearly from violent deaths due to cancer, automobile accidents, heart disease, suicide, and occupational injuries than from murder and manslaughter, but we tend to focus upon the latter categories. Of course, homicide has a readily identifiable victim and offender and is included under the Criminal Code. We also have criminal statutes concerning automobile accidents and suicide, but not concerning occupational death. Nonetheless, the

Table 1-1

Canadian Death Rate by Cause, 1975*

	Number	**Rate**[1]
Heart Disease[2]	56,970	250.0
Cancer	33,998	149.0
Occupational Death[3]	8,265	48.3
Motor Vehicle Accident	5,896	25.9
Pneumonia	5,454	23.9
Suicide	2,808	12.3
Cirrhosis of Liver	2,725	12.0
Peptic Ulcer	735	3.2
Murder	633	2.8

* Sources: *Canada Year Book*, 1978-79, Ottawa: Ministry of Supply and Services and *The World Almanac* and *Book of Facts*, 1980, New York: Newspaper Enterprise Association, Inc.

[1] Rate per 100,000 population

[2] Heart disease deaths will include many work-related causes, in whole or in part, such as short-term and long-term physical and emotional stress and toxic pollutants. While this probably runs into the thousands, no reliable estimates are available.

[3] This total includes adding 25 per cent to the deaths reported by workmen's compensation and 20 per cent of the cancer deaths in Canada in 1975. The base population is those 15 years and older.

yearly toll in lives for occupational carnage is much higher than that for murder. If we look, in Table 1-1, at how Canadians die, we find that occupational hazards are the third leading cause of death, following only heart disease and cancer. We are twice as likely to die from our jobs as from automobile accidents. We are about eighteen times as likely to be victims of the workplace as of murder outside the workplace. In fact, we are more likely to die of peptic ulcers than of murder. It must be emphasized that this is a very conservative estimate of occupational death since it does not include deaths from other industrial diseases, such as lead poisoning.

While Canadians often pride themselves on the fact that they are less violent and more civilized than people in the United States and many other western countries, international statistics suggest otherwise. If we look, in Table 1-2, at Canada's fatality rate compared to that of five other industrialized

Table 1-2

Fatal Accident Incidence Rates by Country and Industry, 1975*

		Industry			
Code	**Country**	**Manu-facturing**	**Construc-tion**	**Railways**	**Mining and Quarrying**
Ic	Great Britain	4	18	19 (Ib)	37
IIa	Federal Republic of Germany	16	35	26	46
Ib	Irish Republic	9	8	40 (Ic)	45
Ic	Canada	15	96	25	198 (Ib)
Id	United States	3	16	10	33
Id	Japan	2	13	4	61

* Adapted from "Canada Ranks High in Workplace Fatalities," *Canadian Occupational Health and Safety News*, Vol. 2, No. 18, September 3, 1979, p. 2. Although different bases are used for the rates, a general picture is provided by comparison.

The codes referring to the basis on which the accident incidence or frequency rates were calculated, are defined as follows. They remain the same for each country unless otherwise noted in parentheses:

Method of notification
I Reported accidents
II Compensated accidents

Exposure to risk
a Rates per 100,000 man-years of 300 days each
b Rates per 100,000 wage earners (average numbers)
c Rates per 100,000 persons employed (average numbers)
d Rates per 100 million man-hours worked

societies, it suggests that in Canada *more* workers are killed by their jobs. Canada is first in fatalities for the construction and mining and quarrying industries and second highest for manufacturing and railways. It would appear that it is quite a bit safer to work in the United States than in Canada in these industries. While Americans are much more likely to be victims of murder outside the workplace, death from the job is more common in Canada. It may be that, as Canadian historian Kenneth McNaught explains, "Canada has a history of violence enacted through legitimate institutions, in contrast to a pattern of individual and group violence in the United States."[3] Much of the violence we experience in Canada may be through legitimate institutions such as work.

It's a Crime

Dr. Samuel Epstein describes his book entitled *The Politics of Cancer* in the following terms: "I view it as a book on white collar crime on the one hand and also on the failed democracy. . . ."[4] Henri Lorraine, president of the Canadian Paperworkers' Union, says employers have killed workers by refusing to invest profits to improve working conditions.[5] Why do these men call it white-collar crime and killing when workers die or are injured and disabled from work? We have been taught to think of crime as involving an easily identifiable victim and offender. For example, if our spouse poisons us and we subsequently die then we have been murdered by our spouse, who is liable to prosecution for murder. However, if our company causes us to be exposed to toxic substances and we subsequently die from this exposure, the company is not criminally liable for our deaths and will at the most be cited for violations of health and safety regulations. For example, it has been revealed that asbestos companies continued to expose workers to that substance in spite of the fact that they had had evidence concerning its fatal effects for some thirty years. Such conscious, premeditated, and rational behaviour undoubtedly led to thousands of deaths and disabilities. Nonetheless, asbestos companies are only liable to civil lawsuits.[6]

Another example is Quasar Petroleum Ltd. of Calgary, which was found guilty of violating job-site safety regulations, resulting in the death of three men. The law provided for a maximum of $5,000 fine and/or imprisonment of up to six months. Quasar was fined $5,000 for killing the three men, who were single and in their early twenties. How did Quasar kill the young men? The company did not provide respiratory protective equipment and an external gauge on an enclosed tank, thus, men had to go inside the tank without protective equipment and subsequently were overcome with toxic fumes. Furthermore, the company had not trained the workers concerning the hazards of the job and the need for such equipment.[7]

Isn't this just an unfortunate "accident"? No, the deaths of these three young men could have been avoided if the proper training and equipment had been provided. While the company undoubtedly did not mean to kill these specific three men, it established the conditions for their death by violating the law. By analogy, we could view murder during an armed robbery as an accident. Most armed robbers do not intend to kill the robbery victim but merely want to make some money. However, their act of robbery with a dangerous weapon sets the conditions for such violence. Likewise, a company saving money by not purchasing safety equipment may be merely pursuing profit, but its action establishes the conditions for an "accident" or "disaster."

> The private corporation (and many Crown corporations) exists first and foremost to earn a reasonable profit and return on investment for their shareholders. Occupational health, and other costs, unless they can be passed on to the consumers, are ultimately an expense which reduces profit, at least in the short run.[8]

Should the company which threatens the workers' safety and health for profit be any less culpable when death occurs than the armed robber who also threatens violence for economic profit? We think not!

The violation of safety and health standards and/or the failure to establish adequate standards is usually a rational, premeditated, conscious choice concerning capital expenses and business profits. In the public sector, it is usually a political decision to streamline a budget. In both the private and the public sectors, the consequences are the same. While deaths and job injuries on the worksite are usually thought of as accidents caused by worker carelessness, research suggests otherwise. It has been estimated that approximately 39 per cent of job injuries in the United States are due to illegal working conditions while another 24 per cent are due to legal but unsafe conditions. At the most, a third of accidents are due to unsafe acts.[9] However, the maintenance of unsafe conditions is rational since the likelihood of detection is low and the penalties are relatively small. No one has ever been imprisoned in Canada for violation of safety and health laws, although prison sentences are available in most provinces. The attitudes among many safety and health personnel reflect a lenient approach toward such law violators. One provincial head of inspection states that:

> We are not dealing with criminals when we take people to court. A guy who breaks into your house knows what he is doing and knows the consequences and probably has been through the process before. To be dragged before a judge and be sentenced to twelve months in jail is not pleasant to him, but it is not unexpected, and it isn't demeaning to him; he will stand there with a smile on his face and be defiant. When we are talking about individuals or entities being prosecuted for infractions of Occupational Health and Safety legislation, we are talking about an entirely different animal. We are talking about a person who basically is honest and an upright citizen. We are talking basically of a person who finds this process of being prosecuted and having that process publicized extremely distasteful.[10]

In this manner the government enforcer of safety and health laws rationalizes why heavy fines or even imprisonment are not as important as the stigma of the court process. However, this same official goes on to say that violators are prosecuted only after serious and/or repeated violations.

> People who go to court have refused to apply regulations they know exist and have in the past been ordered to and instructed—advised—to put those things into effect and they have decided they are not going to. So they are not strangers to the law.

Using the above logic, since a murderer is a solid citizen 99.9 per cent of the time and only murders 0.1 per cent of the time we should not view him or her as a criminal! We must look at the consequences of one's actions or inactions. If violating safety and health laws does not cause a death then the penalty should be less than if it does take a life, just as the penalty for armed robbery is less than that for murder. Unfortunately current penalties for health and safety violations do not adequately consider this distinction between the law violation and subsequent violence and death. This may be due, in part, to the above image of the white-collar criminal who is not considered a criminal.

The Canadian public has tended to view corporate crime as economically harmful but not physically dangerous. The image of the corporate criminal is that of a business person who commits fraud, income tax evasion, bribery, embezzlement, price fixing or some other crime for personal economic gain. This approach fails to consider that organizations are legal entities which may commit crimes against us. For example, if a construction company speeds up work and fails to observe proper safety and health rules, it may kill or seriously injure workers.[11] Two criminologists have defined organizational crime in the following manner:

> Organizational crimes are illegal acts of omission or commission of an individual or a group of individuals in a legitimate formal organization in accordance with the operative goals of the organization, which have serious physical or economic impact on employees, consumers or the general public.[12]

By making the distinction between corporate and organizational crimes we are recognizing the daily impact private and public organizations have upon our lives as workers, consumers and members of the general public. Therefore, the behaviour of individuals is placed within the context of the organization. For example, while an employee who embezzles from the employer is guilty of a corporate offense, the same employee may be involved in safety and health violations as part of the policies, practices and/or procedures of the organization. In the latter offenses, the corporate offender is carrying out organizational goals. This distinction forces us to look at organizational changes and control as a means of addressing workplace violence rather than solely individual sanction. For example, punishing a worker for not wearing safety equipment or failing to follow health and safety procedures may not deter the behaviour if the organizational goals and practices of the company and management reinforce such behaviour.

Attention to organizational crime has largely been upon violations of competition legislation, which although having criminal penalties, are not generally viewed as criminal.[13] This is largely due to the fact that only economic harm occurs. However, does the public view violence from organizational law violation in the same way? No, according to a recent analysis of public survey data by two criminologists. They found that the public ranks organizational crimes having physical impact much higher in seriousness than those with merely an economic impact, *just* as they rank common crimes with a physical impact more serious than those with an economic impact. Therefore, "causing the death of an employee by neglecting to repair machinery" is as serious as impulsive homicide or arson which kills someone.[14] Thus, the belief that the public does not view organizational crimes *as* crimes is wrong, particularly when they entail violence and death.

We should criminalize many of these organizational acts which involve "victims without crimes." Two Canadian lawyers have recently made a case for applying the Criminal Code to violations of health and safety laws. They assert that criminal negligence, duties of master to servant, assault, criminal breach of contract, traps likely to cause bodily harm, causing mischief, common nuisance, conspiracy, and murder all may be used for prosecuting violations.[15] For example, an assault is committed when a person either applies force intentionally to another person or, by an act or a gesture, causes another person to have reasonable grounds to believe that there will be an interference with his or her physical integrity. The daily interference with the physical integrity of workers evidenced in injury and disease statistics amounts to a massive assault on the Canadian workforce. However, one may argue that the victims of workplace hazards really do not see themselves as victims of an assault or other type of crime since they may contribute to their own injuries. In discussing occupational deaths one criminologist states:

> To say some of these workers died from accidents due to their own carelessness is about as helpful as saying that some of those who died at the hands of murderers asked for it. It overlooks the fact that where workers are careless, it is not because they love to live dangerously. They have production quotas to meet, quotas that they themselves do not set.[16]

Do injured workers view themselves as victims of crimes? The following case study tells the story of one worker who was injured in the high-risk construction industry.

PROFILE: Stolen Health

Alberta is seen as the land of prosperity, where employment is plentiful, money abundant, and life euphoric. In quest of black gold, corporations need the support of thousands of employees. Oil companies fuel the growth of other, indirectly related corporations. Petroleum creates the boom economy. But most employees fail to recognize a grim principle behind economic booms. Just as a company can provide a worker with a sizable paycheque, it can also create, in the name of production (i.e., profits), an unsafe workplace.

Alberta's growing need for homes and office space is prompting developers

to promote highrise construction. In 1979 Alberta's construction workers suffered through a record-breaking 17 per cent increase in injuries, making construction one of the most accident-prone industries in the province. Those who gravitate to construction work are, by and large, young, strong, and unhampered by mortgages or family responsibilities. Such was the situation of eighteen-year-old Hubert Maisonneuve. When he arrived in Calgary in the fall of 1978, he planned to work for a year or so, then return to his native French community in Ontario where, hefty bankroll in hand, he would start up a bakery, a trade he had learned from his father.

After two months of unemployment Hubert was hired by a small construction firm and put to work "flying the forms" on a highrise building, though he was non-unionized and inexperienced in highrise construction. One month later Hubert lay in a coma in a southwest Calgary hospital.

On a chilly December day Hubert was working on the forms for the highest level of the escalating highrise. As he reached over to grab a cable—an innocuous movement at ground level—he slipped, flew over the edge, and fell nine floors—a full 120 feet—onto a pile of steel below.

Whisked to the hospital and life-support systems, he lay in a coma for sixteen days. His sturdy muscles had been turned into molten rubber from the impact. One of his lungs had collapsed and a tracheotomy was performed.

Two months after his fall, no doubt to the surprise of onlooking doctors, Hubert was beginning to test his strength in the halls of the hospital. He had aged visibly. His weight had dropped from 150 pounds to less than 110. Tasks that

Hubert Maisonneuve

had once been automatic had to be relearned. Walking or the use of any muscle now required concentration, but his concentration had also been severely weakened by the shock. Six months after his fall, having undergone hours of therapy, Hubert considered it an achievement to be able to withstand the physical onslaught of a ten-minute walk in the fresh air.

> Most of the day I slept. I slept for 20 hours sometimes. Then I started to go outside, sometimes for five minutes, then for 10 minutes, and one day I went out for a whole half-hour. That was really something. I just had to get out.

More than two years after the accident, Hubert is coaxing his body to perform, and trying to regain the stamina and capability he had prior to his fall. Whether he will succeed is a matter of conjecture. There are no physical visible signs of his accident, though his thought processes, along with his gait, have slowed and his speech is cautious.

There's no question that Hubert considers himself a lucky man. He's alive. But his recuperation has given him countless inactive hours to retrace the accident and its causes. Time passes, but the anger remains. Obviously, the fall would not have occurred had he not accepted the job. But his money was running out and despite his lack of experience the foreman offered to hire him. Hubert fell, but he believes it could have happened to another worker just as easily.

There is no hesitation as he points firmly to the company for failing to provide equipment and to educate workers to protect themselves. Also at fault is the government for failing to enforce standards on the job site.

Hubert was not wearing a mandatory safety belt when he slipped. According to him, workers on the site were not briefed on what kind of gear was necessary and most of the crucial safety equipment was lacking. "The company had three safety belts for thirty workers," he explains. Besides preventive measures, Hubert wonders about sanctioning practices. No charges were ever laid against the company for failing to comply with safety regulations by providing adequate equipment, nor was an inquiry into the "accident" ordered by the Workers' Compensation Board. Since then the company has gone bankrupt. What's the sense of having safety standards if a company is allowed to violate them with impunity?

Hubert equates the WCB with a cheap insurance scheme for companies, recognizing one major difference—once a company is covered by the WCB, its employees relinquish their rights through the courts, for either prosecution or compensation. The Board is the only authority allowed to handle such details.

Since the accident, Hubert has been receiving 75 per cent of his wage—$850 per month. He has undergone assessments to see whether he is fit to return to work. So far he has not been, but Hubert doesn't know when the board may conclude he is fit to take on "light duties." At that point a decision will be made as to whether he is permanently or only temporarily disabled. Once a worker's condition "plateaus" (stabilizes), the WCB decides whether an accident has permanently or only temporarily disabled the worker. If the harm is considered permanent, meaning if it will hinder a worker's future earning power, a pension is granted. The pension is based on a percentage of the disability, but no one is quite sure of the board's criteria in arriving at that figure.

Whether Hubert will be covered for future problems stemming from the accident is hard to determine. Muscle damage may lead to premature arthritis . . . but how does one prove the disease had its roots in an accident? Doctors advise that serious head injuries often lead to epilepsy . . . but how does one show unequivocally the cause?

Hubert looks on, well aware of having been robbed of his health, and warns other workers to refuse dangerous tasks and to demand necessary safety equipment. Hubert considers mandatory safety committees who would check worksites daily as priority instruments of safety control.

But one pain will linger—the first-hand knowledge that the government does not enforce safety standards by fining those companies which break the law. Hubert would like to force the issue, but that would mean proving the government's laxity in his case. "But I can't sue the government. You just can't go after the government."

For Hubert, the message from his experience is clear: "Government compensation isn't acting for human rights."

Whose Risk? Who Pays?

The question in occupational health and safety is not necessarily whether a risk will be taken or not, but rather who decides to take what type of risk which endangers whom and for what purposes. There are three sides involved in every hazardous condition or situation: (1) those who create it, (2) those who experience it, and (3) those who regulate it.[17] In the past workers have, knowingly and unknowingly, experienced innumerable risks which they did not create and had no control over. Management created the risks, workers assumed them, and subsequently health and safety officials have attemped to regulate them.

As Dr. Ravetz notes, "a hazardous environment (at work or at home) is part of social powerlessness." The traditional view of management and government was that the worker voluntarily assumed the risks of a job by accepting it. This ignorance of economic reality is no longer accepted and workers are increasingly demanding safer and healthier workplaces. Those workers most subject to physical abuse, including death, have been largely powerless to do anything about it. Canadian journalist Lloyd Tataryn concludes that:

> The principal victims of unsafe environments created by industries generally come from the ranks of the working class and the poorest segments of society. Consequently the victims do not have the resources to mount the concerted scientific and political campaigns necessary to alter their environmental circumstances.[18]

This book is about the hazards faced by the Canadian workforce, and efforts to combat these hazards. It is a book about economics, politics, science, government, corporations, and unions. But most of all, it concerns human suffering and dying, much of which can be prevented.

NOTES

1. "I'm Only a Broken Down Mucker." In Philip J. Thomas, *Songs of the Pacific Northwest* (Vancouver: Hancock House, 1979).
2. Mary Alice Beyer (ed.), *Violence In Canada* (Toronto: Methuen, 1978), p. 1.
3. Ibid.
4. Quoted in *Canadian Occupational Health and Safety News*, June 11, 1979, p. 3.
5. "Industry Kills—Union Head," *The Calgary Herald*, November 13, 1979.
6. "Asbestos Cover Up," *The Calgary Herald*, November 13, 1978; Lloyd Tataryn, *Dying for a Living*, (Ottawa: Deneau and Greenberg, 1979); Subcommittee on Crime of the Committee on the Judiciary, House of Representatives, Ninety-Sixth Congress, Second Session, *Corporate Crime* (Washington, D.C.: U.S. Government Printing Office, May, 1980).
7. *Canadian Occupational Health and Safety News*, July 23, 1979, p. 3.
8. G. B. Doern, "The Political Economy of Regulating Occupational Health: The Ham and Beaudry Reports," *Canadian Public Administration* 1977, p. 18.
9. Nicholas Ashford, *Crisis In the Workplace: Occupational Disease and Injury* (Cambridge, Mass.: MIT Press, 1976), pp. 107-15.
10. Quoted in G. B. Reschenthaler, *Occupational Health and Safety In Canada: The Economics and Three Case Studies* (Montreal: Institute for Research on Public Policy, 1979), pp. 82-83.
11. "Workers Walk Off Job After Steel Jack Falls," *The Calgary Herald*, July 24, 1980.
12. L. S. Schrager and J. F. Short, Jr., "Toward a Sociology of Organizational Crime," *Social Problems*, June 1978: 411-12.
13. C. H. Goff and C. E. Reasons, *Corporate Crime In Canada: A Critical Analysis of Anti-Combines Legislation* (Scarborough: Prentice-Hall of Canada, Ltd., 1978).
14. L. S. Schrager and J. F. Short, Jr., "How Serious A Crime? Perceptions of Organizational and Common Crime," in G. Geis and E. Stotland (eds.), *White Collar Crime: Theory and Research* (Beverly Hills: Sage Publications, 1980), pp. 14-31.
15. H. J. Glasbeek and S. Rowland, "Are Injuring and Killing At Work Crimes?" *Osgoode Hall Law Journal*, December 1979, pp. 507-94.
16. Jeffrey H. Reiman, *The Rich Get Richer and the Poor Get Prison* (New York: John Wiley & Sons, 1979), p. 68.
17. J. Ravetz, "The Political Economy of Risk," *New Scientist* 8 (September 1977): 598.
18. Tataryn, *Dying For A Living*, p. 156.

Part II

Description of the Problem

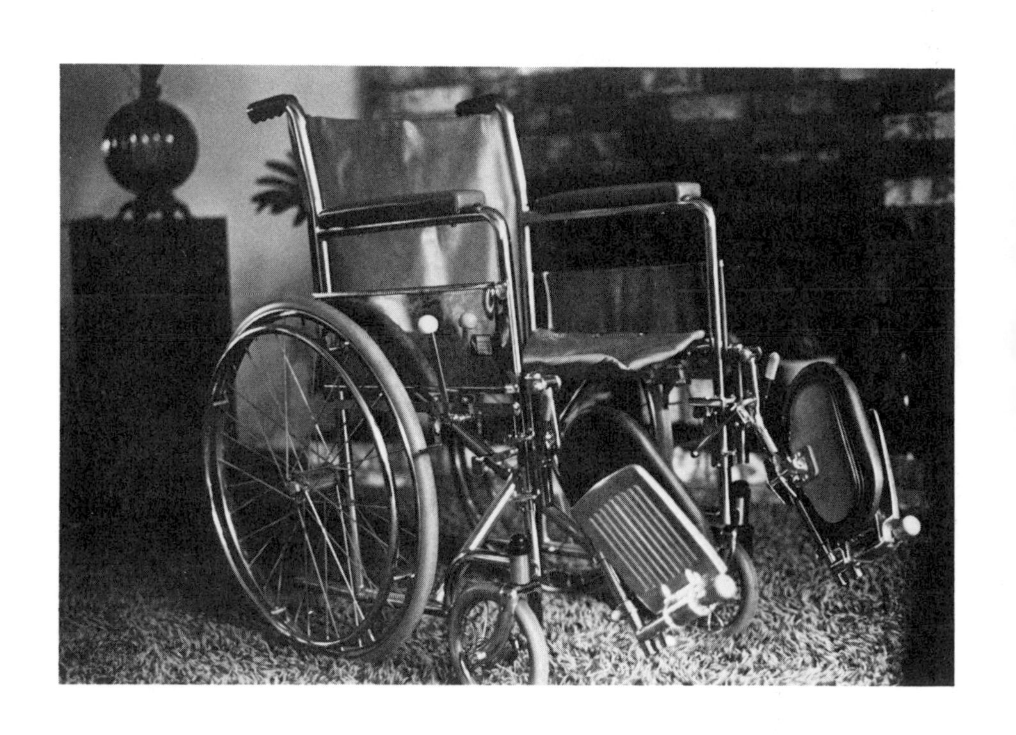

Chapter 2

On Killing and Injuring at Work

A worker dies on the job every six hours in Canada. Most men and women escape occupational death, but many are temporarily or permanently incapacitated because of occupational health and safety hazards. One worker in 10 is injured annually. And many thousands more continue to work, unaware they are harbouring slowly evolving occupational diseases or that physical ailments will painfully show themselves only after a great deal of accumulated damage is done.[1]

Winning the West and Losing Lives

When we think of the building of Canada and the development of the West it often brings images of explorers, settlers, the CPR, Mounties, and Indians. The romantic notion of nation-building and patriotism is contradicted by the actual motives behind the emergence of Canada as a nation-state.

> The myth of Canadian history is that the railway and Prime Minister John A. Macdonald's economic policies were government instruments to build a dominion from sea to shining sea! In fact, Canada as a nation was an invention of the Montreal business community. The St. Lawrence capitalists had been fighting for some time to maintain themselves against the encroachment of their American rivals and Confederation and settlement of the West was to be their coup—the creation of a market that only they would be allowed to service. The three elements of Macdonald's National Policy: western settlement, a transcontinental railway and a tariff wall to protect the market, became instruments for survival and expansion of the St. Lawrence business class.[2]

The reality of life for most workers during this period was one of meagre wages, long hours, unhealthy and unsafe working conditions, disease, injury, and often death. Many of the early workers on the railroad were from eastern Canada, particularly Quebec, and brought out under contracts which they often could not understand. Besides having their transportation costs deducted from their wages, they could buy only from company stores at inflated prices, were charged for medical supplies and room and board, and could not even quit their jobs. The Mounties were there to make sure neither the Indians nor the workers disrupted the construction. Masters and Servants Acts made it a crime for a workman to desert his employer.

This form of slavery occurred in the most horrible conditions. In 1899 the government formed a commission to investigate two workers' deaths. It reported:

> The number of men working upon the road who become ill . . . is, I think, abnormally large. With particularly healthy climate and sufficient good food, how does it happen that there should be in the neighbourhood of 1,500 men requiring treatment in a total aggregate of from 2,000 to 4,000 and all within the space of less than a year? There must have been an utter disregard for the simplest laws of health somewhere and I think it may be found in the lack of sanitary conditions in the camp. How is it possible that sickness could be avoided where 50 or 60 men occupy a bunkhouse, say 24 by 40 feet, with a seven-foot ceiling and no ventilation provided?[3]

The diseases common to the railway workers were diptheria, cough, mountain fever and rheumatism. The two men died of diptheria after what could only be called criminal neglect by the company. From this commission came the establishment of the Public Works Health Act of 1900 to set health standards and provide for inspection of the camps. It wasn't until 1902 that an inspector was hired to enforce the act. The conditions were even worse for the Chinese labourers who worked on the railroad in British Columbia. Between 1901-1918, 3,700 railway construction workers lost their lives in "accidents."

One of the major purposes of the railroad was to ship the raw materials extracted from the West to eastern markets. Mining was one of the earliest and most dangerous industries in Canada. On June 19, 1914, in one of Canada's worst mine disasters, 189 men were killed while working on the Crowsnest Pass line of the Canadian Pacific Railway near Hillcrest, Alberta. Subsequently, the federal commission of inquiry found that the explosion was caused by a methane gas pocket which was ignited and set off an explosion of the thick coal dust. The coal mines in western Canada were among the most dangerous in the world—in the decade ending in 1918, 737 miners were killed in British Columbia and Alberta collieries. Gas seepage in mines on the British Columbia side of Crowsnest Pass was found to be fifteen times greater than in comparable Pennsylvania mines. Men working in western Canadian mines were twice as likely to be killed as those in Nova Scotia or the United States.[4] More than 1,200 miners lost their lives in Alberta mines between 1904-1963 with 134 deaths from 1904-1910. One retired Crowsnest miner recalls that when there was an accident in the mines the management first asked about the horses. "They never asked how the goddamn men was. It took time to train a horse. You could replace a man anytime them days."[5]

Industry Kills: Digging Your Own Grave

my friend's father
died
when the dump car
overturned
on him
& his flesh burnt
one with the slag

& slag became
hill
red
thick air
black rocks
dead father
giants in the night
  a bumped word
  inco
dead father
company town
union
dead father
no grass for long

& slag is
why
for what reason?[6]

As noted in Chapter 1, Canadian mining remains more dangerous than mining in other developed countries. In fact, if we look at death rates by industry (see Table 2-1) we discover that the mining industry has the highest in Canada.

Due to the high number of mining deaths (20 in seven months) a government of Ontario committee was formed in the summer of 1980 to study and make recommendations concerning mine safety.[7] Wenton Newman, president of the Ontario division of Inco Ltd. testified that its 1980 safety record was unacceptable. The company's death rate per man-hours worked was higher in 1980 than at any time in the last two decades. Although Newman agreed that the company's bonus incentive plan could provide more money to those willing to take shortcuts and break safety rules, he asserts there is no evidence to suggest incentive work causes serious injury.[8] Both common sense and more significantly, good sense, would suggest otherwise. Violence to the worker is heightened by speedups and incentives that go along with speedups.

Also, a Quebec public inquiry is being held due to the May 20, 1980 cave-in at Belmoral gold mine in Val d'Or which killed eight miners. The Belmoral mine had only opened in September of 1979 and there were accusa-

Table 2-1

Average Fatality Incidence Rates In Canadian Industry By Industry Division, 1969-1978*

Industry	Rate per 100,000 1969-1978	N[4]	1978
Mining	121.2	(160)	75.8[1]
Forestry	111.1	(80)	98.6
Fishing	73.9	(17)	60.9
Construction	33.7	(204)	22.0
Transport	26.4	(213)	21.3
Manufacturing	11.0	(215)	7.3
Public Administration	10.8	(69)	9.4
Policing[3]	7.6	(4)	(3.6)[2]
Trade	4.5	(74)	3.1
Agriculture	4.4	(21)	1.3
Service	3.0	(75)	1.6
Finance	1.3	(6)	.9

Sources: *Fatalities in Canadian Industry*, Occupational Safety and Health Branch of Labour Canada, 1969-78; 1975 employment by industry data from *Perspective Canada II*, Ministry of Supply and Services Canada, 1977.

[1] These rates are for 1978 only.

[2] This rate is only for 1975 and is derived from Statistics Canada, 1979. It is based upon the total number of police personnel.

[3] This is the annual average incidence for 1966-1975 per 100,000 police personnel. Derived from Ministry of the Solicitor General, 1976:121.

[4] This is the annual average number of actual deaths for the years considered.

tions that it was rushed into operation without adequate concern for safety.[9] Subsequent testimony has pointed out that Belmoral Mines Ltd. operated without an accredited engineer, geologist, or surveyor on staff for the nine months prior to the May 20 cave-in. According to an engineering consultant for Belmoral Mines, stability studies of the ground were not made because of the expense involved. Furthermore, a small cave-in on May 13 should have led to a shutdown of the area for 10 weeks, but the area remained open. Finally, a good mining practice, filling empty cavities with waste rock to prevent cave-ins, was not followed.[10] Again, profit and savings seem to be more important to the company than workers' health. Belmoral Mines Ltd. has subsequently been charged with eight counts of manslaughter.[11]

Table 2-2

Ranking of Provinces and Territories by Fatality Rate, Injury Frequency, and Severity Rate in Mining Industries

Rank	Fatality Frequency[1]	Lost-time Injury Frequency	Severity Rate[1]
1	Nova Scotia & Alberta	Nova Scotia	Alberta
2	—	Alberta	British Columbia
3	Manitoba	Territories	Quebec
4	British Columbia	British Columbia	New Brunswick
5	Saskatchewan	Manitoba	Manitoba
6	Quebec	Ontario	Saskatchewan
7	Ontario	Quebec	
8	Newfoundland	Saskatchewan	
9	New Brunswick	Newfoundland	
10		New Brunswick	

Source: G. W. Gibbs and P. Pintus, *Health and Safety in the Canadian Mining Industry*. Centre for Resource Studies: Queen's University, 1978, p. 45.

Notes: Frequencies are expressed per million man-hours worked. Lost-time injuries include fatalities.

[1] Data available only for places listed. Severity rates are calculated as the number of days lost by injury per million man-hours worked.

As Table 2-2 points out, Nova Scotia and Alberta appear to be the most dangerous provinces for miners to work in. A recent case study of mining dangers and safety policies is the McIntyre Mines Ltd. cave-in in Grande Cache, Alberta on February 28, 1980. In the summer of 1979, McIntyre Mines Ltd. was announced winner of Canada's John T. Ryan trophy for underground coal mine safety for 1978, the third winning year in a row for the Grande Cache mine. The Safety Manager of the mine, Barry Munro, said that the most effective way to prevent accidents is through education. "If people are properly trained and oriented to safety, you avoid problems."[12]

The official government report on the death of three miners in the McIntyre cave-in suggests no amount of training could have saved the lives of these men. Inspection reports as far back as May 1979 note that poor roof conditions existed and the Mine Managers' Support Rules were not being enforced. The roof was not supported properly and thus endangered workers' lives. The report makes the following understatement in its conclusions:

> It is particularly disconcerting to note that no temporary breaker support posts were set during this shift, in fact the District Foreman states that temporary supports are set "When we feel they are required."[13]

Furthermore,

> IT CAN BE CONCLUDED, THEREFORE, THAT THERE WAS DISREGARD FOR THE FULL STATUTORY REQUIREMENTS OF THE MANAGERS' SUPPORT RULES.[14]

Undoubtedly to the loved ones of the three dead miners it was more than "disconcerting" that safety rules were not followed. Violence was perpetrated by the company through an unsafe work environment. Such dramatic killing is overshadowed in mining by the often slow and torturously painful death from miners' diseases, which will be discussed in the next chapter.

On Dying in the Woods

> The cables scraped a tune on the naked rocks.
> We dreamed of beer in the air-cooled bars of town
> and of sparks that might sow flame by the haulback blocks—
> Much hotter they'd close us down.
>
> In our groggy minds we nursed the greed for reprieve.
> It would never come so what the hell was the use?
> Then the hooker yelled and the sidehill came alive
> as the roadline stump tore loose.
>
> We dove for cover and held by horror, we stared
> at the grizzled hooker whose legs were not fast enough
> for the spinning uprooted stump that came like it cared
> and swept him over a bluff.
>
> There's little more. We packed him finally out,
> dead as though he had never breathed or been
> and they closed her down but I heard his words like a shout
> "It's the toughest show I've seen!"
>
> As his grave lies elsewhere, carefully kept and unmarred
> with a floral wreath and a plaque that bears his name
> but his real stone is a cliff-face, pitted and scarred
> on a logged-off logging claim.[15]

Forestry is second in fatalities among Canadian industries with an average rate of 111 per 100,000 workers over the 1969-78 period. Working in the woods has long been dangerous. An average of 25 loggers were killed each year in the first part of this century in British Columbia.[16]

> Sometimes a logger was so horribly injured he begged to die. Once, when a bucker's saw got stuck in a fallen tree, he jumped over the log to attack it from the other side. As he jumped, the log, about three feet in diameter, rolled onto his leg. The men around him tried to lift the tree off but it was too heavy. They began to cut it into pieces while the trapped man yelled in pain and begged to be hit over the head with a hammer. It took agonizing hours to free him and then he faced a long and painful journey to hospital in Vancouver.[17]

In 1979 there were 35 logging fatalities in British Columbia. The most dangerous job is that of the faller, which accounted for 15 of the fatalities. The Workmen's Compensation Board of B.C. *Health and Safety Digest* suggests employer culpability in eight of the cases. The following three examples are taken from their *Digest.*

1. FALLER—22 years experience. Faller had two trees hung up and proceeded to cut the holding tree. He commenced "brushing out" when both hung-up trees fell on him.
   CONTRIBUTING FACTORS: Failing to follow recognized safe work procedures. Firm had no written falling and bucking procedures to follow in event of falling difficulties per WCB 1. H. & S.[18]
   Regulation 60.22 (b).
2. FALLER—20 years experience. Worker was struck by a previously cut-up tree while falling another tree.
   CONTRIBUTING FACTORS: (1) Domino falling, (2) Working in an area made hazardous by a cut-up tree, (3) Lack of supervision and instruction.[19]
3. SKIDDER OPERATOR—1 year experience. Operator was crushed by the snag which he was attempting to fell by pulling with the skidder.
   CONTRIBUTING FACTORS: Attempting to pull over snag with insufficient length of cable.[20]

While logging in the forest is inherently dangerous, company policies and practices may add to the peril. For example, paying loggers on the basis of their productivity (piecework) may create risks due to hurry-up tactics. According to one study, piecework in British Columbia did not affect the accident rates of buckers and fallers.[21] This article was based upon an earlier study produced for the British Columbia Workmen's Compensation Board based upon 1,430 time loss claims for buckers and fallers in 1972. But in a devastating critique, the Health and Safety Research and Education Branch of the Occupational Health and Safety Division, Saskatchewan Department of Labour, has pointed out that the study confuses the issue more than it clarifies it. Specifically, the B.C. Study found that age of worker, size of firm and geography were not related to accidents. What it boiled down to was that younger workers in smaller companies in the interior of British Columbia had the highest accident rates. The study failed to consider that method of payment is related to age of workforce, company size, and location. It appears that smaller firms paid by piecerate more than large companies, and that all pieceworkers were in the interior, with coast loggers on salary. Also, younger workers are less likely to get into union shops, which are more likely to have a normal wage schedule. The Saskatchewan critique concludes:

> Here is a report which laments the data it doesn't have, but which fails to give the basic breakdown of the data it has. A report which goes out of its way to erase the piecework/salary difference it does find. A report which uses statistical methods to hide the effect of its basic variable in three others, and then turns around and claims its basic variable has no effect at all. A report which shows no comprehension that a

form of wage payment is a process of producing a specific kind of workforce. A report which doesn't even hint that piecework/salary may even have the slightest bearing on which accidents get reported and which do not.

If the labour movement has friends like LOG, does it need enemies?[22]

In the fall of 1980 delegates to the thirty-first regional safety and health conference of the International Woodworkers of America in Vancouver called for more positive action on the part of management. They charged that accidents are still largely blamed on worker carelessness rather than hazardous working conditions. Also they complained about the lack of control over new chemicals in the workplace and lax dust control standards. Furthermore, they called for the provincial government to ensure their right to information about the toxic substances sprayed from planes in their work areas.[23] The Canadian Paperworkers' Union is fighting to eliminate PCB's from their workplace. Pulp and paper mills have the greatest accumulation of PCB's and workers are subject to massive chemical assault.[24]

Looking again at Table 2-2, police work, although popularly considered one of the toughest and most dangerous industries, has a relatively low fatality rate compared to several others. Those in the service and finance industry are least likely to meet a sudden and dramatic death in the workplace. However, as will become evident in subsequent chapters on disease and stress, employees in "white-collar" industries such as service, professional, sales, and clerical may be subject to a slower death on the job.

Social Class and Occupational Death

When we look, in Table 2-3, at specific occupations, the same industrial trends are evident. Again, social class is an important factor in one's life-chances, since white-collar occupations are less risky. In a stratified, class-based society such as ours, those closer to the bottom take most of the physical risks which largely benefit those at the top. In a recent English study of national death rates, the highest death rates were among such class-based occupations as labourers and unskilled workers and the lowest among university teachers and physiotherapists. The Working Group on Inequalities In Health found that:

> if you are a labourer, cleaner or a dock worker you are twice as likely to die than a member of the professional classes. You are more likely to have respiratory disease, infectious disease, and trouble with your nervous, circulatory and digestive systems. You are more likely to get cancer and more likely to suffer from mental illness. And with the exception of mental illness—so is your wife.[25]

A former Alberta miner noted the class-based nature of life when he spoke on behalf of workers' compensation in 1907:

> As the working class produces all the wealth, I think there should be legislation providing compensation for them. I think it is only just. All the fatal accidents that have happened here, it has been the working men that have supported the widows.[26]

Table 2-3

Average Fatality Incidence Rates in Canadian Industry 1970-1978 by Occupation*

Occupation	Rate per 100,000 (1970-1978)	Number of Deaths[2]	Rate per 100,000 (1978)
Mining and Quarrying	231.5	(125)	150
Forestry and Logging	117.0	(62)	100
Fishing, Hunting, Trapping	90	(18)	95
Transport Equipment Operation	49.2	(194)	35.8
Construction Trades	23.3	(158)	17.2
Materials Handling	19.4	(48)	2.3
Machining	18.3	(45)	5.7
Processing	16.2	(63)	7.9
Managerial, Administrative	8.4	(54)	5.7
Product Fabricating, Assembling and Repairing	6.0	(54)	5.1
Service	5.0	(71)	6.1
Other Crafts and Equipment Operating	4.8	(6)	5.6
Agriculture	3.8	(19)	1.0
Professional[1]	3.0	(43)	1.4
Sales	2.7	(28)	1.2
Clerical	1.1	(19)	.7

* Fatality data comes from *Fatalities in Canadian Industry*, 1969-78, published by The Occupational Safety and Health Branch of Labour Canada, while the occupation data base is for 1976 from *Canada Year Book*, 1978-79. Ottawa: Ministry of Supply and Services.

1 Professional includes natural sciences, social sciences, religion, teaching, medicine, artistic and recreational.

2 This is the annual average number of deaths for the years considered.

While your chances of being killed by work are greater than being killed in an auto accident, injury and assault from the workplace is even more common.

Injury and Assault in the Workplace

In 1978 there were over one million work injuries and illnesses among some 8.5 million Canadian workers. If we add 25 per cent to the number of injuries and illnesses to adjust for coverage of all workers in Canada, a total of about 1.33 million official injuries occurred in 1978. Therefore, about 16 per cent of the workforce in Canada sustained an injury or illness on the job. Since, for a variety of reasons, reporting to workmen's compensation is lower than the actual incidence of injuries, the number and proportion are undoubtedly higher. For example, a study in the United States found that workers in American industry suffer *ten times* as many injuries as are officially reported by private and public bodies.[27] What this means to us, as workers, is that we have a better than 1 in 10 chance of being injured or becoming ill from our job. According to Labour Canada, 54 per cent of these injuries involved no loss of work except the day of injury, while the remaining 46 per cent resulted in the loss of roughly 12.3 million days lost. Each disabling injury involved a loss of roughly 25 days.[28]

The above governmental statistics are a bare minimum. Dr. Victor Rabinovitch, occupational health and safety program director of the Canadian Labour Studies Centre, has calculated a minimum of 70 million working days lost in 1977 due to job-related injuries and disease. This is six times the time lost due to strikes and lockouts and over five times the government data.[29] Occupational cancer deaths accounted for 45 million days lost, fatal accidents for 6 million, permanent disabilities for 4.9 million, and temporary disabilities for 7.1 million. Rabinovitch adds to this total of 62 million days lost at the start of the disability period: accidents and disease which are not reported and those claims rejected; diseases not yet recognized and those which doctors have difficulty diagnosing; and "general non-specific wear and tear" on the human body, particularly to the back. Thus, he estimates that the total is at least 70 million, and concludes:

> This massive total is clear evidence that a genuine crisis exists in health and safety in Canadian workplaces.[30]

Whether one uses the conservative figures of the government or the more comprehensive labour estimates, injury and illness from the workplace has reached epidemic proportions. Government figures show that between 1969 and 1978 overall injuries increased 35 per cent—disabling injuries increased 69 per cent, compared to only a 15 per cent increase in non-disabling ones. In 1978 work injuries cost approximately 3.5 billion dollars.[31]

We are nearly 28 times as likely to be the victim of a workplace assault as we are of an officially recognized criminal code assault. (See Table 2-4.) Whether due to injury or illness, violence is prevalent in the workplace. Where you work will clearly influence your chances of being assaulted on the job.

Although there are annual statistics concerning death rates according to industry, no such comparable data exists for injuries. However, we do have available a study of injuries for various federal employees for the 1978-79 year. Data from a selected number of federal employee groups are presented in Table 2-5 concerning their injury rate, degree of disability, and the frequency and severity rate for disabling injuries. The employee groups are listed according to their injury rate per 100 employees per man-year. The Freshwater Fish Marketing Corporation has an unbelievably high rate of 90.77 injuries per 100 employees, with 45 per cent disabling. Its frequency and severity rates (which includes deaths) are also high. However, Cape Breton Development Corporation has nearly a 74 per cent injury rate with 76 per cent of those being of a disabling nature. It has

Table 2-4

Canadian Assault Rate* By Type, 1977

	Number	Rate
Criminal Code Assaults[1]	103,931	446.2
Work-Related Assaults[2]	1,296,121	12,346

[1] Source: *The World Almanac and Book of Facts*, 1980, 1979.

[2] 46 per cent of these were disabling.
Source: "Health and Safety," 1977.

* Rate for criminal code assaults is per 100,000 population while rate for work-related assaults is for 100,000 workers. A 25 per cent adjustment is made to work injuries to include workers not covered by Workmen's Compensation.

the highest frequency and severity rate, accounting for most of the deaths, and has a large number of injuries. Third in injury rates is Eldorado Nuclear Ltd., although its figures are much lower than the first two groups. Nearly 1 in 5 Post Office employees is injured with 67 per cent of them being disabled. Working in the Post Office is more injurious than the Canadian Penitentiary Service, which has a rate of 13 injuries per 100 employees. Low on the list is the Royal Canadian Mounted Police with about 4 per cent of its employees being injured on the job. Contrary to the image presented by cops and robbers shows and violent crime dramas, the reality of police work is largely non-violent. In fact, as an employee of Parliament (House of Commons, Library of Parliament, Senate of Canada) you are more likely to be injured than as a member of the R.C.M.P. The safest group of federal employees are those in Justice, where about 0.33 per cent are injured and the severity rate is 0. These differences in injury and disability rates reflect occupational and class differences.

While it may be obvious that those working in construction, mining, fishing, or manufacturing will have high injury rates, what about public employees in hospitals and homes for the aged, municipalities and school boards? A recent study by the Canadian Union of Public Employees notes that:

> CUPE members are not miners, but they still are exposed to silica; they do not produce pesticides, but they use them; they are not loggers, but many use chain saws. CUPE members are welders, garbage collectors, sewer workers, printers, electricians, painters, plumbers, heavy equipment operators, mechanics, and office workers. They work in heat and cold, they are exposed to noise, vibration and radiation. Many of them work with a broad range of toxic substances. The injuries they experience from falling objects, from electrical shocks, from trip hazards and pinch points, as well as from lifting too much, are the same as those experienced by workers in the private sector.[32]

Table 2-5

Number and Type of Injury for Selected Federal Employees, 1978-79*

Employees	Number of Injuries per 100 Employees	Number & % Non-Disabling[1]		Number & % Disabling		Disabling Injury[2]	
		N	%	N	%	Frequency Rate	Severity Rate
Freshwater Fish Marketing Corp.	90.77	98	55	79	45	202.56	2,013
Cape Breton Developments Corp.	73.91	626	24	1,988	76	281.45	11,495
Eldorado Nuclear Ltd.	26.74	213	54	178	46	60.88	840
Northern Transport Co. Ltd.	23.64	61	70	26	30	35.33	810
Post Office	18.62	3,851	33	7,724	67	62.12	1,060
Transport: Marine Services	15.41	545	62	337	38	29.55	1,922
National Harbours Board	15.59	134	40	198	60	46.48	1,029
Canadian Penitentiary Service	13.05	648	47	718	53	34.33	987
National Defense	13.34	2,655	49	2,736	51	33.87	680
Canadian Grain Commission	12.31	61	46	72	54	33.33	368
Royal Canadian Mint	12.29	33	40	49	60	36.73	596
Public Works	6.50	316	49	332	51	16.65	282
Agriculture	6.30	361	56	286	44	13.92	231
Transport: Air Services	6.08	416	50	410	50	15.12	500
Indian Affairs & Northern Development	5.96	413	54	345	46	13.58	459
Parliament[3]	5.36	121	69	55	21	8.38	112
Veterans Affairs	4.93	136	39	215	61	15.09	277
Public Archives	4.44	14	44	18	56	12.48	130
RCMP	3.99	77	60	52	40	8.03	125
National Museums	3.78	26	68	12	32	5.97	161
CBC	3.19	257	65	141	35	5.65	101
National Film Board	2.06	10	48	11	52	5.41	115
Transport: Administration	1.88	17	53	15	47	4.40	60
Employment and Immigration	1.13	157	56	123	44	2.49	40
Justice	.34	3	75	1	25	.43	—

* Adapted from "Injury Experience—Agencies Not Under Treasury Board Occupational Safety Policy, Year Ending March 31, 1979" and "Injury Experience—Public Service Departments, Year Ending March 31, 1979." Both are preliminary figures published by Labour Canada, Occupational Safety and Health Branch, October, 1979.

[1] Excluding fatalities. [2] Both frequency and severity rate are calculated using 2,000 man-hours per man-year. [3] Parliament includes House of Commons, Library of Parliament, and Senate of Canada.

In the United States, a typical municipal worker is three times more likely to be assaulted on the job than an industrial worker. Garbage collectors and street and highway maintenance employees have a rate 5 to 6 times greater than the average industrial worker.[33] Although no comparable national data is available for Canada, the limited studies suggest that public employees in Canada face the same problems. The injury rate for public employees in Ottawa for 1976 was approximately 5 times higher than the United States national average for all industries, while the severity rate was about 1.5 times that of the United States.[34] Nonetheless, the Association of Municipalities of Ontario opposed occupational health and safety legislation covering municipal employees, because, in their words, "Quite frankly, we are at a loss to understand just what is the problem and why the legislation is needed at the municipal level.[35] Katz notes that on the same day that such an argument was being presented, 10 of 50 (20 per cent) of garbage collectors in Ottawa were not working because of on-the-job injuries.

The inventory of *Hazards* produced by a CUPE research team is one of the first attempts in Canada to systematically categorize health and safety problems among various public employees. In addition to physical hazards, they elaborate upon the biological, mechanical, and stress factors in the workplace. For example, 70 pages are devoted to hospital workers and the variety of hazards they are subjected to. The general hospital hazards include standard infections (biological hazards) such as tuberculosis and viral hepatitis, mechanical hazards such as lifting, cuts, falls, and stress due to such factors as shift work and understaffing.

Nearly half of the compensated cases for hospital workers are back injuries. They are often due to lifting patients and falls.

PROFILE: The Walking Wounded

"Now I have one speed and that's standing still." Whenever Cecelia Turpin wants or needs to move from point A to point B she assesses the distance and decides whether the action is vital. Walking from the lounging chair to the couch a few feet away has to be planned carefully. Answering the front door is impossible. Besides having to walk the distance, there are stairs to climb and descend. It's just too physically painful. Cecelia spends her days sitting for hours without shifting her legs because the joints in her knees fill with pain whenever they are bent. Even changing seating position is done cautiously. "I can feel little bits of bone hitting bone. I can feel the bone sticking into my skin."

Looking at her wheelchair and two metal canes, tools of mobility, she recalls the lifestyle she and her husband Merril enjoyed, three long years ago, before the brutal slip on a wet floor in the kitchen of the Vancouver General Hospital. "There was dancing . . . plenty of dancing . . . and camping . . . almost every weekend if the weather was good . . . and . . . oh yes . . . every fall we went hunting. We were very active and enjoyed doing all kinds of outdoor things."

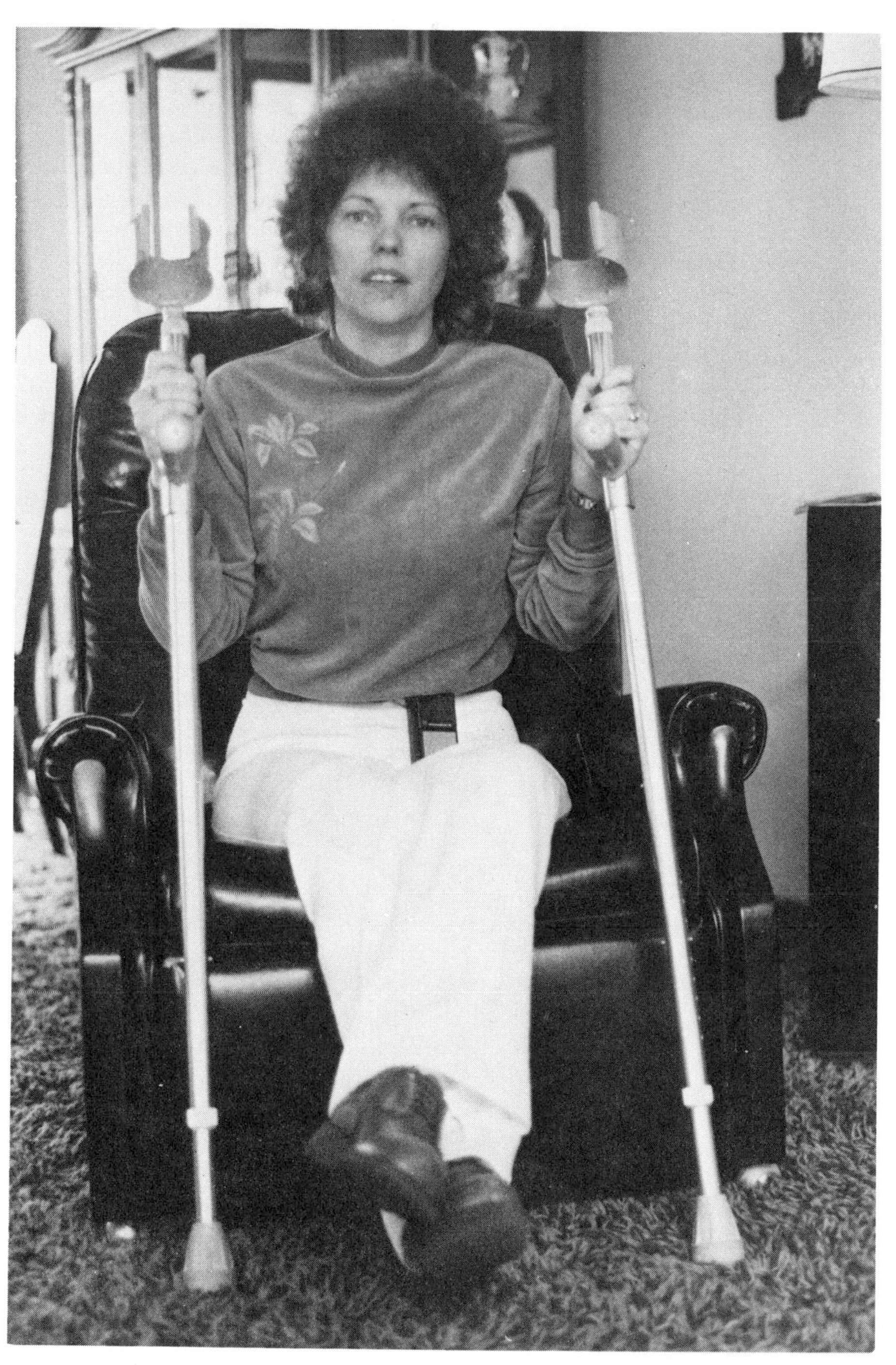

Cecelia Turpin

Now whenever Cecelia embarks on a jaunt to the outdoors—usually for a doctor's appointment—she takes her wheelchair.

Cecelia had worked in hospitals for nine years prior to her accident. In November of 1972 she began working as a kitchen aide in the Vancouver General Hospital. Then in June of 1977 she slipped, fell to her knees and, according to the original assessment of the accident, sprained both knees. It wasn't the first time Cecelia had fallen. A few years earlier, in 1974, her right knee was hurt in a similar accident, the cartilage was removed, "and I never missed a day of work." Since she wasn't in need of financial support at the time, Cecelia never filed an accident report with the Workmen's Compensation Board.

This fall, however, was different, though at the time Cecelia felt confident the injury would be temporary. She spent the summer of 1977 taking therapy at the WCB rehabilitation centre. But when no signs of progress were made, her left knee, which was the most severely damaged, was operated on and the cartilage was removed. Then, once again, she went back to therapy. "The doctors told me that within a year my knee would be as good as new." But therapeutic rehabilitation was not working. Her knees, particularly her left, remained painful and swollen.

Nonetheless, without consulting or even notifying Cecelia, the British Columbia WCB cleared her to return to work and closed her file in January of 1978. Though her family doctor advised against assuming a job, Cecelia tried. The effort lasted a week. When the pain became increasingly worse she was forced to quit. An appeal to the WCB finally resulted in her file being reopened, but a month's wage-loss benefits were not recovered because the board refused to cover the period between the closing of her file and the time when she was able to make an appointment with WCB doctors to prove her physical incapacity to work.

Cecelia has kept a detailed chronology of her injury and problems with the WCB, which reveals a trail of assessments, therapy, countless doctors, operations and job retraining. All of these culminated in frustration, financial woes, and mental anguish, accompanied by continuous physical pain and plenty of determination.

Once her file was reopened, she was placed on benefits again, and sent off to the doctor for yet another assessment of her condition. Her left knee was checked with a scope by the same doctor who had performed her earlier operation. He determined that another cartilage in her knee was damaged and that she had a fractured kneecap that had gone undiagnosed and that she had walked on for eight months. A second operation was performed in the spring of 1978, then Cecelia was off to therapy again for most of that summer. Months later Cecelia would find out that the second operation on her left knee was not authorized by the WCB, despite the fact that the doctor was well aware of the need for clearance. In the earlier operation he had sought the WCB go-ahead. Cecelia and Merril now believe that during the first operation something in the medical procedure went awry and that the second attempt, by the same doctor, was an effort to reverse a problem created during the initial operation. The Turpins admit that their theory is based on informed speculation, but they wonder why a second operation was performed without the WCB authorization, particularly when the first one didn't work. A number of doctors have since confirmed that the operation should never have taken place, when the initial one failed. The second attempt only made matters worse.

A few months after the second operation Cecelia was advised that the damage to her left knee would be permanent. Her right knee, although not as severe, was deemed permanently damaged as well. Ironically, in August the WCB cut off her benefits again. Pending the appeal of her case, Cecelia, on the board's instructions, went through countless job assessments and retraining programs in the fall of 1978—everything from making chesterfields to typing. In between there were doctors' assessments to find out what could be done about or with her knees. The appeal to the WCB to review the closure of her case led the board to suggest that she be assessed for a permanent partial disability as soon as her condition stabilized. The WCB also stated that Cecelia would be able to handle "light duties." But, as Cecelia points out, how many jobs are there for which walking is not a prerequisite? Nonetheless the WCB suggested she return to the hospital to work at "light duties," though her former employer maintained no such "type" of work existed. However, in June of 1979, the Vancouver General Hospital management agreed to hire Cecelia. She accepted a job working as a computer operator at $6.18 an hour. On the fourth day of the job, Cecelia was rushed to Emergency. "The pain was so severe." Her family physician firmly told her not to return to work. Still, the WCB maintained, and does to this day, that Cecelia is capable of holding down a job. "They keep telling me that somewhere out there is a job I can do."

Cecelia doesn't relish her condition anymore than the WCB appears to want to pay for it. She has sought medical opinions from the three top orthopedic surgeons in North America. All of them have simply shaken their heads. Although knee transplants have been performed in the past, the specialists maintain that at 32 Cecelia is too young to have such an operation. The knees would wear out. Perhaps when she gets older, they suggest, or when current transplant techniques are perfected.

In January of 1980 Cecelia spent another three months in the hospital. Her condition continues to deteriorate and doctors have advised that the way in which she walks, because of her knee injury, is adding stress to her back and hips. Cecelia has been forewarned—eventually she will suffer from both back and hip problems. And although an injured worker is not to be put on pension until his or her condition stabilizes or plateaus, the WCB has forged ahead and approved a pension for Cecelia.

Cecelia's eyes flare, her voice exudes restrained disgust, as she explains the procedure of the "meat chart." "They shoot your body into a computer and it pops out with a figure [a percentage of disability]," she notes. So much for a knee which bends, but won't handle body weight. So much for a knee which is fused or locked. So much for a leg amputated above the knee. It makes no difference to the WCB, she explains, whether you have the use of your knee or not. If a leg is amputated the pension is larger than if it is attached despite it being rendered useless by a knee which can't handle the pressure of walking.

According to the WCB, Cecelia has a permanent partial disability in one knee only. The board has recognized and paid for the partial loss of the use of her right knee for more than two years. However, the WCB now maintains that her knee was damaged in the fall prior to the one which occurred in June of 1977—the fall that Cecelia did not report to the WCB and which consequently the Board does not consider to be work-related. Her left knee has been assessed at a 9.3 per cent disability. The maximum would have been 10 per cent. The pension allows for 9.3 per cent of the wage she was earning three months prior to the accident—a total of $65 a month, or $800 a year.

Today Cecelia would have been earning an estimated $1200 a month as a kitchen aide. That figure does not include the possibility of promotions. Along with the capacity to walk, Cecelia has lost her livelihood and nine years of seniority and benefits. Her husband, Merril, now works seven days a week to bring in the income necessary to meet the mortgage and expenses.

Besides the haggling over wage-loss and pension benefits, Cecelia says that other expenses incurred because of her accident are only painstakingly reimbursed by the WCB. For instance, the washroom must be equipped with support bars. And although her family doctor says a homemaker should come in three times a week, the WCB has reluctantly agreed to two days a week. In addition, she needs an electronic device to control the front door, since otherwise she cannot answer it. She also needs a special chair to aid her in the kitchen—a chair which would allow her to make meals and do dishes while seated.

Cecelia has gone from mobility to disability in the short time it takes to slip on a wet surface and fall on a marble-like floor. Her accident has led to a new awareness. "Before, I thought you'd be looked after 100 per cent. I never thought there'd be a hassle with the WCB." She quickly adds: "Of course I'd never had anything to do with them before either." Such sentiments, denoting blind trust, are echoed by most workers across this country. It takes an injury for them to realize the obstacles.

Both Cecelia and Merril agree that when the injury is temporary the board is not likely to create ingenious obstacles to block payment. But once permanent damage is sustained on the job, and the board anticipates "paying out" for the rest of a person's life, nearly insurmountable walls are raised. The Turpins have a succinct explanation for what otherwise might simply be classified as "unreasonable obstinance." The management of the Board essentially has its wages paid by the companies who pay WCB insurance premiums. In other words, the WCB is on the payroll of the companies. "The WCB is there to protect their employer. They are there to safeguard the companies' money."

"The past three years, the trauma I've been through, it was like hell," says Cecelia. But the Turpins aren't about to let go. They have decided to fight the board and its doctors by launching civil suits on the grounds of malpractice.

The Turpins are not asking for an exorbitant sum. They have announced that $600 per month support from the WCB would be satisfactory—not necessarily fair, but enough to aid in easing the financial crisis created by Cecelia's injury.

While monetary compensation is an immediate need, Cecelia craves another type of relief much more. "I hope that one day doctors will come up with a technique to deal with the pain. I'll settle for some of the pain being taken away."

Despite the experience of the past three years, Cecelia considers her family at an advantage compared to those of other injured workers. It was she, as a secondary income earner, who became disabled. Had it been Merril, or had she been the primary earner, "we would have lost everything." The Turpins know of many injured workers who were the major breadwinners in the home and had exactly that happen to them.

Still, "We haven't got a clue what the future holds. My doctor told me not to give up hope . . . they're always coming up with new techniques."

NOTES

1. Larry Katz, "Work: It's More Dangerous for Public Employees," *The Public Employee*, Vol. 1, No. 1 (Spring 1978): 6.
2. Warren Caragata, *Alberta Labour: A Heritage Untold* (Toronto: James Lorimer, 1979), p. 1.
3. Quoted in Caragata, *Alberta Labour,* p. 7.
4. David J. Bercuson, *Fools and Wise Men: The Rise and Fall of the One Big Union* (Toronto: McGraw-Hill Ryerson, 1978).
5. Caragata, *Alberta Labour*, p. 32.
6. Excerpted from Sharon Stevenson, "Slag," in Tom Wayman (ed.), *Beaton Abbot's Got the Contract: An Anthology of Working Poems* (Edmonton: NeWest Press, n.d.). Also on a recording, "Eleven Canadian Poets" (Edmonton: J. M. LeBel Enterprises, 1973).
7. "Right Standard Tough to Find for Mine Safety," *Calgary Herald*, July 23, 1980.
8. "Safety Record Poor, Says Inco President," *Calgary Herald*, September 17, 1980.
9. "Judge Named to Head Cave-In Inquiry," *Calgary Herald*, July 10, 1980.
10. "Mine Went Months Without Engineer," *The Calgary Herald*, September 17, 1980.
11. "Calgary Firm Charged In Mine Deaths," *The Calgary Herald*, April 11, 1981.
12. "Alberta Coal Mine Wins Third Consecutive Safety Award," *Alberta Occupational Health & Safety*, Vol. 3, No. 3 (June 1979): 1.
13. Workers' Health Safety and Compensation, Occupational Health and Safety Division, Mines Branch, *Report on an Investigation Into a Multiple Fatality Incident at McIntyre Mines Ltd. Mine No. 1765/07 Which Occurred on Thursday February 28th, 1980*, p. 24.
14. Ibid., p. 25. Ultimately, it comes down to safety versus savings. See Kirk Makin,

"Alberta's Mining Dispute: Safety Versus Savings," *The Globe and Mail*, January 15, 1981.

15. Peter Trower, "The Ballad of Booted Bondage," in Tom Wayman (ed.), *A Government Job at Last* (Toronto: George J. McLeod Limited, 1976), p. 25.

16. Bercuson, *Fools and Wise Men*, p. 19.

17. Ibid., pp. 19-20.

18. "Logging Fatalities for First Half of 1979." *Health and Safety Digest*, Vol. 14, No. 3 (Fall 1979): 2.

19. "Logging Fatalities for Second Half of 1979." *Health and Safety Digest*, Vol. 15, No. 1 (Spring 1980): 1.

20. Ibid., p. 1.

21. Keith Mason, "The Effect of Piecework on Accident Rates In The Logging Industry (Incorporating a Different Approach to the Exposure Problem)," *Journal of Occupational Accidents* 1 (1976-1977): 281-94.

22. Health and Safety Research and Education Branch, Occupational Health and Safety Division, *Review of the B.C. Workmen's Compensation Board Study On the Effect of Piecework On Logging Accident Rates* (Regina: Saskatchewan Department of Labour, September, 1974), p. 6. This review labelled the study by B.C. "LOG."

23. *Canadian Occupational Health and Safety News*, October 27, 1980, p. 3.

24. *CLV Health and Safety Forum*, January 19, 1981, pp. 1-4.

25. Phillip Knightley, "How the Other Half Dies," *The Sunday Times*, August 31, 1980.

26. Caragata, *Alberta Labour*, p. 32.

27. Jerome B. Gordon, Allan Akman, and Michael L. Brooks, *Industrial Safety Statistics: A Re-Examination* (New York: Praeger, 1971).

28. R. S. Clark, *Work Injury Experience and Cost in Canadian Industry, 1969-1978* (Ottawa: Labour Canada, October 1979).

29. *Canadian Occupational Health & Safety News*, Vol. 2, No. 8 (April 16, 1979): 2.

30. Ibid., p. 2.

31. Clark, *Work Injury Experience and Cost.* These statistics exclude the Northwest Territories and Yukon.

32. *The Health and Safety HAZARDS Faced by Canadian Public Employees* (Ottawa: Canadian Union of Public Employees, July, 1978), p. 5.

33. Ibid., p. 6.

34. Katz, *Work*, p. 8.

35. Ibid.

Chapter 3

Chemical Assault in the Workplace

The toll imposed by industrial disease is probably grossly underestimated. For example, if a retired chemical worker who smokes appears in a doctor's office at age 67 with lung cancer, the physician will almost certainly blame the lifetime habit of smoking for the person's disease. It may be something in the man's industrial past that was responsible. It is unlikely that this illness will, in any way, be recorded as industrial. Similarly, if a worker in a dynamite factory has a heart attack in his bed late Sunday night or early Monday morning, that heart attack is not likely to be attributed to his previous week's exposure to nitroglycerine. So, if we are going to come to grips with the problems of industrial health, we must improve our methods of disease measurement and become more sophisticated in assessing blame.[1]

It was a bright, clean, new oil rig—the most modern that money could buy. The provincial inspector explained to me that this was a showcase rig and would give me some idea of the best the province had to offer.[2] As I accompanied him on the inspection we came upon a young man mixing bags of chemicals. In the adjacent shed were stacked a variety of chemicals for mixing. I asked the inspector about them and their harmful effects and he hesitated, agreeing that we should check them out. On the bag labelled Peis Caustic Soda Beads a warning stated that it was extremely dangerous and that one should wear apron, gloves, rubber boots, and goggles while mixing the chemical. The young man mixing the chemicals had a T-shirt on and no protective gear. When asked if he knew the chemicals were dangerous he replied that he had only been on the job a couple of weeks and didn't really know about the chemicals. At another rig later that day, the inspector wrote up a formal complaint noting a lack of proper safety equipment for handling Dow Caustic Soda and Hydrated Lime. Although he had some 20 years' experience on oil rigs and in the oil fields, the inspector was trained and oriented to identifying and policing safety violations, not health violations.

Diseases and Compensation

Such an approach largely characterizes the operation of health and safety departments and compensation programs. It has only been in the last few years that chemicals and diseases have been given any extensive attention in discussion of workers' health. This is reflected in statistics concerning compensation. The percentage of workers' compensation claims granted for death due to occupational illness in Canadian industry was 13.2 per cent in 1975, 12.5 per cent in 1976, 11.1 per cent in 1977, and 9.6 per cent in 1978.[3] Thus, an average of about 11 per cent of workers during this period died from occupationally-related diseases while nearly 90 per cent died from traumatic injury. How do these figures compare to the causes of death among the general population?

In *The Dimensions of Industrial Disease*, Professor Terence G. Ison notes that for the age group 20-60 years, 75.6 per cent of their deaths were due to disease in 1974, with only 24.4 per cent caused by "accidents, poisonings and violence."[4] Also, only approximately 5 per cent of disability pensions result from trauma, with the great majority (95 per cent) due to disease. Therefore, the great majority of serious disabilities and premature adult deaths are caused by disease, not by traumatic injury. The proportion of these diseases which are work-related is not known; however, we do know that a very small proportion of compensation claims are granted for disease. Why are the bulk of premature deaths and permanent disabilities among the general population the result of disease, while the large majority of workers' compensation claims for death and permanent disability are due to traumatic injuries? The reasons involve medical practice and research, company and state policies, visibility and causation questions and, perhaps most important, economic factors.

The President of the Canadian Centre for Occupational Health and Safety, Dr. Gordon Atherley, suggests there are an estimated 10,000 workers in Canada who suffer from job-related diseases such as cancer, silicosis and asbestosis.[5]

Identifying Health Hazards

Occupational health hazards are of four general types:[6]

1. *Physical*—noise, heat, vibration and radiation
2. *Chemical*—dusts, poisonous fumes and gases, toxic metals and chemicals, and carcinogens
3. *Biological*—bacteria, fungi, and insects
4. *Stress*—caused by physical, chemical and work situation, including psychological factors such as job pressure.

Compared to safety issues and injuries, health hazards are more difficult to recognize and categorize. This is one of the reasons they have not been given the same attention as traumatic injuries.

For example, the potential industrial disease hazards to workers have been indentified in Alberta as:[7]

Chemical hazards—86%
Physical hazards—12%
Biological hazards—2%

Therefore, chemical hazards pose the most prevalent disease threat to workers.

Recently, Ray Sentes, Alberta Federation of Labour Health and Safety Director, attempted to determine hazards in the workplace.[8] In order to get a general overview of the kinds of health and safety problems workers must contend with, a hazard inventory sheet was completed by representatives of 17 unions representing 76,923 members, about 62.9 per cent of the AFL's total membership. Twenty-three broad categories of hazards were listed. The categories were: trenching and excavating, explosives, extreme heat, extreme cold, dermatitis, biological agents, electrical, welding, ultraviolet radiation, scaffolding, material handling, tools and machinery, ventilation, illumination, dusts, vapours, gases, mists, noise, vibration, stress, shiftwork, and toxic substances.

Some of the categories, such as material handling, are of necessity broad and ill-defined. Others, such as noise, are specific and, at least in their effects, more easily described. The list is obviously arbitrary and incomplete. It is little more than a first attempt to provide a rough guide as to what Alberta's unionized workers are exposed to. Nonetheless, it provides an initial idea of the large proportion of workers exposed to hazards generally, and chemical hazards specifically.

Table 3-1

Exposure to General Hazards

Hazard	Estimated Exposed	Estimated Membership	% of Total Membership Exposed
Dusts	20,617	76,923	26.8%
Vapors	14,173	76,923	18.4%
Gases	15,264	76,923	19.8%
Mists	6,549	76,923	8.5%
Noise	25,279	76,923	32.8%
Illumination	22,759	76,923	29.5%
Extreme Heat	15,215	76,923	19.7%
Extreme Cold	14,236	76,923	18.5%
Stress	33,694	76,923	43.8%
Toxic Substances	23,826	76,923	30.9%
Tools and Machinery	26,532	76,923	34.4%
Vibration	8,320	76,923	10.8%
Scaffolding	11,282	76,923	14.6%
Ultraviolet Radiation	3,032	76,923	3.9%
Shift Work	25,283	76,923	32.8%
Dermatitis	15,229	76,923	19.7%
Ventilation	19,587	76,923	25.4%
Trenching and Excavating	3,605	76,923	4.6%
Electrical	3,207	76,923	4.1%
Explosives	2,799	76,923	3.6%
Biological Agents	7,580	76,923	9.8%
Welding	10,527	76,923	13.6%
Material Handling	12,933	76,923	16.8%

The 1908 Workmen's Compensation Act was revised in 1918 to include seven diseases. Except for miner's phthisis, this list is exactly the same as the 1906 English schedule of industrial diseases. Ankylostomiasis was a tropical disease which appeared among English miners who had been in the tropics in 1909, but no such problem apparently arose in Alberta. In 1938, ankylostomiasis was dropped and miner's phthisis was replaced by pneumoconiosis which was defined as silicosis (from silica dust), siderosis (from iron dust and fumes), and lithosis (from lead dust and fumes). In 1978, the enumeration of diseases was essentially the same as the schedule in 1942, excepting the broadening of pneumoconiosis, including the addition of asbestosis. What is particularly surprising is that the 1978 Alberta Enumeration of Industrial Diseases is the same, excepting pneumoconiosis, as the revised British Workman's Compensation Schedule of diseases in 1907. Could it be that life in the colonies was considered less valuable than in the mother country?

Cancer at Work

Cancer is the second leading cause of death in Canada and the United States. It has been conservatively estimated that 90 per cent of cancer is environmentally-caused and that 20 per cent of cancer deaths are occupationally-related.[9] As Table 3-2 demonstrates, cancer-inducing agents are commonly found in the workplace for many who sell their labour for a wage.

Although it may appear that most every chemical is cancer-producing (carcinogenic), only approximately 10 per cent of chemicals studied turn out to be carcinogenic. One of the real problems in Canada is that we have few systematic studies of the extent and nature of chemicals to which workers are exposed.

Recognition that workers may be exposed to a variety of carcinogens in the workplace means that employers must clean up their act. In the area of chemicals and disease there is little room for blaming the victim. Management decides which chemicals and agents will be in the workplace. This has been considered a "management right." After such hazards are detected there are a number of alternative methods of control. All health and safety problems can be attacked at the source by removing or replacing the chemical or noise-emitting equipment. Modification of the equipment or process may be possible by better maintenance or adaptive mechanisms. Such things as ventilation, acoustical enclosures, or relocating the environment around the source of the hazard can be controlled. Jobs could be redesigned and work practices altered—for instance, areas of work could be changed frequently. Removing workers completely from the hazardous area or shortening their exposure time might help. Finally, such personal protective devices as respirators, eye goggles and ear plugs could be provided to the worker.[10] From the standpoint of management, the most economical and least disruptive method is usually providing protective equipment for the worker. Thus, the onus is placed upon the worker to protect himself rather than upon management to change the workplace. This is generally the poorest method of preventing industrial diseases.

> For diseases that result from contamination, the most effective method of control is obviously to eliminate use of the contaminant by switching to an alternative product, or to alternative materials. Where that is not possible, the next best method may be to contain the contaminant in sealed ducts or other containers so that it does not reach the ambient air, or the skin or clothing of workers. Where it is impossible to prevent the contaminant from reaching the ambient air, the next best method may be to adopt remote-control devices, locating workers in sealed booths with a fresh air supply. *Only as a last resort, or a temporary expedient, where the disease cannot be prevented by designing or planning decisions, is it necessary to prevent disease by personal protective equipment, or by other methods that involve operating routines, or other aspects of workers' behaviour.*[11]

A recent U.S. government study found that PCBs and three other toxic chemicals can penetrate the "protective" clothing worn by millions of workers. The study found that most of the materials tested were permeated within a few minutes of contact with one of the toxic chemicals.[12]

Table 3-2

Common Occupational Carcinogens

Agent	Organ Affected	Occupation
Wood	Nasal cavity and sinuses	Woodworkers
Leather	Nasal cavity and sinuses; urinary bladder	Leather and shoe workers
Iron oxide	Lung; larynx	Iron ore miners; metal grinders and polishers; silver finishers; iron foundry workers
Nickel	Nasal sinuses; lung	Nickel smelters; mixers and roasters; electrolysis workers
Arsenic	Skin; lung; liver	Miners; smelters; insecticide makers and sprayers; tanners; chemical workers; oil refiners, vintners
Chromium	Nasal cavity and sinuses; lung and larynx	Chromium producers, processors and users; acetylene and aniline workers; bleachers; glass, pottery and linoleum workers; battery makers
Asbestos	Lung (pleural and peritoneal mesothelioma)	Miners; millers; textile, insulation and shipyard workers
Petroleum, petroleum coke, wax, creosote, anthracene paraffin, shale and mineral oils	Nasal cavity; larynx; lung; skin; scrotum	Contact with lubricating, cooling, paraffin or wax fuel oils or coke; rubber fillers; retort workers; textile weavers; diesel jet testers
Mustard gas	Larynx; lung; trachea; bronchi	Mustard gas workers
Vinyl Chloride	Liver; brain	Plastic workers
Bis-chloromethyl ether, chloromethyl ether	Lung	Chemical workers
Isopropyl oil	Nasal cavity	Isopropyl oil producers

continued overleaf

Table 3-2 continued

Coal soot, coal tar, other products of coal combustion	Lung; larynx, skin; scrotum; urinary bladder	Gashouse workers, stokers and producers; asphalt, coal tar and pitch workers; miners; still cleaners
Benzene	Bone marrow	Explosives, benzene or rubber cement workers; distillers; dye users; painters; shoemakers
Auramine, benzidine, alpha-Naphthylamine, beta-Naphthylamine, magenta, 4-Aminodiphenyl, 4-Nitrodiphenyl	Urinary bladder	Dyestuffs manufacturers and users; rubber workers (pressmen, filtermen, laborers); textile dyers

Source: U.S. National Cancer Institute.

Questions of design, location, structure, equipment, and materials have all been the prerogative of management, therefore it is at the level of worker behaviour that most health practices are initiated. Furthermore, as will be elaborated upon in a later chapter, compensation boards are reluctant to compensate for diseases unless there is absolute proof of causation, otherwise, they tend to assume other causes, such as eating, smoking or "lifestyle" habits. While smoking may have a combined effect with, say, asbestos (called a synergistic effect), asbestos workers who don't smoke have an eight times greater risk of developing lung cancer than an unexposed population. However, asbestos workers who do smoke have a 92 times greater chance. While one's personal habits may contribute to the development of disease, the workplace itself is an independent producer of cancer.[13]

The following excerpt from a brief by the International Association of Heat and Frost Insulations and Asbestos Workers, Local No. 126, Calgary, Alberta to the Alberta Select Legislative Committee, Workers' Compensation, addresses the issue of smoking and compensation.

> **Recommendation 8:**
> The Board should stop immediately its policy of reducing the asbestos-related pension awards of smokers.
> **Reason:**
> The Board reduces pensions by as much as 50 per cent when the claimant is a smoker. There is no medical and probably no legal basis for the Board's practice. The relationship between smoking and asbestos-related diseases has been closely examined during the past few years. Here are some of the scientific findings:
> *(1) Mesothelioma and smoking*—"cigarette smoking seems to play no part in the initiation of mesothelioma";

(2) Asbestosis and smoking—"To this time, therefore, epidemiologic studies of lung function have not been able to elucidate the relationship between airway obstruction and asbestos exposure, or the part played by the cigarette habit (additive or synergistic) . . . until further evidence is available, an open mind should be kept in this regard."

Earlier this year, a study, "Radiological Changes After Withdrawal From Asbestos Exposure," was published. One of its conclusions was that "there were no important differences in age or smoking habit between those with and without parenchymal change."

(3) Lung cancer and smoking—In 1968 Dr. Irving J. Selikoff published the results of his study on smoking and lung cancer. The study, based on 370 members of our Union, concluded that the lung cancer death rate was 6.8 times as high as that reported for the general white male population of the United States. The study also suggested that asbestos workers who smoke have about 92 times the risk of dying of lung cancer as men who neither work with asbestos nor smoke cigarettes. In 1972 Dr. Selikoff published a follow-up study confirming the previous data. These studies were soon being used by the asbestos industry in an attempt to "prove" that but for smoking 97 per cent of asbestos workers who died of lung cancer would not have died of that disease. What the asbestos industry and many others conveniently ignored was the fact that Dr. Selikoff's studies did not include a follow-up of lung cancer rates for non-smoking asbestos workers. In May 1979 Dr. Selikoff appeared before the U.S. House Education and Labour Subcommittee on Labour Standards. He stated that, "Only now, 10 years after following a group of 2,066 non-smoking individuals, are the data sufficient to indicate a positive effect for production of lung cancer in non-smoking workers." His data are as follows:

Cigarette Smoking	Death Rate per 100,000		Relative Risk
	Asbestos Insulators	U.S. Males	
Yes	362.0	74.4	4.9
No	40	9.2	4.4

The significance of the data is that the probability *is about 75 per cent that a lung cancer in an asbestos worker is attributable to asbestos exposure both for smokers and non-smokers.*

Thus, for mesothelioma, asbestosis and lung cancer there is no medical justification for the Board's reduction of compensation awards. . . ."

Nuclear Age, New Diseases

There are approximately 25,000 toxic substances used in manufacturing industries with 500-600 new ones being introduced each year. The Science Council of Canada studied the following six hazards: asbestos, lead, mercury, oxides of nitrogen, radiation, and vinyl chloride. However, it notes that they are but a small fraction of dangerous materials and are not necessarily the most dangerous. In discussing radiation, the report notes that we are daily exposed to radiation and that "Growth of the nuclear industry will place more members of the public at risk of radiation exposure."[14] The radiation exposure standards vary between the atomic radiation worker and the public and, according to the report:

> It appears that the major problems occur during the mining and milling of uranium and during the disposal of radioactive wastes.

Tataryn notes that Elliot Lake uranium miners are dying of cancer at a rate three times that expected.[15] Furthermore, fluorspar miners exposed to radiation in St. Lawrence, Newfoundland show a high rate of death.[16] A recent follow-up study of former miners in Port Radium, Northwest Territories found a high rate of lung cancer. More specifically, underground uranium miners who worked five years or more from 1946-1960 had a lung cancer rate five times that of surface miners and other underground miners who worked less than five years.[17]

Table 3-3

Standards for Radiation Exposure in Canada, 1977 (in rems/year)

	Atomic Radiation Worker	Public
Whole body, gonads bone marrow	5	0.5
Bone, skin, thyroid	30	3.0
Tissues of hands, feet, ankles, forearms	75	7.5
Other single organ or tissue	15	1.5

The above-noted standards for radiation exposure are the "acceptable" levels—acceptable to the government and companies which create the risk and police it, while the workers are subject to its violence. Although it has been claimed that there are "safe" levels of radiation exposure, this claim has not withstood scientific investigation. For example, a study of the effects of low-level (legally permissible) radiation upon workers at the U.S. nuclear facility at Hanford, Washington between 1944 and 1972 found cancer deaths due to this exposure. Although government and industry scientists argue that the Three Mile Island accident had no human victims, several independent scientists suggest that hundreds of babies died due to radiation exposure. In fact, it is being argued now that low-level radiation may be more damaging than high-level exposure. A recent review of the evidence states:

Even more disturbing was the work of Canadian researcher, Dr. Abram Petkan, who, in papers published in 1972 and 1974, showed that the risk of damage to a cell by radiation per unit of radiation absorbed could actually increase, rather than decrease, as the radiation dose rate was lowered to background level.[18]

Of course, nuclear energy means big money for business, government and research scientists. Also, it means jobs. However, it may be necessary to choose between safe and unsafe jobs. In a brief concerning the proposal to build a uranium refinery near Warman, Saskatchewan by Eldorado Nuclear Ltd., the Saskatchewan Division of the Canadian Union of Public Employees notes:

> Clearly, then, there is a public environmental problem posed by radon gas. But we should not lose sight of the fact that by constructing a nuclear refinery, Eldorado would be exposing refinery workers to radon gas on a daily basis.
>
> In Port Hope, Ontario, public buildings were closed because the radiation level was too "high," but workers in the uranium refinery face these high levels day in and day out.
>
> We have found that more and more Canadian workers are subject to "environmental blackmail," having to choose between a safe and healthier working environment and retaining a job in the face of limited or non-existent employment opportunities. This is an unacceptable condition. Priorities have to be changed. In the case of Warman, Saskatchewan, let's not add to the problem by creating an inherently dangerous work environment.[19]

The public cannot necessarily expect private companies or even government agencies to act on their behalf. For example, the public relations director for Ontario Hydro has recently admitted that the utility distributed misleading and one-sided information concerning nuclear energy.[20] The Crown corporation produced, among other things, a pamphlet entitled "What Is Radiation?" which fails to mention that radiation can cause cancer or genetic defects. In the grand tradition of propaganda for profit, Ontario Hydro was seeking to increase its rates, and presented only one side of the story. This was done, according to Hydro's director of public relations, because:

> We just felt at the time we produced that there was so much anti-nuclear stuff and negative information that we had to put out some positive material, so we did.

What are the costs of saving life by reducing radiation exposure? A recent government study found that "the cost per life saved is about $460,000 in 1973 dollars."[21] While it concludes that this is not too much, given the amount of suffering caused by lung cancer, rapid increases in cost may prohibit any further reduction in exposure.

> In view of the rapid increases in capital and operating costs at Denison Mines over the years, which appear to correspond to the reductions of radiation levels in the Denison Mines, the marginal cost of the lost lives saved may well be much higher than the average cost. If this is the case, any further reductions in the radiation levels would be much more expensive in terms of the cost to society per life saved.[22]

We deplore such cost-benefit mentality when it comes to human suffering and death. It is based on faulty logic and the wrong values—placing dollars over life. (See Chapter 10 for a critique of cost-benefit analysis.)

While it has been shown that strict government enforcement will reduce the health hazards of radiation,[23] strict levels and enforcement may not be of concern to a business-oriented cost-benefit perspective.

A classic example of the politics of occupational health is the case of asbestos.

Asbestos: The Political Economy of Lying and Dying

According to the Science Council of Canada, one of the lessons to be learned from our experience with asbestos is:

> Asbestos illustrates the tragedy that can occur when clean-cut, early-warning signs are ignored.[24]

Ignoring signs of harm is negligent; suppressing information of harm is criminal.

The world's first asbestos mine was opened in Thetford, Quebec in 1879, and subsequently Canada has been a leader in asbestos production. We currently account for about 40 per cent of the world's production, with 80 per cent of our mining and milling occurring in Quebec. Thetford, Quebec remains the centre of Canadian asbestos and has been an area of high morbidity and mortality from asbestos.[25] Asbestos is virtually indestructible and highly fire-resistant, and its fibres can be spun into yarn and woven into cloth. It has some 3,000 different uses in such things as cement, asphalt, wallboard, pipes, textiles, insulation, food and beverage processing, and brake linings. Tragically, its inhalation accounts for approximately 50,000 deaths per year in the United States from cancer and other diseases and undoubtedly thousands in Canada.[26]

Both U.S. and Canadian insurance companies stopped selling life policies to asbestos workers in 1918. Subsequent studies in the 1950s and 1960s found excessive death rates for asbestos workers, particularly from lung cancer. Conditions at the Johns-Manville plant, opened in Scarborough, Ontario in 1946, provide insight into the causes of such deaths. Men worked at the plant without respirators in dust so thick that they could see only a few yards. In the mid-1960s, Dr. Irving Selikoff, internationally-recognized authority on occupational diseases, visited the plant and predicted a high incidence of cancer deaths in the coming decade. Dismissing the claim as alarmist, management made little effort to improve conditions. Subsequently, over fifty workers (10 per cent of the workforce) have been disabled by chronic respiratory diseases, with 27 deaths from lung cancer.[27]

Documents released in product liability suits against the asbestos industry in the United States show that a conscious, rational, well-organized cover-up of the ill-health effects of asbestos was engineered by representatives of Johns-Manville Corporation, Raybestos-Manhattan Incorporated and other asbestos companies. The Subcommittee on Crime of the Committee on the Judiciary, U.S. House of Representatives, notes in its report on Corporate Crime:

> South Carolina Circuit Court Judge James Price (who reviewed the material), is quoted as saying "it shows a pattern of denial and disease and attempts at suppression of information" so persuasive that he ordered a new trial for the family of a dead insulation worker whose earlier claim had been dismissed. Judge Price noted that correspondence further reflects a conscious effort by the industry in the 1930s to downplay, or arguably suppress the dissemination of information to employees and the public for fear of promotion of lawsuits. Judge Price also noted compensation disease claims filed by asbestos insulation workers against several companies—which quietly settled them—including eleven asbestosis cases settled out of court by Johns-Manville in 1933, all predating the time (1964) when these companies claim they first recognized the hazard to insulators.[28]

In a 1949 survey of a Canadian Johns-Manville plant entitled *Industrial Hygiene—Survey of Men In A Dusty Area*, seven workers were found to have asbestosis. However, the medical director deemed it "inadvisable" to warn the workers of the problem.[29] Labelled the Asbestos Pentagon Papers, the documents, revealing deceit and cover-up, have led to numerous lawsuits and compensation claims. But legal action cannot give back lives or good health. We will continue to reap the violence of asbestos for some time, notwithstanding reduced levels of exposure and more public concern. As a recent newspaper headline states, "Asbestos Finally Catches Up."[30] For both workers and non-workers, asbestos will continue to take its toll.[31] The worker in the following profile is one of its many victims.

PROFILE: The Rude Awakening

Everyone likes to have a bit of respite from the workaday routine. When Tony Vidrih and his co-workers were in a particularly playful mood, they'd toss chunks of asbestos at each other. If only they'd known . . . but obviously they didn't. Despite, or perhaps because of, the fact that they were being inundated with asbestos insulation, and despite the fact that insurance companies since shortly after the turn of the century have upped their rates to insure asbestos workers, the workers in this warehouse hadn't been told of impending health dangers.

Now they know—largely because of Tony Vidrih's case. Exactly how many of them wonder about the possibility of their premature doom due to asbestosis will never be recorded. In this particular warehouse Tony is the acknowledged case and, perhaps in a sense, the herald of days to come.

Every six weeks Tony has chest X-rays to see how his condition is progressing. In 1978 Tony was diagnosed as having oat-cell carcinoma. In 1979 he became one of the first workers in this country to have his lung cancer recognized by the Workmen's Compensation Board as being indirectly related to his intake of asbestos fibres.

Tony Vidrih

Tony and his wife Gertrude sit at the kitchen table in their Sherwood Park home, on the outskirts of Edmonton. Stelco, the steel company where Tony worked for 17 years, is only a few miles away. Though he doesn't work there any more, that company's name and Tony's misfortune will stick in the minds of his wife, children, and co-workers long after Tony is gone. And Tony is well on his way, as he readily admits.

To an outsider, it's amazing how Tony and Gertrude are able to relate, with hardly a hint of emotional trauma, details leading to the factor that will eventually separate their lives.

Tony came to Canada from Yugoslavia in the late 1950s to work as a farm labourer. In 1962 he began working for Stelco. During his 17-year service, Tony held jobs in the melting shops, dealing with molten metals, in the furnace, and later as a janitor in a warehouse where the ceiling had been sprayed with asbestos insulation. In the course of making a living at Stelco Tony worked with a host of chemicals, a few of which were carbon, arsenic, lime, sulphur, chrome, nickel oxide and, of course, asbestos. The heat from the furnace demanded protective equipment such as wrappings and leg garments made of asbestos.

After a severe back injury in the early 1970s, Tony was off work for a year before he returned to Stelco as a janitor. The warehouse where he worked, and where the lunchroom for some Stelco workers was located, dropped a continuous stream of asbestos. Large clumps fell to the floor and were left there until they became pulverized by forklift and pedestrian traffic into small fibres. Then they wafted through the air, apparently like any other dust.

On occasion, Tony would nap after taking a painkiller to ease his strained back. "That asbestos was dropping down like rain. I'd get up and I was all full of it, like someone had dropped flour all over me."

In the lunchroom, located in the same warehouse, workers would eat their sandwiches and, unknowingly, asbestos, which settled on anything at rest for more than a few minutes. It was a messy, dirty job—the workers thought that's all it was. And work went on.

In 1971, Tony realized that he had become unusually susceptible to chest colds. He'd never had any health problems, let alone any related to his chest. After visiting doctors from time to time to see about his chest-related illness, he was usually sent home for a week's rest, with doctors diagnosing his problem as bronchitis. In 1978 after one of his sporadic bouts, Tony visited a doctor and was once again diagnosed as having bronchitis. A month later, Tony noticed a lump on his shoulder. He returned to get a physician's knowledgeable advice, and was told that he had oat-cell carcinoma of the right lung. Gertrude was pregnant with a fourth child at the time.

Initially, the Vidrihs, while trying to cope with the understandably difficult fact that cancer had struck their family, thought they were just one of the multitudes randomly victimized by cancer. But, then, during one of the Vidrihs' regular visits to the W.W. Cross Cancer Clinic in Edmonton, Gertrude haphazardly began reading a magazine when an item caught her attention. It was the story of a worker in the United States who was launching legal action in an effort to be compensated for his cancer, which he believed to be related to his work with asbestos. It was the first time the Vidrihs had heard asbestos could cause cancer. Gertrude began to wonder if Tony's cancer was related to the same substance. "I felt sure he had worked with it." He had, and after garnering the strength to deal with the raw reality of death, and collecting the energy needed to concentrate on other efforts, the Vidrihs contacted the Steelworkers local that Tony belonged to. That led to six months of meticulous research in an effort to prove that Tony's health had been stolen by his exposure to asbestos.

Tony's work history was traced right back to the work he had done in Europe. The union and the Vidrihs scoured the country for doctors who had information relating to the cause and effect between asbestos and cancer, not an easy task when physicians generally avoid controversy. Then the family doctor was approached to detail his version of Tony's condition. Though the family physician did not directly admit that Tony's condition was caused by his work, he left little doubt that it was the likely reason. "We thought we had a big fight on our hands. People said that it was no use to try, that the WCB wouldn't even accept it," recalls Gertrude.

The Vidrihs note a major factor, one which was instrumental to their success, in winning the case. "The family doctor was behind us. When he filed the form it left little doubt that it was asbestosis. He was convinced that Tony had asbestosis and said verbally that he was ready and willing to go to court and say it if he had to."

The Vidrihs, with the help of their union, caught the company unaware. "The company didn't expect us to fight," says Tony. The amount of research they had done in six months, detailing Tony's 15-year indirect exposure to asbestos, was overwhelming. "It was worth it, we thought, even if we didn't win—as long as we could present a strong enough case to make it easier for someone else."

In the fall of 1979, three months after filing the WCB claim and after nearly six months of working for recognition of Tony's work-related problem, the WCB granted Tony total permanent disability—full compensation. Currently he receives $523 every two weeks—$1,046 a month. Still, it's only monetary compensation and can't be considered even so much as a consolation prize. As Tony remarks: "Maybe the company won't like this . . . but I'm very proud to have won this case. Not because I have better security, but maybe I'll open the door to lots of other people who really are going to need help before dying or after dying . . . for the wife and the kids. My pension will help Gertrude a little to pull through."

The warehouse where Tony contracted his disease has been cleaned up, largely due to pressure from the Steelworkers Local #5220. Workers still on the job no longer breathe in the asbestos that Tony did. But no one yet knows how many feel the effects of the fibres they were once subjected to.

Both Tony and Gertrude call the circumstances they are facing "a rude awakening." Gertrude holds down a full-time job as a foreperson of mechanical maintenance for the local school board. Ironically, asbestos is now being detected in schools across the country, where it was installed as a "fire-free" insulation. Her attitude toward the job has changed enormously since the discovery of Tony's health problems. At one time, they both trusted their employers. Tony now says that if he'd known the dangers he would never have handled the material. And if he were back at work today and noticed an infraction of health and safety regulations, he says he would go directly to the occupational health and safety office to see about corrective action.

Gertrude now refuses to do any tasks which she senses may endanger her health. As a foreperson, she advises fellow workers to adopt a similar attitude.

"It really bothers me, you know. You go out there to work. You do your best to keep your employer happy. You're there to make a living and then all of a sudden you get sick because of your job, because of your employer's negligence. Those people are out there making a living. I don't think they should have to die because of company ignorance," says Gertrude.

The Vidrihs say they aren't bitter. But they have both turned into vigilant supporters of worker health. Tony is busy fighting for his life. At the age of 44 he is going through extensive chemotherapy and wondering how much longer he can hang on. And Gertrude is busy keeping a protective eye open for health problems in her workplace. "If a worker wouldn't want to fight for compensation for his work-related problems, I'd do my best to encourage it. Do it . . . maybe it won't help you . . . but there's other people. If you fight maybe it will open up the area for the next person. We can't do anything for Tony but maybe we can do something for other people," says Gertrude.

Tony sits pensively. His four children are playing actively. Gertrude tries not to let it show. Her work, her children, keep her busy. But once in a while there is a glimmer of pain at the thought of what could have been. Tony tries to smile, as though all is well.

No one can sum it up better than they. Tony: "The lady from the compensation board asked me "How does it feel to die?" . . . I don't feel nothing 'cause I'm going to die one day or another . . . but you think about it . . . I'm ready; whenever the time will come I'll have to go . . . but what I'm thinking about is her and the kids. If the kids were bigger they could help her, but the little one was only two years old on Valentine's Day and the oldest one is only fourteen. They are still small. . . . Otherwise about dying . . . I'm ready . . . whatever comes . . . and I know it won't be long . . . 'cause I can feel I'm going . . . but I won't give up till the last minute." Gertrude: "It hurts, it hurts deep. And you always wonder why. But I think I've pretty well grown to accept it. I can't say I'm bitter with the company or anything like that . . . because the guys were in ignorance . . . I'm not bitter about the case . . . I honestly do hope, though, that every place else is cleaned up. I don't think anybody else should have to go through what we're going through. It's hard on Tony, it's hard on me and it's hard on the kids."

On August 6, 1980, Tony Vidrih's name was placed on the growing list of occupational health and safety fatalities.

NOTES

1. Robert Morgan, "Tracing Causes of Industrial Illness," *Canada Labour* 23 (1) (March, 1978): 19.

2. One of the authors, Charles Reasons, accompanied provincial occupational health and safety officers on several site visits in the summer of 1980.

3. *Fatalities In Canadian Industry, 1969-1978* (Ottawa: Occupational Safety and Health Branch, Department of Labour, October 1979).

4. Terence G. Ison, *The Dimensions of Industrial Disease* (Kingston, Ontario: Industrial Relations Centre, Queen's University, 1978).

5. Linda McQuaig, "Occupational Death," *Maclean's*, May 19, 1980, p. 45.

6. Nicholas A. Ashford, *Crisis In the Workplace: Occupational Disease and Injury* (Cambridge, Mass.: MIT Press, 1976), p. 73.

7. This material comes largely from Yessy Byl, *Compensation for Industrial Diseases in Alberta* (Unpublished paper, University of Calgary, 1979). Stress will be treated in a separate chapter.

8. Ray Sentes, *Hazards in the Workplace: Responses and Recommendations of Alberta's Unionized Workers* (Edmonton: Alberta Federation of Labour, 1981).

9. Samuel S. Epstein, *The Politics of Cancer* (New York: Anchor Books, 1979).

10. Ashford, *Crisis In The Workplace*, p. 74.

11. Ison, *Industrial Disease*, p. 5.

12. "PCB, Other Toxic Chemicals Penetrated Safety Clothes," *The Calgary Herald*, February 16, 1981.

13. Janet Bertinuson, "Occupational Cancer," *Monitor*, Vol. 8, No. 2 (March-April, 1980): 6.

14. Science Council of Canada, *Policies and Poisons* (Ottawa: Ministry of Supply and Services, 1977), p. 20.

15. Lloyd Tataryn, *Dying for a Living* (Ottawa: Deneau and Greenberg, 1979) pp. 61-105.

16. Elliott Layton, *Dying Hard* (Toronto: McClelland and Stewart, 1975).

17. M. Grace, M. Larson, and J. Hanson, "Bronchogenic Carcinoma Among Former Uranium Mine Workers at Port Radium, Canada—A Pilot Study," *Health Physics*, Vol. 38 (April 1980): 657-61.

18. Thomas Pawlick, "The Silent Toll," *Harrowsmith*, June, 1980, p. 39. Also see Karl Z. Morgan, "How Dangerous is Low-Level Radiation?" *New Scientist*, April 5, 1979, pp. 18-21.

19. Brief regarding the proposal by Eldorado Nuclear Ltd. to build a uranium refinery near Warman, Saskatchewan, presented on behalf of the Saskatchewan Division of the Canadian Union of Public Employees to the Federal Environmental Assessment Panel, January 18, 1980, Saskatoon, Saskatchewan. It should be remembered that Eldorado Nuclear has a high rate of accidents, according to the figures in Chapter 2. Although the Warman site has been initially turned down, alternative Saskatchewan sites are being considered. See "Uranium Refinery Ruled Out," *Calgary Herald*, August 6, 1980; and Andreas Schroeder, "A Small Town Faces Up to a Big Question," *Today Magazine*, January 31, 1981, pp. 6-8.

20. "Utility Admits to Misleading Public," *The Calgary Herald*, July 22, 1980.

21. Bruce Montadar, *A Case Study: Occupational Health Regulations Limiting Radiation In Uranium Mines* (Ottawa: Ministry of Supply, 1980).

22. Ibid., p. 24.

23. Jessica L. Pearson, "Organizational Response to Occupational Injury and Disease: The Case of the Uranium Industry," *Social Forces* 57 (September 1978): 23-41.

24. Science Council of Canada, *Policies and Poisons*, p. 17.

25. For an in-depth analysis of Thetford and the politics of asbestos, see Tataryn, *Dying for a Living*, pp. 15-60.

26. Epstein, *The Politics of Cancer*, p. 79-102.

27. Ibid., pp. 82-83.

28. Subcommittee on Crime of the Committee on the Judiciary, House of Representatives, Ninety-Sixth Congress, Second Session, *Corporate Crime* (Washington, D.C.: U.S. Government Printing Office, May 1980): 24.

29. Epstein, *The Politics of Cancer*, p. 93.

30. "Asbestos Finally Catches Up," *The Calgary Herald*, June 28, 1980.

31. Unsafe asbestos levels have been found in schools and government buildings. The New Brunswick government buildings were closed due to an "unacceptable amount of asbestos in the air." ("Hazard Halts Government," *Calgary Albertan*, June 12, 1980). Ironically, even the Consumer Product Safety Commission of the United States found itself subject to assault from flaking asbestos ("Asbestos Hazard Found at U.S. Watchdog Agency," *The Calgary Herald*, June 26, 1980).

Chapter 4

Work-Related Stress

> *Job stress is the tolerated bedfellow of the worker. It can't be left in the locker room with the hard hat and coveralls at the end of the work day. . . . Although sources of stress at various work situations may vary, the nature of work and technology determines the quality of life of a particular workforce. It is also, perhaps, the single most important variable affecting the environment, family life, recreation, leisure and the general health and safety of workers.*[1]

Work as a Social Problem

Your work, or lack of it, is a major aspect of your social identity. Work is a social issue for several reasons. Since it's defined as an obligation for most of the population, when not all people can obtain it, we have the unemployed, the marginally employed, and the underemployed, and, more often than not, guilt—a sign that many people are discontented with their work. Consequently, since having a job is pivotal to the North American lifestyle, lack of work or dissatisfaction with work can greatly affect one's qualtiy of life. How often have you encountered the question "What do you do?" While all of us occupy several different roles such as parent, spouse, lover, friend, volunteer, neighbour, son/daughter, etc., all of these are considered inappropriate answers. Instead, you are expected to respond with one role such as engineer, truck driver, carpenter, plumber, teacher, fireman, housewife, secretary, etc. In this society, having a job justifies your existence. Work becomes a social problem for exactly that reason.

Since work and personal identity are tightly intertwined, the nature and quality of our job and our satisfaction with it affect our health and safety on the job, as well as off. Job stress may injure us physically and mentally and damage relationships with others—whether we are actually at work or not.

What is stress? According to Webster's Dictionary, stress is defined as pressure and strain, especially a force that tends to distort a body or also a factor that induces bodily or mental tension. Structural engineers talk about stress factors and stress systems in bridges, steel girders, skyscrapers, and other physical structures. What about psychological and physiological stress? All of us have probably been under stress to finish a task, make an appointment, do well on an exam, or excel in cooking, dating, childbearing, lovemaking, or any number of feats! While stress is recognized as an important motivator, it can also have ill consequences.

A Variety of Stressors

Studies of the workplace have generally found the following work-related stress hazards present:

1. *Job dissatisfaction* produces ill health and a shorter life span.
2. *Physical conditions* such as noise, vibration, extremes of temperature, poor lighting and ventilation and safety hazards produce stress.
3. *Overload/underload* occurs when there are dull, repetitive and machine-controlled tasks (underload) or when too many responsibilities and competing demands are placed on one's time (overload).
4. *Scheduling* such as shiftwork and compulsory overtime are job stressors.
5. *Unclear demands* by superiors are stress-producing.
6. *Concern for job security* is stressful, particularly for women and minority group members who are most likely to hold tenuous positions.[2]

As will become evident in discussing several of these stressors, physiological, psychological, and social harm may follow excessive stress.

What are some of the biological aspects of stress? In Table 4-1 we find that some of the adverse effects include increased risk of artery disease, heart disease, and kidney disease. While the stress response is a natural mechanism for adapting to the environment, excessive stress can lead to a variety of ill health effects. Heart disease is the number one killer in Canada and stress is an important factor in producing heart disease. Hypertension (high blood pressure) and subsequent heart disease are not uncommon in certain occupations. Besides high blood pressure, stress contributes to peptic ulcers, another major disease in our industrialized society.

Noise as a Stressor

Excessive noise is a stressor which produces not only physical damage to the ear but also both physical and emotional drain. It causes the body to produce more hormones, such as adrenalin, which increase one's pulse rate, blood pressure and rate of breathing. Blood clotting ability is increased and the vessels in the body, except those in the muscles and brain, constrict. Excessive noise levels are related to increased rates of heart disease, circulatory and digestive problems, and ulcers. One's balance and vision are also affected by noise.[3] This, combined with the annoyance factor, contributes to many accidents in noisy work areas. Ultimately, since it produces such stress-related ailments as heart disease, noise can kill you.

The Canadian Union of Public Employees *Hazards Inventory* notes the effects and remedies for noise hazards, shown in Table 4-2.

A hearing protective device, the least effective method of curbing the prob-

Table 4-1

Selected Biological Aspects of the Stress Response*

Selected Effects on Target Organs	Selected Biological Responses	Selected Potential Adverse Effects
Pituitary and Adrenal Function Stimulated	Indirect: (a) Affects all systems listed below Direct effects: (b) Increased concentration of cholesterol in blood (c) Increased concentration of blood sugar	Risk factors in heart disease
Blood	Increased clotting time	Risk factor in heart disease
Kidneys	(a) Cell structure can be damaged by adrenal corticoid hormones (b) Secrete pressor substances which constrict blood vessels, and possible decreased excretion ability	(a) Kidney disease can result (b) Can result in hypertension, which in turn is risk factor for kidney and heart disease
Thyroid	Stimulates metabolism in all organs	(a) Increased heartrate—risk factor in heart disease
Fat Tissue	Releases free fatty acids	Risk factor in heart disease
Gastrointestinal Tract (stomach and intestines)	(a) Suppresses movement; changes surface conditions (b) Stimulates gastric acid secretion	(a) Risk factors for duodenal and stomach ulcers, ulcerative colitis (b) Colon cancer (??)
Blood Vessels	Inflammatory changes resulting in constriction	Risk factor in artery disease, heart disease, and kidney disease
White Blood Cells and Lymph Gland	Depression synthesis and function	Decreased immunological response: increased disease susceptibility (??)

* From *Women's Work, Women's Health: Myths and Realities*, by Jeanne Mager Stellman. Copyright © 1977 by Jeanne Mager Stellman. Reprinted by permission of Pantheon Books, a Division of Random House, Inc.

lem, is the most likely approach to be taken, since it involves little or no capital investment or change in the workplace. The widespread use of such protective devices demonstrates that economic priorities of the workplace are more important to management than the health and safety of workers. In one shop which the first author scrutinized with a provincial inspector, the workers had to pay for ear plugs or other protective gear. According to the inspector and plant safety supervisor, if workers were given such devices they would not look after them, "but charge them and they will be careful." While we were sitting and discussing this in the plant safety manager's office, a young man came in complaining about headaches and ear problems. He had a large, abnormal growth on one ear and appeared in pain, possibly due to the hearing protective device and/or the abnormal noise level. The plant safety officer first suggested that his problem might not be industrially-caused. However, the provincial inspector intervened and suggested that the worker see a doctor and have it checked out. The plant safety officer reluctantly agreed, but the worker could not leave for several hours because the plant manager was not around to O.K. his trip to the doctor.

Although the most serious consequence of exposure to occupational noise is permanent loss of hearing, many other negative consequences ensue, all of which can be tied to stress. Non-occupational noise has been linked to increased deaths around high-noise airports.[4] A Danish survey of 960 women in 28 separate communities found that with increased nuisance due to increased (from 56 decibels to 72 decibels) traffic noise, the percentage of women with a high degree of psychic well-being declined from 63 per cent to 30 per cent, while the number using sedatives increased from 23 per cent to 43 per cent, and the consulting of doctors due to psychic problems increased from 3 per cent to 30 per cent of the sample.

Stress and Heart Disease

As noted in Chapter 1, heart disease is the leading killer of Canadians, claiming 56,970 lives in 1975. A recent study of heart disease published in the *American Journal of Public Health* found that clerical workers who are or have been married and who have children are twice as likely to have heart disease as are other working women and housewives.[5] The research showed that secretaries and other clerical workers had the most suppressed anger, created by a combination of job and home circumstances which didn't allow for the venting of this anger. These workers complained about unsupportive bosses and were on the same job for ten years or longer. The researcher, Suzanne G. Haynes, stated that "They had almost no control over their jobs. They were told what to do and when to do it. They had no freedom of movement."

An important cause of stress in the workplace is the lack of control over the environment, including tight rigid schedules set by others, close supervision, and little physical or intellectual mobility. A large proportion of the 40 per cent of the workforce that are women work in female job ghettos as typists, secretaries,

Table 4-2

Noise Hazards*

Hazard	Where Found	Effects	Controls
Noise (constant)	Found in virtually every workplace to some degree.	Noise can cause hearing loss which affects both the ability to understand speech and the ability to hear other sounds (e.g., some high frequency musical instruments)	Virtually any noise can be controlled through improved engineering.
	Noise is defined as unpleasant or unwanted sound.	Noise can affect balance as well as visual acuity.	In many instances simple measures can reduce noise levels (e.g., use of 3 narrow belts rather than one wide one)
	Ranges from compressors or pneumatic tools to trucks, to heavy equipment to printing presses to electric typewriters to computers.	High noise levels cause people to shout in order to communicate—may result in voice disorders.	Every workplace should be analysed to determine and evaluate noise sources.
		Noise has been linked to numerous other internal problems including digestive, circulatory and coronary heart diseases.	Noise can be controlled at the source (e.g., enclosure), or on the path to the worker (e.g., acoustical barriers) or at the worker (e.g., enclosed control booth).
			Hearing protection such as ear plugs or muffs is the least effective way to control noise.

			In many instances such devices do not afford protection, such as cases where workers are required to wear both safety glasses and ear muffs.
			Hearing protection is uncomfortable especially in hot environments and it may interfere with communication on the job.
			Hearing protection is not a solution to a noise problem because it does nothing to reduce or eliminate the noise.
Noise (impact)	Impact noise is defined as noise where peaks occur at intervals of greater than one second. Examples include rivet guns, drop hammers, punch presses, etc.	It is believed that combinations of impact and continuous noise are the most hazardous.	Equipment needs to be redesigned to minimize noise production.
		Single loud impacts from an explosion can rupture the ear drum.	
		This type of injury is less common in occupational exposures.	

* Source: Canadian Union of Public Employees, *The Health and Safety Hazards Faced by Canadian Public Employees*, Ottawa, 1978, pp. 18-19

CAMROSE LUTHERAN COLLEGE
LIBRARY

health aides, nurses, and textile workers, where there is a rigid authority structure and little control over the workplace. The traditionally low status of women in industrial societies is more conducive to stress than the higher status associated with men's work. For example, housework is considered unskilled and assigned little prestige compared to men's work. Also, "women's jobs" bring low esteem and are psychologically unrewarding. Finally, the role expectations for women are generally diffuse and unstructured, thus producing anxiety and stress. For example, it is easier to measure steel production than the emotional and physical output required for child-rearing. These factors not only account for more stress for women, but also for sex differences in rates of mental illness.[6]

An example which illustrates the important link between stress and heart disease comes from Japan. Although highly industrialized and urbanized, Japan has one of the lowest rates of coronary heart disease in the world, while Canada and the United States have among the highest. In a study depicting this stark contrast, Y. Scott Matsumato presents the following hypothesis:

> The etiology of coronary heart disease is multiple and complex, but in urban-industrial Japan, the in-group work community of the individual, with its institutional stress-reducing strategies, plays an important role in decreasing the frequency of the disease. If adverse and stressful life experiences may be translated through physiological mechanisms into bodily disease, then the converse seems reasonable.[7]

Matsumato points out that the Japanese are less self-centered and egocentric than North Americans and more dependent upon the social group. The employee in Japan is hired essentially for life and gets a major part of his or her identity from the company. The employees can be open and relaxed with their fellow employees, not competing and closed. This strong collectivist orientation means there is no distinction between work and leisure or between public and private life. Most socializing is with other employees, and many stress-reducing activities are provided by work, including after-work socializing such as vacations with the work group and after-work tea. The mobility, individual competition and isolation which is stress-producing in North America is much less evident in Japan. The workplace is a communal, family-oriented organization which enters into all aspects of life from celebrating holidays to group vacations. The employer provides security and a sense of self-worth which is usually absent in the North American setting.

"Take This Job and Shove It"

Job dissatisfaction is a key factor in occupational stress and is associated with coronary heart disease. Poor working conditions such as tediousness, lack of recognition, and impoverished interpersonal relations can produce low self-esteem and heart disease.[8]

If a happy worker is a happy citizen, then an unhappy worker is an unhappy citizen. The dissatisfied worker may come home from work and vent anger by kicking the dog. If there isn't a dog, the victim may be the cat, spouse, children, or oneself. Thus, dissatisfaction with your job can lead to cruelty to animals, child beating, spouse beating, divorce, or suicide, and other traumatic events. Disliking your work and consequently yourself may also produce excessive use of alcohol or other drugs, homicide, automobile accidents, and other harmful events which go beyond the workplace. Such dissatisfaction also leads to carelessness—and if a worker *cares less* about the work, he or she is more likely to have an on-the-job mishap.

What do workers say when asked whether or not they are satisfied with their current jobs, "all things considered"? The great majority of workers responding to this question in different countries over the last 25 years have said they are satisfied. In a 1975 study 82 per cent of Canadians surveyed revealed their jobs were at least "somewhat enjoyable." Such figures are startling given the extent of strikes, sabotage and absenteeism in the workplace. On an average day in this country more than 530,000 workers don't report to work and absenteeism annually accounts for eleven times the number of man-days lost due to strikes and lockouts.[9] In *The Tyranny of Work*, James W. Rinehart suggests there is a war at the workplace as evident in strikes, wildcat strikes, restriction of output, and making the workplace liveable through horseplay, talk, and sharing of food, drink and sabotage.[10] Why, if workers say they are satisfied, is there such a war at the workplace?

If we ask workers a different set of questions we find less satisfaction. For example, the level of satisfaction expressed in answer to the question: "What type of work would you try to get into if you could start over again?" declines rapidly. In one study the extent of satisfaction with one's job ranged from a high of 93 per cent for urban university professors to a low of 16 per cent for unskilled auto workers.[11] More specifically, we see a direct relationship between declining satisfaction and jobs which afford little opportunity for independent control of the work process.

Table 4-3

Job Satisfaction by Occupation

Occupation	% Satisfied
Urban University Professors	93%
White-Collar Workers (21-29 yrs. old)	46%
White-Collar Workers (30-55 yrs. old)	43%
Skilled Auto Workers and Skilled Steelworkers	41%
All Blue-Collar Workers	24%
Unskilled Steelworkers	21%
Unskilled Auto Workers	16%

Only 50 per cent of a Canadian sample indicated they would "take the same job without hesitation" when asked, "Knowing what you know now, if you had to decide all over again whether to take the job you now have, what would you decide?"[12] Unfortunately, the survey was not broken down into occupational groups. Nonetheless, one-half of Canadian workers sampled wouldn't accept their jobs again without thinking twice.

From a variety of studies it is evident that commitment to one's job is based upon its relative status compared to other occupations and, significantly, the amount of control an individual exercises within the job. In a recent study of 22,000 workers in 130 occupations in the United States, those under the most stress were unskilled labourers, secretaries, assembly-line inspectors, laboratory technicians, mid-level office managers, foremen, managers, waitresses/waiters, machine operators, farm owners, miners, and house painters.[13]

Social scientists often use the term *alienation* to designate the feelings of powerlessness and meaninglessness often produced by such jobs. This feeling of alienation is evident in the following remarks by an automotive plant worker in Southern Ontario:

> Oh, it can drive you. It can really drive you after a while, especially with all the repetition. You're a robot. You're a number, "who are you? I don't know, I'm 3518." Getting written-up, getting into trouble is the only way you get recognition. A "pinkie" is an award—they still remember your badge number and name. You gotta lead a wild-cat if you wanna be a foreman. Sabotage too, that helps break the monotony. Sure. How many guys in there are divorced because they are working there. It's a great place to become an alcoholic—7 days a week, 12 hours a day. How greedy are you? Sure, I hit the sauce pretty bad for a while till the wife threatened divorce. But they treat it like a game. I would like an apprenticeship. I really want an apprenticeship bad. I love working with my hands. I put in for one—they had three openings. I figured that would be my college education, that's where it's at for me. But I didn't get it and I know why—it's my union involvement. They make a game of it, when it's not really a game. It's people, human lives you're dealing with. These people aren't games. It's a corporate game. It's the corporation that counts and nothing else. Production is all they care about. Everything else—safety, quality, people—they couldn't give a shit. That frustrates me when I start thinking about that. I don't daydream anymore. I save that for when I go to bed at night—going hunting or what have you. Oh yeh, that's a real freedom. The last time I went up to the woods I told my wife before I went I might not come back and she knows I'm serious. Things are just moving entirely too fast. I guess that's the reason for escape. We are rushing . . . pushing buttons, we're busting our ass to create new objects to save time so we can spend more time figuring out how to save more time. It's just out of control.[14]

What are the sources of alienation in our contemporary industrial society? Rinehart argues that there are three basic sources for worker alienation: First, the means of production are concentrated into the hands of a small dominant class. Second, markets have been created in land, labour, and commodities which make us feel separate, and like obsolete items. Land, labour, and other commodities are viewed in terms of prices and profits, and workers are viewed as commodities. Finally, there is an elaborate division of labour which produces hundreds of distinct, minute tasks which are often repetitive and boring.[15] Another consequence of alienation, as noted in the quote above, is excessive drinking.

One More for the Road to Alienation

In Canada in 1974 there were approximately 482,300 alcoholics—3 per cent of the adult population over 20 years of age. Only 3-10 per cent of alcoholics fit the stereotyped skid row image, with more than 50 per cent of alcoholics being fully employed members of the labour force, representing about 3-6 per cent of the labour force.[16] While alcoholics are found in different income and occupational categories, one Ontario study found that three occupational categories accounted for over one-half the alcoholic population: (1) service and recreation; (2) craftsmen and production workers and (3) unskilled labourers.[17]

Employers have responded to this massive problem with a variety of programs to help the employee with his or her problem.[18] Why? The following submission by New Brunswick to a national study of alcoholism in the workplace provides an answer.

Cost To the Company

- Sub-standard or deteriorating work performance
- Absenteeism—2½ times as frequently as the general population
- Employee turnover and costly training of replacements
- Friction with co-workers
- Lower morale
- Poor executive decisions
- Deteriorated customer or public relations
- Accidents on the job—3 times the company average
- Loss of trained and experienced workers with lengthy service, administrative costs resulting from processing grievances, discharge and suspensions
- Forced, premature disability retirements drain retirement funds.[19]

Therefore from a cost-benefit perspective it makes good business sense to deal with the problem of excessive alcohol use among employees. But how is it dealt with? The principal method is "constructive coercion." This amounts to confronting the employee with his or her problem, and giving him or her the option of solving the problem or being fired. This approach essentially views the problem as stemming from outside the workplace but affecting one's work. Thus, the structure and nature of work as a cause of stress and subsequently excessive alcohol use is not really addressed. No wonder people drink!

In the summary of results of the national survey on alcohol in the workplace, the Directorate of the Non-Medical Use of Drugs states:

> Most persons felt that the workplace was not a causal agent in the problem of

alcoholism. It was further felt that this issue should not be raised as it would provide an excuse for the alcoholic to avoid responsibility. Others felt addiction services had no business examining this, that the emphasis should be on treatment.[20]

In spite of this prescribed ignorance, the Ontario submission notes that:

> We assume that the workplace does act on the individual to cause many personal problems including alcoholism. Our primary focus in approaching employers is to encourage them to identify problem employees and to establish policies and procedures that may reduce work problems. *We do not approach employers with the notion of redesigning their internal operative structures.*[21]

It is well established that the social patterns of some occupations call for more drinking than others. Organizations may stimulate the idea that drinking is an important part of performing the job. For example, alcoholism symptoms of business executives correspond with their career development in the mid-thirties and early fifties. In groups such as the military, merchant marine, and isolated work camps, the monotonous and protective, yet controlled, routines are broken by drinking opportunities. Drinking becomes a preoccupation to reduce the routine of the job, sexual deprivation, and loneliness of an all-male society.[22]

For example, a case is currently before the British Columbia Workers' Compensation Board asking the board to include alcoholism in its definition of a work-related disability. Co-author and Vancouver lawyer Craig Paterson is claiming his 42-year-old client developed alcoholism as a consequence of his years of working in hard rock mining in isolated camps. Osgoode Hall law professor Terence Ison, former chairperson of the B.C. Workers' Compensation Board, believes that "where drinking is encouraged by the employer as part of the job, looking after the bar, for instance, or salesmen entertaining customers, any consequent alcoholism might be seen as a result of employment."[23] While Paterson is not overly optimistic that the Board will rule in his favour, the challenge has been made and he sees victory eventually for such workers' claims.

Bill Rozel, enforcement head for Alberta Workers' Occupational Health, Safety and Compensation recently noted, when talking about the high accident rate on oil rigs:

> Senior executives bring booze onto a dry rig in the belief that this will endear them to the men; this is not helpful to the toolpush (rig manager) who then has to get through a shift with a less-than sober crew.[24]

The reason that alcoholism and other problems usually show up last in the workplace is succinctly stated by the Saskatchewan head of occupational health and safety, Robert Sass:

> Workers do whatever possible to adapt to the demands of the workplace. This apparent adaptation shows up as maladaptation outside work—in the form of marital problems, poor digestion, tiredness, strained relationships with children, alcoholism, drug abuse, etc. In fact, 85% of breakdowns occur first outside of work, only

> lastly does it spill back into work in the form of absenteeism, low productivity, insubordination, and friction with fellow workers. Thus, the workplace is the first cause but the last effect in the chain of psycho-social illness.[25]

Our jobs—no matter how hard—justify our existence. We give our all—even ourselves.

The fact that job dissatisfaction and other stress factors may produce excessive drinking is evident in the occupationally-determined differences in rates of alcoholism. For example, labourers tend to evidence more alcoholism than many other occupations. As one study in Alberta concludes:

> This data suggests that the labour type of work may produce greater stress than other jobs. This may promote a life style that results in a higher incidence of alcohol abuse.[26]

The relationship between alcohol use and the working class has some important historical lessons for contemporary students of stress and drug use.

Institutionalizing Booze

During the eighteenth and nineteenth centuries drinking places became working-class refuges in England. Taverns provided many social services which later were taken over by other institutions. As centres of recreation they provided gambling, cockfights, games, music, circuses, theatricals, dances, and prostitutes. Also, they offered food and lodging and lavatories. Their lights, heat, furniture and sociability were comforting to the working class. Drinking places were also trading places and news stations.[27] Workers were compelled to go to taverns to be paid on paydays or when their jobs terminated, and the tavern-keeper who also acted as paymaster would often keep workers waiting until the workers would owe the tavern a large part of their pay in drink.[28] Also, the sellers of drink would allow workers to drink on credit and extend small loans, creating indebtedness and continued patronage.

Since taverns acted as employment agencies, workers depended on tavern-keepers to get a job. Hatters, smiths, carpenters, weavers, boot and shoe makers, metal workers, bakers, tailors, plumbers, painters, glazers, and book-makers had to periodically hang around a tavern to get a job. Coal miners and iron workers were hired by small contractors who kept drinking places and compelled their workers to spend a good portion of their pay on drink. "Coal heavers" on coal-carrying ships were required to drink a certain amount daily at work, with it being deducted from their wages. The hiring policy was based on the motto, "The hardest drinker is the best man." Many employers of common labourers and craftsmen such as candle makers, bakers, and tailors sold drink at the workplace and charged what the workers consumed against their wages. Gin was drunk by women and sedentary workers while beer was consumed by hard labourers because it was believed that beer was necessary for strenuous work. It was a custom to give drinks to workers instead of wages. Central to these policies was that alcohol production was big business and with the combination of coercion and the supply of a variety of services by taverns, hard drinking and drunkenness became associated with lower class life. Thus, distilling and brewing interests helped create drinking patterns among the working class.[29] In a similar fashion, the distilling industry in South Africa kept African mine workers in alcohol through canteens catering to the disposed workers.[30] The history of drink suggests that, contrary to the assumption that demand creates supply, supplies of booze created a demand which is becoming bigger business each year. The increasing sale and consumption of alcohol may tell us something about the increasing stress found in the workplace by the harassed worker.

Harassment as Stress; Stress as Harassment

One source of stress on workers is harassment on the job. Sexual harassment epitomizes the major characteristics of abuse of power: employees (male) in a position of power over other employees (female) exploit this dominance.

> Sexual harassment is any sexually oriented practice that endangers a woman's job, that undermines her job performance and threatens her economic performance. It is also any repeated and unwanted sexual comment, look, suggestion or physical contact that a woman finds objectionable or offensive and causes her discomfort on the job.
>
> It can range from unwanted suggestions or comments to attempted rape and rape. Physically, it can include pinching, grabbing, hugging, patting, leering, brushing against and touching. Psychologically, it can include subtle hints, sexual jokes, and requests for dates or sexual favours.[31]

While sexual harassment is real, it is not acknowledged by Workers' Compensation. In the summer of 1980, Astrid Davidson, Director of Women's Programs, British Columbia Federation of Labour wrote the director of Workers' Compensation concerning sexual harassment. The following response was received by Davidson.

September 5th, 1980

Ms. Astrid Davidson,
Director of Women's Programs,
B.C. Federation of Labour,
3110 Boundary Road,
Burnaby, B.C.
V5M 4A2

Dear Ms. Davidson:

Re: Sexual Harassment on the Job

This will acknowledge your letter of August 20th, 1980, about the above subject and referring to the case of Joseph Albanese (Mass. 389 NE 2d 83).

Joseph Albanese was awarded compensation for a "chronic anxiety state mixed with depression and somatized reaction and neuro-circulatory asthenia" which was considered to have been causally related to a series of emotional episodes related to his job as a "working foreman" and which consisted largely of his being stressed and embarrassed by actions of his immediate superior, and which resulted, at least in his mind, in humiliation and in an impaired relationship with his workers. In addition, it was possible to define clearly a series of such incidents over a period of about 20 months.

As a consequence of reading about this case, you have posed certain questions which I will attempt to answer in the order in which you have raised them.

1. What is the reaction of the B.C. Workers' Compensation Board to cases concerning stress and specifically sexual harassment?

Our Act (Section 5(1)) allows compensation to be paid for personal injury ". . . arising out of and in the course of employment." While we would have no problem in including psychological injury as a compensable illness under certain circumstances, we do not believe generally that "sexual harassment" arises "out of" the employment. It seems, rather, to be a matter which can be better dealt with by labour relations mechanisms and by civil legal action.

2. Do such cases come before the Board?

To my knowledge, no such claim has been presented to the Board, although the Board in Reporter Decision #102 dealt with disablement through exhaustion arising out of stress (see attached). The board of review also discussed an aspect of the same problem in a claim for compensation in a claimant with an intestinal disease (see enclosed).

3. How are they handled?

Since no claims have come before the Board, this question is not applicable. If such a claim did come before the Board the adjudicator would investigate and make a decision based on the facts of the case.

4. What section of the Act would apply?

As I mention above, Section 5(1) would seem particularly applicable. Other sections may apply depending on the circumstances of the case.

I trust this information will allow you to understand our present situation in regard to this subject.

Yours truly,

Adam S. Little, M.D.
Chairman.

According to research, 70-90 per cent of working women experience this type of assault during their working lives. However, many men do not think it is at all prevalent. A recent survey in the United States found that two-thirds of the male business executives surveyed believe that "reports of sexual harassment in the workplace are greatly exaggerated." Over two-thirds of the female executives (78 per cent) surveyed felt reports of sexual harassment were not exaggerated.[32] As we point out in Chapter 5, women have not been included in Workers' Compensation Boards, where decisions about such charges are rendered.

In a comprehensive study of compensation claims in California, Professor Carroll M. Brodsky shows that harassment increases a worker's chances of having accidents and committing sabotage, and can increase physical problems such as hypertension, gastrointestinal and musculaskeletal disorders.

> Harassment behaviour involves repeated and persistent attempts by one person to torment, wear down, frustrate, or get a reaction from another. It is treatment that persistently provokes, pressures, frightens, intimidates, or otherwise discomforts another person.[33]

She points out that the conditions for harassment are established by the stratification of positions, with differences in status, power, and privilege. For example, the belief that fear motivates and controls people is used by those in positions of power to harass those below them. Humour and teasing are one form of harassment. Other forms include scapegoating, name-calling, physical abuse, and the hurry-up tactic. She identifies name-calling as the most destructive form of abuse because it usually refers to a trait one can't change, such as sex or race.

Harassment by the system is systematic injustice to specific subgroups. For example, racial minorities and sexual minorities are more subject to such harassment. Work pressure harassment is based on the fact that profits are the motivating force of business and labour costs are a major expense. "Get the most out of the worker" is a pervading maxim. This is also true in government, where employees such as police, social workers, teachers, and others may have their workload rather than the size of the staff increased.

Brodsky found that reaction to harassment followed three phases: (1) confusion, shock, overwhelmed feelings; (2) random behaviour and (3) continued random behaviour, depression, and/or the decision to fight the problem.

Learn to "Cope" – The Buzzword

According to the Canadian Mental Health Association, there are two basic methods for coping with stress: (1) Being able to have a feeling of mastery and control over your environment, particularly those events which are stressful, and (2) being able to relax and adapt to one's environment.[34] Since the structure of the workplace is believed by many to be the social prerogative of management, much of the material on job-related stress focuses upon methods of coping for the worker by adapting and changing his or her lifestyle. As mentioned earlier, workers will often adapt to the demands of the workplace by maladapting in their off-the-job activities. Therefore, marital problems, excessive drinking, violence, and other problems will appear and eventually affect the job. The job may create the stress leading to such problems in "lifestyle" but, rather than being viewed as a source of the problems, it is often seen as a consequence of such "external personal problems."

No understanding of stress would be complete without talking about fitness. There is a large and growing emphasis on physical activity. Politicians and the government have taken on fitness like a fad. We have "Participaction" at the federal level and the pumping of more government money into amateur sport across the country. One can see the progression among politicians in just a few short years.

Whereas Pierre Trudeau rocketed to fame in the 1960s with his famous somersault dives off swimming pool boards, scuba diving and downhill skiing, one remembers fondly Mike Pearson sitting in front of a television set watching his beloved baseball games. And who could imagine John Diefenbaker or Louis St. Laurent engaged in anything requiring overall body movement?

Iona Campagnolo, the recent Liberal Cabinet minister—Fitness and Amateur Sports—seemed to be attired in jogging gear throughout her entire political career, perhaps including Cabinet meetings. The late Judy La-Marsh—Minister of Health and Welfare fifteen years ago—could never have been imagined attired in anything bespeaking physical leisure or recreation. Bob Stanfield might have helped the Tories win an election if he had been able to catch a football.

The business journals and newspapers are filled with advice to executives on the need for physical fitness, both for themselves and for their employees. A huge business has emerged in management fields—in the manufacture of fitness clothing and equipment, fitness institutes, fitness books, medical and recreational employee fitness programmes, and the like.

The key element used in the sale of physical fitness to business and for business is "productivity." Management and executives require fitness because it will prolong their skill utility for the company, set a good example for employees below them in the hierarchy, and assist in creating a stabler social harmony at work and at home which provides benefits to the company in solidity and tranquility. Also, of course, it fills the extra leisure created for them by the productive capacities of the workers. Executives can afford the longer lunch hours or shorter days or more flexible work hours to allow them to indulge in physical fitness. Who else can afford the expensive and extensive clubs and facilities of tennis and golf, handball and squash, sauna and swimming pool, heat treatments, whirlpools, massage, and weightrooms? This is especially true for office executives in cities. A large part of these executive activities are paid for by Canadian workers in the form of corporate or individual executive tax write-offs for business expenses. The trucker who plays in industrial league hockey in the winter and on a city fastball team in the summer can't claim his equipment or membership as a tax deduction. Nor is his company likely to offer to pay for these activities, except in indirect and limited ways, such as buying team sweaters. Truckers aren't given time off work or flexible hours to engage in these recreational sports. Thus it is much easier for an executive than for a worker to become physically fit and to retain physical fitness. Ads constantly remind workers they should be fit, but workers are not provided with the opportunities of the executive. If most workers are realistically to participate in such physical fitness programs, then they should have appropriate facilities and/or opportunities provided through the workplace. Workers can use the collective bargaining process to win on-the-job recreational facilities.

What about adapting the workplace to fit the needs of workers? Business-inspired slogans and programs have emerged in recent years with catchy new titles. Business, trade, and financial publications—and government documents—have featured a new series of articles, seminars, conferences, studies and management techniques. "Renewing the work ethic," "humanization of work," "quality of working life," "overcoming worker alienation," and "the absenteeism problem" are some of the slogans which are increasingly used.

The Ontario Ministry of Labour established an "Ontario Quality of Working Life Centre" in December, 1978 and began publication of a newsletter, "Q.W.L. Focus," in July, 1980. A joint union-management advisory committee was struck. It includes the President of the Niagara Institute, a leading Toronto corporate lawyer, the Presidents of three large companies—A.E. LePage Ltd., General Foods, and the Valleydene Corporation. It also includes the Presidents of the Ontario Federation of Labour and the Ontario Public Service Employees Union and the Canadian Directors of the Steelworkers and Auto Workers.

There are many related purposes put forward for "Quality of Working Life" programs: a more open, democratic workplace, designing or re-designing workplaces to achieve better harmony between social and technical features, improving the dignity and utility of work. No one would dispute that these are excellent objectives. But are programmes like this the best way for workers and unions to get there?

Insofar as workers' health is concerned, the purpose of these programmes is clearly to keep health and safety issues as far as possible out of traditional collective bargaining relationships. "Discussion" is preferred to traditional "confrontation." And the discussion and planning are meant to take place in informal, higher-level tripartite or multipartite consultative bodies—not through shop-floor or local union committees, demands, grievances or bargaining issues.

As the "Q.W.L. Focus" reveals:

> Collective bargaining is a useful form of conflict resolution. Q.W.L. is also useful because it offers a way of dealing with win-win as opposed to win-lose situations. *In win-win situations, management and labour can co-operate to achieve gains in areas such as the redesign of work or improvements in health and safety conditions.* Collective bargaining and Q.W.L. are different, but complementary processes.[35]

According to this, collective bargaining is for crass economic issues such as wages, which are "win-lose" situations, while Q.W.L. is for safety and health issues, which are "win-win" situations. This thinking is dangerous and unhealthy for workers if it results in keeping health and safety issues out of the normal shop-floor grievance and collective bargaining settings.

The federal government has also been active in this game over the last three years, attempting to introduce Q.W.L. into various sectors of the federal public service, such as the Post Office.

How can we really get at the sources of stress? This will entail a major change in the nature of relationships between workers and management. Rinehart concludes:

> The only genuine solution to alienation involves a total restructuring of the workplace, the economy, and the society. No less than such a radical change can overcome alienation. Recall that alienation in the first instance is a structural condition in which workers are detached from control of their labour and its products. The antithesis of alienated labour is worker's control—not just over their immediate jobs but over the venture work process and its objectives. Workers' control strikes at the fundamental sources of alienation. It entails a transfer of power to working people from elites.[36]

In a more practical and pragmatic way, Sass emphasizes the need for a shop-floor emphasis in attacking work-related stress. Worker participation at the shop-floor level is crucial to eliminating the source of stress-alienated labour. By establishing the three R's of occupational health and safety for workers—the right to know of dangers, the right to refuse dangerous work, and the right to participate in formulating and enforcing rules—the problem will be addressed by those most affected and most interested—workers themselves.[37]

The following case from Saskatchewan is an example of stress reduction brought about through the initiative of workers.

ON A MATTER PERTAINING TO

A STRESSFUL CONDITION

AT THE PRINCE ALBERT PULP COMPANY LTD.,
PRINCE ALBERT, SASKATCHEWAN

I BACKGROUND:

In late March, the joint Occupational Health and Safety Committee established pursuant to Section 24 of *The Occupational Health and Safety Act (1977)* at the Prince Albert Pulp Company Ltd., agreed to submit an unresolved problem pertaining to a complaint of stress by four recovery boiler operators to the Occupational Health and Safety Branch of the Saskatchewan Department of Labour.

II THE PROBLEM:

In December, 1977, a new recovery boiler came into operation at the pulp mill. The new boiler is only half the capacity of the old boiler and according to management is fitted with every conceivable self-regulatory and safety device. The main control panel is fitted into the old boiler control room, on the opposite wall, but the evaporator panels for the new boiler are on a lower floor.

In mid-March, the recovery boiler operators complained that they were feeling the effects of stress due to the extra responsibility of looking after two boilers whereas they had previously looked after only one. They felt that the stress is having an effect on their health, and that this in turn creates a danger to other workers anywhere in the vicinity of either boiler. The four boiler operators believe that the explosion hazards of black liquor recovery boilers are greater than ordinary steam or power boilers, and they were not getting sufficient support from supervision.

III JURISDICTION:

The above unresolved Occupational Health and Safety Committee problem was appropriate for resolution by the Occupational Health and Safety Branch, Saskatchewan Department of Labour. Section 2, Sub-section (k) of *The Occupational Health and Safety Act (1977)* defines "occupational health" as follows:

> (i) the promotion and maintenance of the highest degree of physical, mental and social well-being of workers;
> (ii) the prevention among workers of ill health caused by their working conditions;
> (iii) the protection of workers in their employment from factors adverse to their health; and
> (iv) the placing and maintenance of workers in occupational environments which are adapted to their individual physiological and psychological conditions.

Increased stress or distress not only can produce disease but also increase the potential for accidents to the individual and fellow-workers.

Further, *The Boiler and Pressure Vessel Act (1977)* is also applicable to the above matter. Section 7, Sub-section (d) states that the boiler and pressure vessel inspector may

> give instructions orally or in writing to the owner, chief engineer, shift engineer or other persons responsible for or in immediate charge of a boiler, pressure vessel or plant on any matter pertaining to the construction, fabrication, installation, operation, care, maintenance or repair thereof and require that those instructions shall be carried out within a specified time;

further, Section 37 states that

> where exceptional circumstances exist, rendering strict compliance with the regulations impracticable, the chief inspector may subject to such conditions as he may prescribe, grant special exemptions in individual cases if satisfied that such exemptions are not inconsistent with safe practice.

IV APPROACH:

In order to make a judgement two aspects of the problem require investigation.

(A) First, an assessment of the stressor—that is an assessment of the new working conditions resulting from the additional boiler. This evaluation should also address itself to the following questions:

1. What change in *responsibility* occurs as a result of additional boiler?
2. What additional interactions between the new conditions and other features of work emerge?
3. Are there any increases in hazards to workers, other workers and property, etc., as a result of additional boiler?

In other words, *do increased responsibilities result in increased dangers?* The investigation of the above was appropriately assigned to the Boiler and Pressure Vessel Unit within the Occupational Health and Safety Branch, Saskatchewan Department of Labour.

(B) At the same time, the chief Occupational Medical Officer was asked to investigate the matter regarding stress or distress of the boiler operators as a result of the changed working conditions, or additional recovery boiler. The Chief Occupational Medical Officer's report would contain a medical evaluation of the operator as to the psychological and biological effects due to the "increased" stressors in their work environment.

V. SUMMARY OF INVESTIGATION:

(A) Medical Assessment of Stress

On March 29, 1978, Dr. L. E. Euinton visited the pulp mill and interviewed separately and privately the four recovery boiler operators. They all worked for Prince Albert Pulp Company Ltd., for ten years and have been recovery boiler operators for five to six years. For approximately one year, they have been working a 12-hour shift. More specifically, 4 days on day shift, 3½ days off, 4 days on night shift and 4½ days off, etc. The employees support this arrangement and maintain that their wives do so as well.

Afterwards, Dr. Euinton interviewed the boiler operators' supervisors. One supervisor stated that the responsibility of attending black liquor recovery boilers is not substantially greater than any other boilers, and that it is well within the compass of one operator to attend both boilers. He acknowledges that there have been recovery boiler explosions in the past with tragic results, but usually because someone has ignored signs that something was going wrong. His operators are experienced, are kept fully informed of the advisory committee's meetings, and are fully authorized to close down boilers or otherwise to act to avert serious mishaps, with no pressure to do otherwise for production motives.

The conclusion of Dr. Euinton's report is as follows:

> There is no doubt whatsoever in my mind that these recovery boiler operators are feeling under considerable stress, and that they are worried about the dangers to other men that their stress may cause. What I think most difficult is to allocate the causes of the stress, since I think it comes from a combination of extra responsibility and 12-hour shifts. One of the operators, for instance, lives on a farm of three acres and although he says that he does not substantially "moonlight" he has a wife and a young family and he does have to travel 45 miles to work. Under winter conditions, surely this in itself adds substantially to the strain of 12-hour shifts. The other three operators all live in their own homes in Prince Albert, which is about 14 miles away, also with wives and families.

(B) Report of the Boiler and Pressure Vessel Inspectors

On April 3, 1978, both Mr. Jim Crook and Mr. N. Uhrich, Inspection Engineers within the Boiler and Pressure Vessels Unit, inspected the boilers with a view of assessing the degree of responsibility in attending the black liquor recovery boiler, and whether this is substantially greater by having two boilers to look after instead of one.

The most significant and relevant findings in this report are as follows:

> We find that there appears to be a stress situation. The cause could be through lack of communication, lack of training, working a 12-hour shift, personality clashes between personnel or being over-committed on days off.
>
> We feel that a realignment of job responsibilities should take place to provide for one man per shift to act as relief panel operator. This relief panel operator would be competent at operating the recovery panels . . . .
>
> If, in the future, the turbine control panel is moved up to the control room, a further realignment of responsibilities could take place, however, there should be no reduction of manpower at that time.

VI DIRECTOR'S OBSERVATIONS:

As a result of the above two reports, I met with both the Chief Occupational Medical Officer and the Chief Boiler Inspector to discuss appropriate resolution to the matter. All agreed that the boiler operators are genuinely feeling under stress, with a great deal of concern for safety. Further, we were quite convinced that the situation would worsen if the recovery boiler operators were to continue to look after two boilers on a 12-hour shift.

Because of the degree of stress combined with responsibility, we concluded that the situation is intolerable.

Further, we could not understand why the workers at the Prince Albert Pulp Company Ltd., including the boiler operators, support a 12-hour shift, apparently with no account of the responsibility of the work and the fact that most are married men with families, and some with travelling to do under seasonally hard conditions.

VII REMEDIES:

In order that the boiler operators properly cope with the additional recovery boiler while working a 12-hour shift, the following remedies are to be implemented forthwith:

1. That there be a realignment of job responsibilities so as to provide for one man per shift to act as relief panel operator.
2. The relief panel operators ought to be competent at operating the recovery panels and should assume greater responsibility for training the spoutmen.
3. The relief operator may be assigned other duties during upsets in the system, when required, so as to assist in the levelling out condition. This reassignment is not to contradict the prime or major purpose of this determination, which is to make an assistant available to the operator of the recovery boilers, but rather to allow for flexibility during critical periods. Consequently, such reassignments would be infrequent and for short periods of time.
4. If in the future the turbine control panel is moved up to the control room, a further realignment of responsibilities could take place, however there should be no reduction of manpower at that time.
5. Greater efforts must be made for proper training of the spoutman who is essential in the operation of the recovery boiler because he manually controls the liquor bed and the air flow over the bed.
6. Finally, consideration to the present communications system should be reviewed by higher management. This review should also take into consideration lack of support to the boiler operators by existing supervision.

We believe that the implementation of the above will greatly contribute to the reduction of stress for the boiler operators, and to a more competent and smoother operation of the mill, making for a safer and healthier work environment.

ROBERT SASS,
Director, Occupational Health & Safety Division.

DR. L. E. EUINTON,
Chief Occupational Medical Officer.

RICHARD V. CURRY,
Chief Boiler Inspector.

April 20, 1978.

Although the above-mentioned case was resolved satisfactorily for the workers, attempts at receiving compensation for stress have generally met unsympathetic ears. The following case is one of the few in Canada to be decided upon concerning stress-related compensation. While the job stress was real, the British Columbia WCB decided to ignore its mandate of concern for workers' health.

RE: DISABLEMENT THROUGH EXHAUSTION[38]

Application Considered by:
T. G. Ison, Chairman
G. Kowbel, Commissioner
T. R. Watt, Commissioner

Decision No. 102
13th March, 1975

A claim has been received at the Board for compensation for a state of physical and emotional exhaustion alleged to have been caused by the stress of work.

There being no established principles for the guidance of adjudicators in deciding a claim of this kind, the claim has been referred to the Commissioners to determine the principles applicable.

Both the claimant and the employer seem aware that the Board is unaccustomed to paying claims on this ground, and the claim has therefore been presented in some detail. The facts as stated by the claimant are as follows:

> I have worked six years at [residential treatment centre for children] with children who have behaviour disorders. The nature of the work itself is very demanding of physical energy and emotional resources: we take care of the day to day needs of each child in a residential setting, we modify and build in appropriate behaviours for each child on an ongoing basis, we prepare the child and his family for his return home with the use of methods that we have found effective and that the parents have learned to use comfortably, we prepare the child to return to his school and community, and once returned we follow up his progress with a period of aftercare.
>
> Beyond that, in the past six years I have adjusted to several changes in treatment methods which have evolved into our present structure, have dealt with the effects of the expansion of our program into access or day care where I work each day with nearly half again as many children as when I began, and for the past several years have been introduced to and have actively participated in regular sessions with the families of children in treatment.
>
> These six years have been rewarding but exhausting. As the fatigue accumulated, I found myself becoming less efficient, less able to deal with everyday challenges without draining myself to do so. I was becoming edgy, nervous, depressed at not functioning as smoothly as I was used to doing, depleted in performing just my usual duties. Though apparently physically healthy, my energy and spirits were low. I went to my doctor, with the resulting diagnosis: physical and emotional exhaustion due to the nature of my work. He has prescribed approximately two months off work with reassessment after the first month and has urged me to go away for a few weeks if possible. My employer, ____________, agrees with this request for time off and supports my application to the Workmen's Compensation Board.

It appears that a period of rest of about 6 to 8 weeks is required for recuperation.

For the purpose of clarifying the applicable principles we will assume, without deciding, that the facts stated by the claimant are correct.

A state of physical and emotional exhaustion caused by stress over time does not come within the popular understanding of the word "injury," nor is it an "injury" as that word has been construed and understood by the Board. The question, therefore, is whether this kind of disablement should be recognized by the Board as an industrial disease.

For several reasons, we do not feel that recognition of exhaustion as an industrial disease would be practicable, or sound policy. Almost every occupation involves some physical and emotional demands. To prevent those demands from having a debilitating effect involves a range of judgments. There are the intial judgments by employers in selecting workers for jobs and by workers in selecting employment. Then there are judgments relating to workload, working conditions, working hours, and other factors relevant to stress. There are judgments relating to overtime, and to vacations. These matters often involve judgment both by employers and by workers, though to some extent they are regulated in labour legislation. It has not traditionally been regarded as a compensable disability when a worker is engaged for a position which he subsequently finds is too much for him, or becomes run down through working excessive overtime, or for other reasons finds that the demands of the job have a debilitating effect.

Many people cope with problems of this kind by changing their employment. Others cope by taking a vacation. In other cases, unions and employers cope with the problem by negotiation or arranging for time off in lieu of overtime. In other situations, where an employer recognizes that exceptional work demands have subjected a worker to a period of stress, sick leave may be arranged, or some other arrangement may be made by the employer for paid leave. But where an employer does not make such an arrangement, it would hardly seem fair that he should be able to pass on the costs of such leave to other employers who do.

Third, claims of this kind would be extremely difficult to adjudicate. For example, how could the Board conclude that the emotional stress resulted from work without considering whether it resulted from other causes; and how could this be decided without going back perhaps as far as childhood history? The answers may be obvious in some cases, but they would not be in others. Moreover the answers could not be determined in many cases without engaging in a kind of enquiry that many people would resent. For example, how could the Board determine the emotional significance of stress at work without enquiring into the domestic affairs and other aspects of the private life of the worker concerned?

Even apart from problems of causation, there would be obvious difficulties in distinguishing between someone who is suffering from physical and emotional exhaustion, and someone who simply needs a vacation. This is in addition to the problem of justifying the distinction when made. To make these distinctions in cases where someone needs a period of rest would involve substantial administrative costs, both at the Board and elsewhere, to determine whether that rest period should be paid for out of the Accident Fund, or in other ways. Overall and in the long run, we think it in the public interest that this administrative cost should be avoided, and that rest periods of this kind should be provided for through provisions of vacations, time off for overtime worked, sick leave, or in other ways that are provided for by collective agreement, or by arrangements between employers and workers.

RESOLVED that:

1. A state of physical and emotional exhaustion is not recognized by the Board as an industrial disease.
2. There will be no conclusions of fact reached on the particular claim, because assuming the facts as stated by the claimant to be correct, the claim should be denied.

NOTES

1. Robert Sass, "Stress: The Tolerated Bedfellow," *Canadian Dimension*, June 1980, p. 30.
2. "Stress: The More You Know About It, The Better You Cope," *Mental Health* 4, 2(May 1980): 4-7.
3. *Stress At the Workplace*. Prereading for A.U.P.E Conference on Health and Safety, June 12-14, 1980, Edmonton, Alberta.
4. B. E. Dunn, "The Noise Environment of Man," in H. W. Jones (ed.), *Noise In the Human Environment*, Vol. 2 (Environmental Council of Alberta, n.d.), pp. 195-257.
5. "Clerical Workers Face Higher Risks," *The Calgary Herald*, February 19, 1980.
6. Minaka K. Maykovich, *Medical Sociology* (Sherman Oaks, California: Alfred Publishing, 1980), pp. 118-20.
7. Y. Scott Matsumato, "Social Stress and Coronary Heart Disease In Japan," in H. Dreitzel (ed.), *The Social Organization of Health* (New York: Macmillan, 1971), pp. 127-28.
8. Maykovich, *Medical Sociology*, p. 124.
9. Joseph Smucker, *Industrialism In Canada* (Scarborough: Prentice-Hall, 1980).
10. James W. Rinehart, *The Tyranny of Work* (Don Mills, Ontario: Longman, 1975).
11. Harold L. Wilensky, "Work as a Social Problem," in Howard S. Becker (ed.), *Social Problems: A Modern Approach* (New York: John Wiley & Sons, 1966), pp. 117-66.
12. Smucker, *Industrialization in Canada*, p. 285.
13. "Stress," *Mental Health*, May 1980, p. 5.
14. Smucker, *Industrialization In Canada*, pp. 288-89.
15. Ibid.
16. Donald G. Finlay, *Constructive Coercion and the Alcoholic Employee: Problems and Prospects* (B.C. Alcohol and Drug Commission, 1975).
17. *Final Report of the Commission of Inquiry Into the Non-Medical Use of Drugs* (Ottawa: Information Canada, 1973), p. 702.
18. Christian Desjardins, *A Study of Occupational Alcoholism Programs In Canada* (Ottawa: Canadian Addictions Foundation, 1977).
19. Wayne Corneil, *Summary of Results and Submissions Received on Alcohol In the Workplace Study* (Ottawa: Non-Medical Use of Drugs Directorate, 1976), p. 62.
20. Ibid., p. 12.
21. Ibid., p. 147. Emphasis added.
22. Marshall B. Clinard and Robert F. Meier, *Sociology Of Deviant Behaviour*, 5th ed. (New York: Holt, Rinehart and Winston, 1979), pp. 358-59.

23. Mark Budgen, "Seeking Compensation for the Disabling Drink," *Maclean's*, January 26, 1981, p. 41.
24. "Provincial Official Shocked by Oil Industry Safety Record," *Edmonton Journal*, November 16, 1979.
25. Sass, "Stress," p. 32.
26. Deborah Kantz et al., *Alcoholism In the Workplace of Drumheller* (Ottawa: Department of Health and Welfare, n.d.).
27. Brian Harrison, *Drink and the Victorians: The Temperance Question In England 1815-1872* (London: Tabor and Tabor, 1971).
28. Dorothy M. George, *London Life In the 18th Century* (New York: Knopf, 1925).
29. Robert E. Popham, "The Social History of the Tavern," in Yedy Israel et al. (eds.), *Research Advances In Alcohol and Drug Problems* (New York: Pleman Press, 1978).
30. Charles Van Anselen, "Randloads and Rutgut, 1886-1903: An Essay on the Role of Alcohol in the Development of European Imperialism and Southern African Capitalism," *History Workshop* 2 (Autumn 1976).
31. Farida Shaikh, "Sexual Harassment: The Social Disease and How to Fight It," *C.U.P.E.: The Facts*, Vol. 2 (March 1980): 107.
32. "Harassment Exaggerated, Say Men," *The Calgary Herald*, February 18, 1981.
33. Carroll M. Brodsky, *The Harassed Workers* (Lexington, Mass.: D.C. Heath and Company, 1976), p. 2.
34. "Stress," *Mental Health*, May 1980, p. 5.
35. "Q.W.L. Focus," Vol. 1, No. 1 (Toronto: July 1980), p. 3.
36. Rinehart, *Tyranny of Work*, p. 166.
37. Robert Sass, *Stressors and Work Populations* (Regina: Occupational Health and Safety Branch, 1979).
38. *B.C. Workers' Compensation Reporter Series*, Vol. 2, pp. 25-27.

Chapter 5

Women's Work/ Women's Health

Any occupational hazard which may lead to disability, chronic illness or death of any worker or his or her potential offspring can and must be altered to provide maximum safety for the most susceptible worker in the labour force. The hazard, not the worker, must be controlled and the workplace must be designed to provide protection for the most vulnerable worker.[1]

Work*men's* Compensation

In reviewing the numerous reports and articles concerning occupational safety and health in Canada, one is struck by the almost total absence of women in the discussion. For example, only Saskatchewan publishes data on age, by sex, for all workmen's compensation claims.[2] It therefore seems appropriate that the government agencies which deal with health and safety are called Work*men's* Compensation. While the term "workers' compensation" is emerging as a non-sexist alternative, only in recent years has public attention been focused on the occupational hazards for women in the work force.

One searches almost in vain for the sign of a female Commissioner or department head throughout all twelve Canadian workers' compensation boards.

From 1917 until 1980 in British Columbia, there have been over twenty WCB Commissioners, as Chairmen, Labour or Industry representatives. Not one has been female.

Approximately 60-65 per cent of all Canadian WCB employees are women; they are heavily concentrated in the clerical, secretarial, stenographic, reception, typing, food, and janitorial services aspects of the Board and work largely under the direction of male middle managers.

In recent years, the Ontario WCB has had a Positive Action for Women Program with a women's advisory whose function has been to improve career opportunities for women as Board employees. What success this has met with is unclear.

Responsibility for this situation rests upon not only the WCBs, but also labour, industry and provincial cabinets.

WCB Annual Reports virtually ignore women. Women have been more financially disadvantaged as a class than men have by historical under-compensation from WCBs. This is dramatically the case in the area of permanent disability pension awards and rehabilitation assistance. Because women have fewer alternative employment opportunities and live significantly longer than men, inadequate WCB pensions and rehabilitation (either as workers or as surviving spouses) will have a much greater economic impact on women than on men.

Functional impairment systems are still the prevailing method of estimating income loss due to injury or disease. The "meat charts"—Permanent Disability Evaluation Schedules—which set fixed percentages for such things as lost limbs, fused joints, and so on, do not make a distinction between men and women. Therefore, they do not expressly take into account that a lost hand may have a much greater impact upon women workers generally than upon men who suffer a similar injury but who, even if also severely limited, have greater alternative employment opportunities.

Unless all Canadian WCBs move to a complete system of basing pensions on real income loss, reviewing pensions regularly, and building in by regulations some sensitivity to the special relative disadvantages suffered by women, decades more of discriminatory compensation injustice face us.

In 1979 in British Columbia, some 2,376 allowances were being made to surviving spouses, virtually all of whom are women. Some 2,602 allowances were being paid to children. Neither the average payments nor the range of payments are indicated in the WCB's annual report.

For Canada as a whole, using 1977 data, up to 45,000 women were receiving WCB survivor's pensions.[3]

Vocational placement assistance is available in British Columbia to surviving female spouses of workers who are killed on the job. No overall analysis of this service across Canada is available. It is uncertain whether all surviving females receive the vocational assistance they must require, beyond informal counselling. Such services must include aggressive and costly educational and vocational retraining and job placement. Otherwise, women trained to become dependent wives and mothers will be placed in very difficult circumstances by the death of the male "breadwinner." Another economically-forced marriage, or public welfare and subsistence, can easily be the result if such assistance is not provided.

On the research side, even a small portion of the billions of dollars held in WCB pension funds and investments could well be used to fund research and action programmes on women's compensation and health and safety issues. There is no defensible excuse for the failure so far to do this across Canada.

WCB legislation itself has had expressly discriminatory features and language, reflecting the culture and economy out of which it grows. Until the 1974 amendment in British Columbia, all such legislation was called

"Workmen's," not "Workers'." Male pronouns and adjectives have been used throughout such Acts. The employee is virtually always portrayed as a man, with a dependent "wife." "Women," or even "female," are not terms usually found. According to most of the Acts, a woman is still a widow or a wife.

And it is still possible to find expressly sexist provisions such as this one in the Ontario Workmen's Compensation Act:

> Where it is found that the widow or common-law wife to whom compensation has been awarded is a common prostitute or is openly living with any man in the relation of man and wife without being married to him, the Board may discontinue or suspend compensation to such widow or common-law wife or divert such compensation in whole or in part to or for the benefit of any other dependent or dependents of the deceased employee.[4]

To focus on women's health and safety is necessary for a number of reasons.[5] First, women are approximately 40 per cent of the labour force and their rate of participation is increasing much faster than that of men. Also, women are moving into traditionally male-dominated jobs. Because women are on the low rung of the occupational ladder (last to be hired, first to be fired), their health and safety concerns are even less likely to be addressed than men's. Given the neglect of health and safety by industry and government, it follows that women would be more neglected given their position in the workforce. Furthermore, epidemiological studies on health and safety have generally not included women, therefore little is known about their health and safety concerns. Women work in largely segregated female "ghettos" such as clerical, teaching, sales, or health care industries which are purportedly safe and free from hazards. However, we are increasingly coming to recognize the numerous health hazards associated with so-called "safe" white-collar occupations, where most women work. Finally, while both male and female reproductive hazards may exist in the workplace, women and their fetuses are susceptible to certain hazards which men do not encounter.

A Woman's Place Is . . .

The neglect of women in the workforce generally, and their health and safety needs specifically, reflects such factors as a history of paternalism, lack of occupational alternatives, composition of women in the labour force, degree of unionization, changes in labour demands, and the ideological bias of workmens' compensation boards.

> Victorian ideology defined women as inferior to men, fragile, emotional and in need of protection. This ideology was as prevalent in Canada as an import as it was in Britain. The ideal of womanhood combined religious piety, moral purity, and first and foremost—a complete commitment to domesticity. A woman's primary role, her natural contribution, was as a wife and mother. These beliefs were held most strongly in Quebec, where the strength of the family was regarded as the root of national survival.[6]

This ideology has been dramatically challenged since World War II because of the great increase in womens' participation in the workforce. In 1977 women represented 37.9 per cent of the total Canadian labour force and, as Table 5-1 shows, their participation rate is rising rapidly. In the same year, 45.9 per cent of all Canadian women aged 15 years and older were employed outside the home.

Table 5-1

Labour Force Participation Rates by Sex, 1921-1977

Year	Male	Female
1921	89.8%	19.9%
1931	87.2%	21.8%
1941	85.6%	22.9%
1951	83.9%	23.5%
1961	79.8%	28.7%
1971	76.1%	36.5%
1977	77.7%	45.9%

Source: Statistics Canada, Perspective Canada, Ottawa, 1977, Table 6.1 and Labour Canada, *Women in the Labour Force*, Ottawa, 1978, p. iv.

The enormous increase in the female participation rate is largely due to the needs of our economic system and changes in the institution of the family. While the family was once an important economic unit in agrarian Canada, it has become less important and labour in the household has been devalued and viewed as uneconomical. While in the traditional family the wife played an important part in the economic viability of the farm and/or ranch, in today's urbanized, industrialized society such a role has almost entirely disappeared. Furthermore, child rearing was, and largely remains, an integral part of the production process and a significant aspect of women's responsibilities. However, with compulsory school attendance, day care, television, youth groups and other activities outside the family, the socialization role of the mother has been partially replaced.

Also, since the turn of the century the labour demands of our economic system have changed, with a great increase in white-collar jobs and a decrease in unskilled, manual jobs. The demand for cheap labour, particularly in the service sector, is reflected in the fact that in 1901, 15.2 per cent of the work force was white-collar, while the 1971 work force was 42.5 per cent white-collar. Women moved into the labour force in increasing numbers not to compete with men for existing jobs, but to fill the new, emerging needs of our economic system, particularly the demand for clerical work.[7] Thus, women were 75.4 per cent of all clerical workers in 1977, representing 35.4 per cent of the female labour force. As one student of the labour force explains:

> Clerical work as we now know it is largely a product of the period of monopoly capitalism. . . . As small enterprises grew into large corporations, offices expanded until each function was separated into different sections or departments of the corporation.[8]

In Table 5-2 the dramatic increase in the female labour force generally, and clerical work specifically, is quite evident. While the proportion of women employed in the service industry has decreased, service work remains largely "women's work." Also, reflecting change in the institution of the family is the fact that married women have greatly increased their participation in the labour market, with 60.4 per cent of female workers being married in 1977. Between 1967 and 1977 the percentage of all married women who were in the workplace increased from 32.9 per cent to 42.8 per cent.[9]

The increase of married women in the workforce reflects not only changing attitudes about the role of women in society but, more importantly, the economic realities of inflation, consumerism, and market demands. In order to make a mortgage payment, raise a family, and live a "relatively" comfortable existence it is becoming necessary for two members of the family to work. Of course, this applies particularly to working-class and middle-class families. The higher up the socio-economic ladder you go, the less frequent are working wives. In a recent analysis of data concerning married women in the work force, sociologist M. Patricia Connelly concludes:

> In summary, it would appear that as the standard of living in Canada rises, married women whose husbands earn low incomes must work outside the home to maintain their relative standard of living. Married women do not work in order to close the gap between rich and poor families; rather they work to prevent the difference from increasing.[10]

The dual careers of working wife and mother are additional demands placed upon women in the second half of the twentieth century.[11] Since the roles of wife and mother have been devalued in terms of their economic significance, women are increasingly pushed into the workforce, thus increasing their workload and subsequent hazards such as fatigue, stress, and accompanying health and safety problems.

Women's Work

> Ten hours a day of labour
> In a closely lighted room
> Machinery was her music
> Gas her sweet perfume.[12]

The fact that women are noticeably absent from workers' compensation statistics is largely due to the areas of their labour force participation. Where is the "safe" and "non-harmful" work of nearly 40 per cent of our labour force? As previously

Table 5-2

Major Trends in Labour Force Participation of Women 1901-1976

Year	Female Labour Force (in thousands)	Women as % of Labour Force	Married Women as % of Female Labour Force	Clerical Workers as % of Female Labour Force	Personal Service Workers as % of Female Labour Force
1901	238	13.3		5.3	42.0
1911	365	13.4		9.4	37.1
1921	489	15.5		18.7	25.8
1931	665	17.0	10.0	17.7	33.8
1941	834	18.5	12.7	18.3	34.2
1951	1,164	22.0	30.0	27.5	21.0
1961	1,764	27.3	49.8	28.6	22.1
1971	2,831	33.3	56.7	32.7	22.3
1976	3,859	37.4	59.6	35.8	16.7
1977	4,022	37.9	60.4	35.4	17.3

Source: 1901-1961 figures from Department of Labour, *Women at Work in Canada*, 1964, various tables. 1971 figures from Women's Bureau, Department of Labour, *Women in the Labour Force 1971: Facts and Figures*. 1976-77 figures from Women's Bureau, Labour Canada, *Women in the Labour Force: Facts and Figures*, 1978, Part 1, and 1977.

mentioned, "women's work" has been largely concentrated in areas which are "female ghettos." Table 5-3 shows that the major "female ghettos" are medicine and health, clerical, teaching, and sales. Over half of the workers in each of these occupations are women, and they collectively account for nearly three quarters (72 per cent) of the female labour force.

In the occupations which have high official rates and frequencies of recognized deaths and injuries according to workers' compensation statistics, such as mining, forestry, fishing, and construction, women are essentially absent. Therefore, given the bias of workmen's compensation towards accidents and injuries rather than health issues such as disease and stress, few women are to be found in official statistics. This, of course, does not mean that the occupations where women are largely found are free from injury, illness and stress. Women in these occupations are particularly susceptible to health problems of disease, chemical poisoning and stress-related illness. However, disease, stress, and illness have not generally been recognized by government as compensible. The focus has been upon safety hazards, particularly of a dramatic, easily recognizable nature. For example, 78.4 per cent of all women workers are in the service, trade, finance, and public administration industries, which have relatively low claim rates for "recognized" compensation categories. Furthermore, women are in sectors of the work force which are less unionized, with only 27 per cent of the female labour force unionized as compared to 43 per cent of the male labour force.[13] As will be evident in subsequent chapters, attention to health and safety issues is more likely among the unionized work force.

The lack of unionization does not necessarily reflect disinterest or failure to attempt unionizing by women. For example, in 1975 women were 72 per cent of the banking industry's labour force. Of nearly 7,600 bank branches across Canada, only about 65 were unionized in 1979. Why? Not because tellers and other bank employees were not attempting to unionize. Rather, the low rate of unionization has been primarily due to the banking industry mounting a huge campaign opposing unionization of its largely female staff. This campaign has included harassment and illegal action by the banking industry. The Canadian Labour Relations Board has found banks in violation of numerous laws, including the following illegal actions:

—firing staff for union activities
—transferring workers involved in a union in one branch to a different branch
—denying promotion to an employee due to union activity
—hiring additional workers at a branch in the process of unionizing in order to undermine the majority of union members required to form a union
—holding both group and individual meetings during working hours ("captive audience" meetings) to apply pressure to employees to prevent them from unionizing, meetings sometimes attended by high-ranking officers of the bank, who had not been heard of previous to the meetings
—requiring workers at unionized branches to make up any cash shortages at the

Table 5-3

Employed Labour Force in Occupational Categories by Sex, Women as Percentage of the Total Employed Labour Force, and Percentage Distribution of Women and Men, Canada, 1977[a]

Occupation	Women (1,000's)	Men (1,000's)	Women as Percentage of the Total Employed Labour Force for each Occupation	Percentage Distribution by Sex for each Occupation: Women	Percentage Distribution by Sex for each Occupation: Men
Medicine and Health	324	103	75.7	8.9	1.7
Clerical	1,290	420	75.4	35.4	6.9
Teaching	250	198	55.8	6.9	3.2
Service	629	602	51.1	17.3	9.8
Social Sciences	66	72	47.8	1.8	1.2
Artistic, literary and recreational occupations	45	77	36.9	1.2	1.3
Sales	380	698	35.3	10.4	11.4
Farming, horticulture & animal husbandry	114	384	22.9	3.1	6.3
Product fabricating, assembling and repairing	194	691	21.9	5.3	11.3
Managerial and administrative	146	526	21.7	4.0	8.6
Religion	5	23	18.5	0.1	0.4
Processing	62	306	16.8	1.7	5.0
Materials handling	41	204	16.7	1.1	3.3
Other crafts and equipment operating	21	114	15.6	0.6	1.9
Natural sciences, engineering and mathematics	35	290	10.8	1.0	4.7
Machining	15	233	6.0	0.4	3.8
Transport equipment operation	15	377	3.8	0.4	6.2
Construction trades	7	667	1.0	0.2	10.9
Fishing, hunting and trapping	*	20	*	*	0.3
Forestry and logging	*	54	*	*	0.9
Mining and quarrying	*	53	*	*	0.9
All occupational cat.	3,642	6,113	37.3	100.0	100.0

[a] Adapted from Labour Canada, Women's Bureau, *Women In the Labour Force, 1977 Edition*, Ottawa: Ministry of Supply and Services, Canada, 1978, Table 26b.

* Figures too small to be reliable.

end of the day out of their own pay, while this was not required at non-union branches.[14]

Besides the low level of unionization in "ghettoized" industries, women usually occupy the lower rungs of these industries. For example, nearly 100 per cent of nurses are women while only 10 per cent of doctors are women. Likewise, women educational administrators are few compared to their predominance in teaching, mainly in the primary grades. Finally, while only 20 per cent of the Canadian labour force works part-time, women make up 70 per cent of all part-time workers. Of course, part-time workers are usually excluded from various fringe benefits of the job, are poorly paid and unorganized, and are often excluded from protection if a collective agreement exists.

Therefore, it is due to the nature of their labour force participation, compensation board bias, low level of unionization, and part-time nature of employment, that women are largely absent from health and safety statistics. However, women experience a variety of job hazards.

Hidden Dangers In the Office

What are the special hazards which women are most likely to encounter? The Canadian Advisory Council on the Status of Women has presented some of these hazards in a special chart reproduced in Table 5-4.[15] As previously mentioned, the hazards are largely due to chemicals and stress, which result in a variety of diseases and physiological changes. For example, while women are only 3 per cent of the dentists, they are still subject to the health hazards of liver disease, spontaneous abortions, mercury poisoning and radiation effects, as they constitute 68 per cent of the dentists' support staff. They are disproportionately subject to the hazards of dental work without the economic benefits which accrue to the dentist.

Women made up 75.4 per cent of the clerical work force in 1977, with 35.4 per cent of all women workers occupying this type of job. A more detailed analysis of the hazards of clerical work is provided in Table 5-5. While you might not readily recognize these hazards, they are real to the thousands of women who experience them daily. Because of the "nice" office setting and the lack of dramatic injuries, such work is devalued in terms of status, wages, and power. A recent study in the United States found that clerical workers face twice the rate of heart disease as other working women or housewives. This was explained as largely due to stress, lack of control over the workplace, unsupportive bosses, and the often accompanying jobs of wife and mother.[16] The chemical hazards facing clerical workers are numerous and we are only now beginning to recognize them. While there has been a great deal of attention given to stress and health problems of executives, little attention has been given to those of clerical workers. However, in front of every successful executive/manager type you will find an excellent clerical staff bearing the brunt of the administrator's hassles. In fact, it is more often the case that an office runs smoothly and effi-

Table 5-4

Special Health Hazards for Women Workers

Just as some jobs have traditionally been filled by men only, some have employed women largely or exclusively. These are sometimes known as female "ghettos" to suggest the undesirable aspects of this unnecessary segregation of jobs. This summary looks at some health hazards in female "ghettos."

Occupation	% Women (if known)	Hazard	Possible Health Problems
Airline flight attendants	86% (1976)	Fatigue caused by changes in time and climate, jet lag, work stress, noise, loss of sleep	Changes in heart-rate, body temperature, blood pressure, liver & kidney function menstrual cycle
Cleaners (house & office)	19%	Cleaning products	Skin irritations and housemaid's knee
Dentists Dental nurses, assistants & technical hygenists	3% women 68% women	Exposure to radiation, anesthetics and mercury vapours	Liver disease, spontaneous abortion among dentists' wives, central nervous system changes, mercury can cross the placenta & radiation is very dangerous for fetus
Electrical & electronic workers	42% (1971) 67% (1971)	Many chemicals, e.g., arsenic, asbestos, lead, mercury, phosporous radiation, etc.	Skin irritations, poisonous if inhaled or swallowed
Farmers & farm workers	3% (1971) 24% (1971) usually the wife also farms	Pesticides, insecticides, fungicides, climatic extremes, commercial solvents	Allergies, bacterial infections and viruses, lung diseases, skin cancer

Hairdressers	51%	Commercial products, long hrs. of standing, hair tonics, soaps, detergent, perfumes, nail polishes and dyes, hairspray	Bacterial infections Skin irritations and possible cancer, liver and bladder ailments, respiratory diseases
Hospital employees: nurses, doctors, lab. techn., cleaning & laundry staff, cooks and dieticians, physiotherapists	60% approx.	Anesthetic gases (long term exposure exposure through faulty equipment), radiation, contagious stress and mental pressure	Spontaneous abortion; congenital abnormalities in children, cancer, leukemia, reproductive problems, kidney & intestine problems & nausea, viral hepatitis, tuberculosis, rubella
Laboratory workers and related personnel	73% approx.	Bacteria and viruses, radiation	Infections—many viruses can cross the placenta, bone marrow damage, etc.
		Toxic chemicals	Skin irritants, marrow damage, reproductive products, liver damage, red blood cell damage.
Launderers and dry cleaners	62%	Chemicals and dirty clothes, solvents	Sores, pimples and scaling skin, accidents common, cancer may be danger during pregnancy
Office workers	75% (1975)	Poor ventilation, lighting, noise, monotony, alienation from work, lack of exercise, stress	Physical and mental stress most usual results Heart disease, ulcers, hypertension
Salesclerks	66%	Standing	Varicose veins, foot problems
Teachers	60% pre-university level	Contact with children, stress	Contagious diseases, ulcers, hypertension, etc.
Textile industry	80%	Chemicals, lint and dust, noise, fatigue, asbestos	Asbestosis (lung cancer)

Source: Canadian Advisory Council on the Status of Women, *The Person Papers: Health Hazards at Work*. Ottawa, 1976.

Table 5-5

Hazards of Clerical Work*

Hazard	Health Effects and Prevention
Video display terminals (VDTs) also known as cathode ray tubes (CRTs) which are inside the screen	Paperwork of today is the VDT input of tomorrow: More and more clerical workers are working with this TV-like equipment. VDTs can cause eyestrain with possible permanent vision damage, temporary colorblindness, headaches, tension, neck and back pain. VDTs also emit low levels of ionizing radiation and radiofrequency which may damage genes. Frequent rest breaks reduce harmful effects on vision from VDTs. VDTs should have adjustable screens for user comfort and built-in lead screens to reduce radiation.
Photocopying machines	Most photocopiers emit *ozone* gas. Ozone irritates the eyes, nose, throat, and lungs. Ozone may also cause damage to chromosomes. A chemical used in Xerox brand toner called *nitropyrene* may be a potential cancer-causing agent. Photocopiers should be located in well-ventilated areas. If necessary, ventilation ducts should be attached directly to the copier. Ozone levels should be checked and maintained below the OSHA standard level (.1 parts per million parts of air). Clerical workers should know what chemicals are in the toners presently being used, and make sure they do not contain nitropyrene.
Lighting	*Natural light,* or lighting which reproduces the *full spectrum* of the sun, is the healthiest and most comfortable light. *Fluorescent lighting* has been found to cause hyperactivity in children and animals, and is not full-spectrum light.
Ventilation	General ventilation in clerical offices, usually furthest from windows, is often poor. Ventilation systems have been shown to cause outbreaks of what seems to be the flu, but what is actually *pneumonitis,* or "humidifier lung." This occurs when bacteria which has been allowed to build up in the cooling fluid is dispersed throughout the building. Badly-designed ventilation systems also carry *dusts and fumes* from other parts of a plant or from outside into clerical offices. Proper design and regular maintenance prevent illness induced by ventilation.
Noise	Although scientists have declared 67 decibels and under to be the comfortable noise range, electric typewriters and other office machines may be as loud as 80 decibels. Simple solutions such as plastic typewriter shields, carpeting, and room dividers help tone down office noise.

Opaque correction fluid	Until 1979, most opaque correction fluids contained the highly-toxic solvent *trichloroethylene* or TCE. In that year, after a 14-year-old girl died from sniffing the fluid, and after it was found that TCE may lead to liver cancer, it was removed from these products. But many bottles containing TCE are still on the shelf. If correcting solutions are used, keep the bottle away from your face and cover immediately after using.
Stencil machines	Chemicals used in the mimeograph process contain *solvents* which may be irritating to the eyes, nose, and throat. Stencils should be made and reproduced in well-ventilated areas.
Excessive wrist action	For those who must use constant, repetitive motions of the wrist, like cashiers, typists, and keypunch operators, painful muscle strain can occur. Known as "keypuncher's wrist," *tensoynovitis* should receive medical attention. Another problem that may develop is *carpal tunnel syndrome*, a disabling disease of the nerves in the wrist.
Sedentary work	Many clerical workers are confined to their desks. Sitting all day in poorly fitting chairs causes *backstrain* and may *impede circulation*. Smoking is an added drawback for the clerical worker who sits all day. Carbon monoxide from cigarettes stays in the bloodstream longer during low physical activity, having harmful effects.
Stress	Stress is one of the major health hazards of clerical work. A study found that women clerical workers have a *coronary heart disease* rate of *12%*, much higher than the rate of 7.1% for women who don't work outside the home. This rate is most likely related to additional stress faced by the clerical worker on the job. A National Institute of Occupational Safety and Health study of stress-related disease rates of 22,000 people in 130 jobs found clerical workers to be the *second highest*. The low pay and status, lack of control over workload and decision-making, inaction all contribute to stress in the office job. Clerical workers can effectively get together to discuss conditions which are stressful and how to change those conditions. General rights and benefits such as those gained by unionized clerical workers help to cut down on stress on the job.

---

* Labour Occupational Health Program, July, 1980. For a detailed bibliography and packet on the Hazards of Clerical Work, write to the Labor Occupational Health Program, Institute of Industrial Relations, University of California. Berkeley, CA 94720.

ciently without the executives rather than without the clerical staff. For example, if there was a strike among city officials such as the mayor and city councilmen, it would be much less noticeable than one by the city's clerical staff. The stress and frustration of clerical work is well presented in the following poem:

> Some day I'm gonna stand up on my desk
> take all my clothes off
> and hurl the typewriter at your head
>
> And I'll squirt gestetner ink
> all over your board room
> with its rosewood chairs
>
> Some day I'll shove every paper clip
> into the xerox machine
> and set it at a million
>
> And then I'll throw your file cabinets
> on your antique carpet
> and piss on them
>
> Some day I'm gonna force you to lick
> 1000 envelopes cross-legged
> with nylons on dear
>
> And I'll make you chew three dozen
> shiny new pencils
> and watch you die of lead poisoning
>
> Someday I'm gonna claim compensation
> for mind rot
> and soul destruction
>
> And for sure I'm never gonna write
> one folksy line about the heroism
> of women workers[17]

A more recently discovered hazard of particular significance to women arises from a major technological change in the workplace—video display terminals (VDTs). These machines appear more and more at airports, in offices, libraries, and even in grocery stores, providing instant information at the tip of a finger. There are about one-quarter million of these machines in Canada, with at least 100,000 Canadians (mainly women) using them throughout their workday. Heralded as a great time and money saver, they have a number of health hazards.[18] According to an international conference on VDTs, 50 per cent of VDT users reported eye strain; 29 per cent, headaches; 43 per cent, anxiety; and 40 per cent, depression. Between May 1979 and May 1980 four female employees of the Toronto Star delivered children with birth defects. These women were among seven pregnant workers using the VDTs at the Star during that period. While the causal connection is difficult to make, the issue of low-level radiation was raised. Industry's position has been that there is no relationship between birth defects and low-level radiation emitted by VDTs. But women in unions are forcing an examination of this issue by asking that women have the right to avoid exposure. However, the Ontario Labour Minister said that all 49 terminals tested at the Star emitted radiation below the "level considered safe."[19] It will probably take about 20 years to scientifically determine the specific effect of VDTs upon those currently working with them. However, as noted in Chapter 3, low-level radiation may be more damaging than previously thought. One union organizer for the airlines predicts that "Cathode-tube [VDT] operators are going to be the asbestos workers of the future."[20]

The Hazards of "Sweat Shops"

Does the term "sweat shops" conjure up in your mind an image from bygone days of burly, unshirted men with rippling muscles sweating over forges in the steel mill or foundry? While this may be one's image of sweat shops, their historical reality was the hellhole in which women worked in the garment and textile industries. The 1896 *Report Upon the Sweating System In Canada* paints a vivid picture of the exploitation of women in the large industrial shops and in their private homes. Drawing on unskilled, predominantly immigrant women, large and "respectable" companies such as Eaton's benefited from the sweat of these women.[21]

A recent report by the Centre for Labour Studies, Humber College, Toronto, points out that the hazards of sweatshops still exist today. Entitled *Hazard Inventory for Garment and Textile Workers*, the following hazards are listed as common to both textile and garment workers.[22]

I Physical
(a) Heat
(b) Noise
(c) Illumination
(d) Vibration

II Chemical
(a) Synthetic fibre dust

III Ergonomic
(a) Physical organization of workspace
(b) Work overload
(c) Faulty equipment
(d) Hazardous equipment and materials
(e) Faulty equipment design

IV Stress
(a) Climatic
(b) Chemical and biological
(c) Ergonomic
(d) Organizational
(e) Sex stereotyping

Table 5-6

Physical Hazards

Hazard	Where Found	Effects	Controls
A. HEAT A-1) Heat stress (heat, or heat & humidity)	Everywhere	—*acute* (heat exhaustion or syncope) —occurs primarily in people not used to heat —general effect produces heat stress with abdominal pain, red face with dry, non-sweating skin, rise of body temperature, vomiting, usually results in fainting —*chronic*—headache, fatigue, apathy; lack of concentration, judgment, & efficiency; can lead to accidents —skin fatigue can lead to dry, cracking skin and generalized dermatitis.	—more frequent rest periods —modification by engineering controls, low humidity and ventilation to assist skin to sweat and body to lose heat —workers can become acclimatized to hot environments in a short time (less than a week) —body temperature, heart rate are lowered, more stable blood pressure—however even after acclimatization, worker may remain heat sensitive, especially to heat fatigue (see below) —continued dermatitis may necessitate transfer of workers from area.
A-2) Heat fatigue	Everywhere	—the emotional reaction to a hot environment —results in weariness, irritability, easily fatigued —may affect personal relationships at work and home —may produce greater susceptibility to accidents —*chronic*—little is known about long-term effect of heat disorders, as form of stress is likely to use up body's total energy reserves.	—rest periods (away from hot environments) —engineering controls as above
A-3) Steam		—Burns	

A more specific detailed analysis of heat problems in Table 5-6 indicates why they are "sweat shops."

The report goes on to detail the general hazards for both occupations plus the specific, distinct hazards of garment and textile workers, respectively. As noted in Table 5-4, 80 per cent of textile workers are women. Drawn largely from the immigrant populations in Ontario and Quebec, they have been particularly subject to job hazards without recourse due to their immigrant status, language problems, lack of unionization, and need for work of any kind. The following case suggests that the "sweat shop" remains a major part of our economy and takes its daily toll in suffering and hardship.

PROFILE: A Dime a Dozen

Until she became an injured worker, Anita didn't realize workers in this country are covered by an insurance scheme called workers' compensation. When she finally stumbled on the information, she applied for support for her work-related disease. Almost simultaneously her area manager at the factory where she was employed began insisting that Anita come to his office, "just for a chat." Anita obliged. Once inside the secluded quarters, alone with her superior, she was asked to sign a piece of paper. It was, said the manager, just a general form which all workers at the factory must sign. Fortunately Anita's skepticism overrode intimidation; she did not sign. But, had she been more trusting, her pen would have etched a mark forever relinquishing her employer of liability for health problems she incurred during the course of work.

Anita can't speak or read English. She is one of thousands of immigrant women in Canada who work for low wages and are prime targets for employers seeking profits with a minimum of expenditure and accountability required.

Immigrant women lack knowledge of the working language, are usually unskilled and consequently forced to seek salaries within a limited sphere and one which is all too often saturated by anxious job seekers. Most immigrant women, of necessity, gravitate to factory work, usually within the textiles industry in Eastern Canada. With the guarantee of a wage, often no matter how low, they silently agree to maintain their place without complaint or challenge in the face of appalling working conditions.

Their fear is that any other course, even an assertion of basic human rights, will find them crossing the threshold between income and unemployment. Those who have entered the country illegally have the additional need to remain inconspicuous. And for those who would like to assert their rights, the language barrier is often enough to discourage any concerted effort.

Anita came to Canada from Ecuador in 1973. Her husband had emigrated a year earlier and, after finding stable work, sent for his family. Though Anita has been here for eight years, she is still subjected to discrimination. In her east Toronto home, she chats, at first cautiously. She reluctantly granted this interview through an interpreter under the condition that her real first name would not be used. She chose the pseudonym Anita, and as an additional safeguard, never divulged her last name.

Shortly after arriving in Canada, Anita found a job working in a non-unionized textile factory in Toronto. For $3.70 an hour she knitted socks. The daily quota was seven dozen pairs and if that mark was surpassed the company provided a bonus. But if a worker failed to meet production expectations, the supervisor was on hand to provide firm warnings.

Despite the working conditions, Anita worked at the factory in silence for six years. After three years of bending over a dust-laden machine she began sneezing, almost uncontrollably. Nonetheless, she continued to work. A few years later she was forced to see her family doctor. Her nasal passages had blocked. A specialist diagnosed her problem as a crooked bridge and performed an operation to straighten it. But the problem persisted after the operation. "Then the doctor said, 'I'm sorry, you didn't need the operation. It is an allergy,' " recalls Anita. The allergy, according to the specialist, was nonspecific. He attributed it to household dust.

After having a local injured workers' group analyse the fibres used in knitting the socks, Anita discovered that she worked mainly with cotton. The company had maintained the fibres were synthetic. Cotton dust is thought to cause respiratory problems and eventually a condition known as brown lung or byssinosis. She believes her problem is work-related, but the Ontario Workmens' Compensation Board disagrees. In Ontario, the board does not recognize cotton as a health hazard, and consequently it refuses to believe that Anita suffers from more than an allergy to dust. Anita says that at work the dust was not noticeable in the air, but that after a few hours of knitting, her weaving machine and her hair net were covered with small white particles.

Once the board has made a decision not to compensate, new evidence is needed to open a case. To advance through even the initial stages of a compensation case, let alone reopen the case, Anita needs the backing of a physician. One has acknowledged the source of her respiratory problem as being related to cotton dust, but only verbally and only privately.

"The family doctor continues to say what he has been saying for the last three years . . . that the inflammation is caused by those specific cotton fibres." But he refuses to put it on paper for the WCB. Other specialists say that Anita suffers from a perennial allergy.

After applying for Workmen's Compensation three years ago, Anita underwent severe pressure from her employer to drop the application. Initially the company refused to fill out the necessary form allowing the WCB to begin an investigation into the complaint and, consequently, the worksite. The investigation was eventually conducted, after some delay, but the board decided no hazards existed.

Within the same time-frame the company tried to have Anita sign the piece of paper relinquishing the company's liability in any health problem. If the company was found to be at fault for a health problem, it could have been forced to supply masks and proper ventilation systems, and insurance premiums might increase as workers filed compensation claims for dust-related illnesses.

When Anita continued to refuse to sign the document, her daily quota of seven dozen socks, which Anita says was already difficult to meet for many workers, was increased to eight. The company also saw to it that the cost of needles broken in the course of knitting the socks was garnisheed from her wages. The company was trying to find ways to either have Anita quit her job of more than seven years or to trump up cause to fire her. Anita continued to meet her quota, paid for needles and refused to quit. But, as with most power plays, the side which wields the most force is the side which usually becomes the final arbiter of what is reasonable or valid.

In the end Anita's illness became her downfall. She had been missing work due to her respiratory problems. Since these were not recognized as work-related, the WCB did not pay for her absences. Nor did the company. And her employer made it clear that future absences would not be tolerated. Anita knew that it would be only a matter of time before she was out of work. The company's opportunity came when Anita was preparing to take annual leave and visit her native Ecuador for three weeks. Though the company had cleared her holiday, a day before her departure they reneged, saying they hadn't. Plane ticket in hand, Anita was forced to quit.

Months later Anita sits amid the household dust that supposedly causes her non-specific allergy. Yet, she says, her nose is taking in oxygen much more easily these days. Still, it will never be quite the same. . . . Her lungs have not been tested for brown lung. They may harbour more vestiges of her work with cotton. But, for the time being at least, the major problem is that of finances—with three children, a second income is necessary.

Anita is an immigrant, female, and unskilled. Despite seven years of work at low pay, and a respiratory problem, she's once again looking for work in a market that has more workers than it does quotas to fill. "I'll take any job except one with dust or one as part of management," she quips. Then again, she might just head back to Ecuador.

The Assault on Future Generations

An important role for women in the past and now has been that of giving birth and subsequently providing for the child until maturity. Women by biological necessity must perform the first function and by tradition have carried out the second. As women assumed a significant role in the official labour force the issues of maternity and child-raising became important to the woman worker. Employers have often refused to hire women on the grounds that they would subsequently become pregnant, quit, and stay home to raise the child. We believe women should not have to sacrifice employment opportunities for their children *or* their children for employment opportunities. Yet maternity is increasingly being identified by management as a health hazard to women, while women have identified it as a health issue for both men and women workers to address. Workers, led by womens' groups, are attempting to have pregnancy and birth recognized as a health hazard for which leave and compensation should be given. One of the major areas of concern has been maternity leave.

The most liberal maternity leave benefits in Canada are in Quebec, where, in the fall of 1979, women working in the public sector began receiving 20 weeks with full pay.[23] Most women who are eligible receive federal unemployment insurance, which gives 60 per cent of regular pay for 15 weeks, after a two-week waiting period. Therefore, the change in Quebec is an obvious advance. The maternity leave benefits were won through organized labour struggles in Quebec, as part of broader demands concerning the family and parental rights. Covering approximately 20 per cent of women workers in Quebec, there were other gains for the health of both parents and child. A woman working during pregnancy retains the right to all sick leave, sick pay and health insurance benefits, and continues to accumulate benefits while on maternity leave, including annual leave, pension, seniority, etc. Either the father or mother may take up to two years unpaid leave to care for the newborn child and must be returned to the same position after leave. An expectant father has the right to 5 days paid leave at birth. In cases of adoption, 10 weeks are allowed the mother *or* father as well as 5 days for the parent not taking the 10-week leave. Also, the employer is responsible for informing all workers of any outbreak of disease which may harm the fetus. The woman worker is allowed transfer to another job in the same category, if available, or different category, if both the worker and the union agree.

The protection of pregnant workers from potential hazards in the workplace is particularly significant. As White notes: "Common Front workers, including teachers subject to outbreaks of German measles and hospital workers in operating rooms and X-ray departments, are exposed to possible dangers."[24] It is also important that the father is recognized as playing an important part in the health of the child.

The recognition of hazards to both potential fathers and mothers is now occurring. While it is often thought that only pregnant women need worry about hazards to the fetus, this is not true. As Tables 5-7 and 5-8 show, the fetus may be harmed by the hazards faced by either parent in the workplace. Undoubtedly, the list will grow as more research and attention is given to the problem.

Since both parents are susceptible to transmittable damage, it makes no sense to discriminate against women. Canada made international news when a woman was voluntarily sterilized in 1976 in order to save her job at a General Motors battery plant in Oshawa, Ontario. In Fort Saskatchewan, Alberta, women of childbearing age were denied employment at Diamond Shamrock Polyvinyl Chloride Plant because of possible exposure to carcinogens.[25]

The Canadian Advisory Council on the Status of Women has recently issued a *Position Paper on Reproductive Hazards in the Workplace*. It begins by noting that women currently make up almost 40 per cent of the Canadian work force and should not be discriminated against on the basis of health and safety.

Table 5-7

Reproductive Hazards of Work: Mother*

The first column shows major biological changes of pregnancy. Also listed are some chemical conditions and occupations associated with possible adverse effects on these systems. Occupations which employ relatively few women are not listed even if they involve exposures to these substances. The table is not complete. More information can be obtained from the references listed in the Bibliography.

Body System	Potential Hazards	Some Occupations Where Might Be Found
Lungs: Air is breathed more deeply, mixed more efficiently. There may be more effective absorption of toxic materials and deeper penetration of harmful dusts.	Toxic gases, fumes, and vapors Dusts	Agricultural workers; bookbinders; dental technicians; dentists; dry cleaners; electrical-parts workers; hairdressers and cosmetologists; lab technicians; meat wrappers; operating-room personnel; postal workers; sewers and stitchers; textile workers
Blood: Reduced percentage of hemoglobin and iron. There may be an enhanced effect of oxygen-depriving toxic chemicals and conditions.	Solvents—particularly benzene and other aromatics Chlorinated hydrocarbons (e.g., carbon tetrachloride, vinyl chloride, chloroprene) Carbon monoxide Aniline dyes and nitro compunds (methemoblobinemia formers) Amines and nitrates Metals (e.g., lead, nickel, cadmium) Pesticides (particularly chlorinated hydrocarbons)	Agricultural workers; bookbinders; cosmetics and drug manufacturing workers; dye workers; electrical-part workers; hairdressers and cosmetologists; laboratory workers; lead-battery workers; packers and canners; rubber workers
Circulatory system: 30-40 per cent greater blood volume; expanded blood vessels in legs and uterus, increased heart output; increased body weight. There may be a greater effect from jobs involving physical exertion or lack of it.	Standing or sitting too long Too strenuous activity Unreasonable lifting and carrying Stress (including noise & heat stress) Nitrates & other chemicals which affect circulation and heart function Rotating shifts	Agricultural workers; assembly-line workers; hotel workers; laboratory workers; laundry workers; nurses and nurses' aides; office workers; postal workers; retail clerks; service workers: cleaning and caretaking

* From *Women's Work, Women's Health: Myths and Realities*, by Jeanne Mager Stellman. Copyright © 1977 by Jeanne Mager Stellman. Reprinted by permission of Pantheon Books, a Division of Random House, Inc.

Table 5-8

Effects of Selected Occupational Health Hazards on Male Reproduction

Those agents which have been found to have adverse effects on male reproduction are listed. There has not been extensive research in the area.

Agent	Effect
Benzene	Exposed workers found to have significantly higher chromosomal aberrations. Possible genetic effects on offspring.
Cadmium	Cadmium chloride can induce severe damage to testicular tissue and permanent sterility in test animals. Damage to the blood system of the testes and other parts of the male reproductive organs has also been observed in humans.
Lead	Low levels of lead have been reported to interfere with spermatogenesis in humans, yielding low sperm counts.
Manganese	Impotence and a decrease in libido have been reported.
Kepone	A high percentage of kepone-exposed workers suffered sterility.
Deuterium oxide	Mice exposed to this substance have become sterile. No results from human studies reported.
Radiation x-rays	Male radiological technicians in Japan found to have elevated incidence of sterility. Ionizing radiation also associated with chromosomal aberrations.
Gamma rays	Sterility in mice has been induced by gamma-ray exposure.
Excessive heat	Elevated temperature adversely affects male fertility.

At the time of printing, another chemical, a pesticide known as DBCP, has been implicated as causing sterility in male workers. However, several companies have not officially confirmed this because they now "suspect" that other anti-fertility agents may be present, such as ethylene dibromide and ethylene oxide, two substances not previously related.

* From *Women's Work, Women's Health: Myths and Realities*, by Jeanne Mager Stellman. Copyright © 1977 by Jeanne Mager Stellman. Reprinted by permission of Pantheon Books, a Division of Random House, Inc.

One of their underlying principles is:

> Any occupational hazard which may lead to disability, chronic illness or death of any worker or his or her potential offspring can and must be altered to provide maximum safety for the most susceptible worker in the labour force. *The hazard, not the worker, must be controlled* and the workplace must be designed to provide protection for the most vulnerable worker.[26]

The recommendations of the Position Paper to reduce violence against future generations include the areas of legislation, federal/provincial/territorial co-operation, standards, enforcement, protective measures, right to refuse dangerous work, medical training, research and information dissemination. Concerning legislation, it is recommended that the Canada Labour Code and Canadian Human Rights Act be amended to prevent employment discrimination on the basis of reproductive physiology, such as reproductive capacity, pregnancy or childbirth. Also, there is a call for a central, unified administrative body to deal with occupational health and safety under federal jurisdiction. Furthermore, the federal government is urged to increase its efforts at co-ordination with the provinces and territories in order to provide uniformly high standards.

In terms of specific standards, the position paper recommends a single standard for each hazard be established to ensure maximum protection for the most susceptible worker of any age or either sex. Furthermore, there should be pre-use listing of new substances or processes for teratogenicity,[27] mutagenicity,[28] carcinogenicity,[29] and evidence of effects upon lactation,[30] and subsequent re-examination periodically with strict enforcement of standards.

Concerning enforcement, all workplaces over a designated size should have health and safety committees proportionately representing male and female workers and employers to regularly monitor and enforce standards. Recommended protective measures include workplace monitoring and record-keeping. When a hazard is found the employer should first try to substitute less harmful substances, secondly re-design the workplace to isolate the hazard, and, as a last choice, provide suitable and effective personal protective equipment and/or clothing until other measures are implemented. When this last policy is chosen, the equipment and/or clothing should be designed to fit all workers, be fit tested and shown to provide suitable and effective protection, and workers should be instructed in its use. The position paper further recommends the right to refuse work by male and female workers because of risks to their reproductive physiology without recrimination and with maintenance of employment.

Concerning medical training, the Advisory Council says there should be accurate up-to-date training for health professionals and continuous monitoring of the workplace. Also, all workers should have full access to their medical records and should be fully informed of medical examination results. Finally, research and information is deemed necessary in order to establish new standards, with more attention given to occupations with high concentrations of women workers.

This partial listing of the recommendations of the Canadian Advisory Council on the Status of Women reveals a number of issues which are pertinent to the entire scope of health and safety, such as access to medical records. The concerns of women workers specifically are part of the larger struggle to make the workplace a healthier and safer place. Hopefully, Canada will take the lead in protecting not only its current workers, but future generations of Canadians.

NOTES

1. Canadian Advisory Council on the Status of Women, *Position Paper: Reproductive Health Hazards In the Workplace* (Ottawa, June 1980), pp. 7-8.
2. Statistics Canada, *Workmen's/Workers' Compensation*, Cat. #86-501. (Ottawa: Ministry of Supply and Services Canada, 1980), p. 27. Male claims decrease with age, being highest in the 20-34-year-old group, while claims by women remain relatively stable, with slight increases from 25 years up.
3. Statistics Canada, *Workers' Compensation*, Cat. #86-501, p. 31.
4. Workmen's Compensation Act, R.S.O. 1970, C.505, S.48 as amended to date.
5. These are derived largely from a speech given by Janet Bertinuson entitled "Special Occupational Health Hazards for Women Workers," Alberta Union of Provincial Employees Second Annual Health and Safety Conference; *Stress At the Workplace*, June 14, 1980, Edmonton, Alberta.
6. Julie White, *Women and Unions* (Ottawa: Ministry of Supply and Services Canada, 1980), p. 2.
7. Dan A. Chekki and John R. Hofley, "Women and Inequality: Some Indications of Change," in John Harp and John R. Hofley (eds.), *Structural Inequality in Canada* (Scarborough: Prentice-Hall of Canada Ltd., 1980), pp. 378-400.
8. Patricia Connelly, *Last Hired, First Fired: Women and the Canadian Work Force* (Toronto: Canadian Women's Educational Press, 1978), p. 61.
9. Labour Canada, *Women In the Labour Force* (Ottawa, 1978), p. 36
10. M. Patricia Connelly, "The Economic Context of Women's Labour Force Participation In Canada," in John Allen Fry (ed.), *Economy, Class and Social Reality* (Toronto: Butterworths, 1979), p. 222.
11. Single women have always had a higher rate of labour force participation. In 1977, 78.8 per cent of single women aged 20-64 years were in the labour force compared to 47.6 per cent of married women. Labour Canada, *Women in the Labour Force*, p. 43.
12. "A Factory Girl" from the *Ontario Workman* (1870s), cited in Charles Lipton, *The Trade Union Movement of Canada: 1827-59*, 2nd ed. (Toronto: Canadian Social Publications, 1968), p. 54.
13. White, *Women and Unions*, pp. 21-51.
14. Ibid., p. 45.
15. For an extended discussion of the Council's analysis, see Ann George, *Occupational Health Hazards to Women: A Synoptic View* (Ottawa: Advisory Council on the Status of Women, October 1976).
16. "Clerical Workers Face Higher Risk," *The Calgary Herald*, February 19, 1980.
17. Dierdre Gallagher, "Some Day," in Tom Wayman (ed.), *A Government Job At Last* (George J. McLeod Limited, 1976), p. 57.
18. Larry Black, "A Worrying Case of the VDT's," *Maclean's*, July 28, 1980, pp. 42-43. A recent study of VDT users in the U.S. found numerous problems with the machines. "Memo to Participants in the Bay Area VDT Evaluation" (Department of Health, Education and Welfare, Center for Disease Control, June 26, 1980). The Labour Education and Studies Centre of the Canadian Labour Congress has undertaken a survey of some 2,500 employees in St. John, Moncton, Toronto, Ottawa, Winnipeg, Saskatoon, and Vancouver concerning the nature and extent of health problems related to the use of VDTs. The results should be available in the summer

of 1981. *Canadian Occupational Health and Safety News*, Vol. 3, No. 24, November 24, 1980, pp. 1-2.

19. "Radiation Emissions from VDT's Called Trivial," *The Calgary Herald*, July 28, 1980.

20. Black, "VDT's," p. 43.

21. White, *Women and Unions*, p. 6.

22. Centre for Labour Studies, Humber College, *Hazard Inventory for Garment and Textile Workers* (Toronto, 1979).

23. This discussion of Quebec's maternity benefits is based upon White, *Women and Unions*, pp. 109-14.

24. Ibid., p. 113.

25. Alberta Union of Provincial Employees Second Annual Health and Safety Conference; *Stress at the Workplace: Prereading* (June 1980), p. 38.

26. Canadian Advisory Council on the Status of Women, *Position Paper: Reproductive Health Hazards In the Workplace* (Ottawa, June, 1980), pp. 7-8 (emphasis added). The term "most susceptible worker" is defined as "any worker, male or female, who is at risk from exposure to hazardous substances which may adversely affect their reproductive system and potentially, their ability to produce healthy offspring."

27. Teratogenicity is the ability of substances to cross the placenta and cause defects in the embryo or fetus.

28. Mutagenicity is the ability of substances to cause changes in the genetic material of living cells.

29. Carcinogenicity is the ability of substances to cause cancer.

30. Lactation is secretion of milk by the mother

Chapter 6

Farming May Be Dangerous To Your Health

Farming is the third most dangerous occupation in North America in terms of death rate. Surveys show the death rate in farm accidents has increased so much that today the chance of a farm dweller being accidently killed is greater than the city dweller. The high accident rate and the improperly monitored high incidence of debilitating long-term chronic ailments adds to the risk of farming.[1]

It probably comes as a surprise to many of us that farming is a dangerous occupation. As Canadian society has become increasingly urbanized, attention has been directed to urban problems, including the health and safety of urban workers. The neglect by government of the hazards of farming has been due in part to the lack of a unionized farm labour force, opposition from large agribusiness interests, and the "out of sight, out of mind" attitude toward farming.

Although farming was a major occupation in Canada in the early part of this century, agricultural workers were not included in compensation legislation. As will be noted in Chapter 9, this apparently was due to "public opinion" in the form of agricultural interests who did not want to have their workers included. Although there were a few attempts to form farm worker unions, they were met by great opposition from management. For example, the Beet Workers' Industrial Union which emerged in Alberta in the 1930s was subsequently destroyed through the combined efforts of growers and buyers.[2] Small farmers tend to view themselves as small businessmen having their allegiance to the corporate/business ideology, rather than the farm worker/labour ideology.

While the farm population and the number of farms in Canada has decreased, the size of the remaining farms has increased within the consolidation of agribusiness.[3] However, there are still thousands of agricultural workers in Canada who constitute sizeable proportions of the labour force in some provinces. (See Table 6-1.) Nonetheless, agriculture is covered by Workers' Com-

pensation on a compulsory basis in only Newfoundland, Ontario, and the Territories, where agricultural workers are a relatively small proportion of the workforce. In Saskatchewan, agricultural workers include 30 per cent of the male and 14 per cent of the official female labour force, but only a small number are covered.[4] Since most agricultural workers are not covered by workers' compensation schemes, the hazards of farming do not show up in official WCB statistics on deaths and injuries. That farming is dangerous becomes readily evident when we look at some of the available materials concerning health and safety.

Table 6-1

Agricultural Workers as a Percentage of the Labour Force, for Canada and Provinces, 1978

Sex	Canada	Nfld.	P.E.I.	N.S.	N.B.	Que.	Ont.	Man.	Sask.	Alta.	B.C.
Both Sexes	4.5%	—	10.0%	2.3%	1.8%	2.7%	3.3%	9.3%	24.5%	8.8%	2.3%
Male	5.5%	—	12.9%	2.8%	2.4%	3.3%	3.9%	12.2%	30.2%	10.5%	2.5%
Female	3.0%	—	—	—	—	1.8%	2.5%	4.9%	13.7%	5.9%	1.9%

Source: Statistics Canada, *Labour Force Annual Averages, 1975-78* (Cat. #71-529), Table 10, p. 54.

Some Hazards of Farming

In 1975 the Prairie Institute of Environmental Health published a report on farm accidents requiring hospitalization during 1971.[5] The hospitalization rate for farm accidents was nearly twice (1.8) that for the general population. Nearly half (45 per cent) of farm accidents were work-related while only about one eighth (13 per cent) of hospitalized accidents among the general population were attributed to work. Most of the work-related hospitalizations for farm accidents were due to tractors and other machinery (47 per cent), with less than 1 per cent (16 of 2,590) of the hospitalized accidents covered by workers' compensation.

Dr. Fayek Kelada, senior toxicologist for the Saskatchewan Department of Labour, notes that farmers have poorer hearing than the general population. "A recent study has shown that 78 per cent of a sample of farmers show warning signs of excessive noise exposure and that 26 per cent of these suffer speech hearing difficulty."[6] The prevalence of respiratory diseases is higher among farmers due to exposure to mouldy hay, grain dust, silo gas, fumigants and dust. Also, back injury appears to be more prevalent than in the general population, due to vibrating machinery and heavy lifting. Finally, the long-term effects of exposure to pesticides and other farm chemicals undoubtedly takes its annual toll in death and disease.

The following list of accidents for Saskatchewan Wheat Pool, Country Elevator Division gives us some indication of the violence involved in the grain industry.[7]

September 1978	Climbing out of coopered box car, fell INJURED LEG AND CARTILAGE
September 1978	Set of box car wheels inside box car attempted to move INJURED BACK
September 1978	Car jack slipped INJURED FINGER
September 1978	Car mover rope recoiled (hopper car) BRUISED LEG
November 1978	Coopering car stepped on debris with nail PUNCTURED FOOT
November 1978	Jacking car, handle flipped hit jaw BRUISED JAW, BROKEN TEETH
November 1978	Set brake on car bottom rung ladder broke, fell BRUISED ARM
November 1978	Rail car jack slipped INJURED WRIST
December 1978	Car mover rope recoiled BADLY BRUISED LEG
December 1978	Steel car mover rope recoiled BRUISED CHEEK, BROKEN GLASSES
December 1978	Brake failure hopper car, spout hit head FOUR CHIPPED TEETH

December 1978	Caught finger in car mover rope LOST PART OF FINGER
December 1978	Putting brake on hopper car slipped on ladder RIGHT LEG
December 1978	Barring door closed, bar slipped CHEEK BONE
January 1979	Removing spout from box car SPRAINED ANKLE
January 1979	Jack slipped INJURED BACK
February 1979	Jacking car, helper with tractor, jack slipped STRAINED SHOULDER
March 1979	Coopering car STAPLED THUMB
April 1979	Jacking box car, slipped PINCHED NERVE AND MUSCLES IN BACK
May 1979	Loading spout off push rod INJURED FINGER
May 1979	Coopering STAPLED FINGER
May 1979	Climbing into box car over coopered door BRUISED RIB CAGE
June 1979	Closing box car door CUT AND BRUISED FINGER
June 1979	Pushing box car STRAINED FOOT MUSCLE
August 1979	Using bar to close door TORN SHOULDER MUSCLES
September 1979	Car puller—rope struck employee in back *FATAL*
September 1979	Jack BRUISED LEG, RUPTURED BLOOD VESSELS.

Many of the above-noted accidents concern boxcars and railway equipment. Canadian Pacific and other railroads have found it doesn't pay to transport grain since the Crow Rates have kept their profits down. Therefore, repair and maintenance of equipment has been minimal. One of the consequences of such negligence is derailments. In Saskatchewan alone, there were 26 derailments in 1979 and 11 through April 17, 1980.[8] Inadequate safety standards were blamed for the derailment of rail cars containing dangerous chemicals which resulted in the mass evacuation of Mississauga, Ontario in November 1979. The Executive Secretary of the Canadian Railway Labour Association, E. G. Abbot, speaking on behalf of the 15 unions representing Canadian railway workers before the Mississauga Railway Accident Inquiry, criticized the Railway Transport Committee of the Canadian Transport Commission for not enforcing railway safety measures, letting the railways "police their own operations and write their own rules." He pointed out that the committee in 1970 found companies operating below safety standards in several crucial areas, but nothing was done about it. Abbot specifically noted that certain mechanical changes, such as sufficient hot box detectors and roller wheel bearings, were available and safer but no one had forced the companies to adopt them. He concludes that self-serving economic causes are at the bottom of such failure.

> The level of safety at which Canadian railways have been allowed to operate has been dictated not by what is needed and is technologically feasible, but solely by the economics of the individual companies.[9]

To remedy the problem entails more rigid enforcement of existing safety regulations by the C.T.C.'s railway committee.

> The C.T.C. has a duty to regulate the railway system so as to ensure the maximum level of safety that is possible. Safety must override the companies' balance sheet approach to their operations, and the C.T.C. has a responsibility to make sure that is the case.[10]

While the immediate cause of many farm accidents may be the misjudgment or mistake of the injured farmer or farmworker, the indirect causes include long hours, lack of enough manpower, time constraints, and lack of adequate capital to invest in newer, safer equipment and processes. Such stressful conditions are created by the economic and political structure of rewards which emphasize agribusiness, profit, and production. Farmers and farmworkers do not want to be injured. As the opening quote for Chapter 7 states, workers are injured and die largely because they have quotas to meet and time constraints for meeting them. Such demands are largely imposed from outside. Finally, a large proportion of deaths are from disease, which is out of the control of the worker.

Chemical Assault on the Farm Worker

In 1962 Rachel Carson wrote the book *Silent Spring*, which warned of the dangers of pesticides. Nonetheless, the pesticide industry is a booming business, amounting to over $2 billion in the United States in 1975.[11] A report by the U.S. National Academy of Sciences concluded in 1976:

> The pest control enterprise places a billion pounds of toxic materials into the environment each year, but it is "normal" for us to have only the vaguest idea of how much of each compound was used and where and even then only after half a decade's lag.[12]

A 1978 National Research Council study of 3,300 Saskatchewan grain elevator operators and farmers found that ill effects such as nausea, weight loss, headaches, and double vision were experienced by 10 per cent of them during seasonal spraying of 2,4 D. This was reported in the 1977-78 Saskatchewan Environmental Advisory Council annual report.[13] In a recent conference on alternatives to chemicals used in food production, Bruce Small, President of the Human Ecology Foundation, noted that the "chemical solutions" to our food problems are actually creating greater problems than they resolve. Mr. Small further stated that farm families are particularly at risk because of the variety of agricultural chemicals they are exposed to.[14]

Why have farmers become so reliant upon chemicals? One important reason is the warnings by the multi-billion dollar, multi-national pesticide industry of the dangers of not using pesticides. For example, representatives of the Canadian Agricultural Chemicals Association (C.A.C.A.) forecast additional crop losses of 30-50 per cent for those brazen enough to cease the use of chemical pesticides. The President of the C.A.C.A., A. D. St. Clair, when challenged on a Regina radio open-line program to back up the 30-50 per cent claim, is reported to have admitted that he was not aware of any scientific studies that would back up those figures. We do not need a degree in agronomy or political economy to understand where the C.A.C.A. is coming from. They are in the business of pushing drugs to farmers and have a vested interest in maintaining high sales.[15]

Thus, chemical manufacturers are strong proponents of the use of pesticides, herbicides, and fertilizers, forecasting reduced productivity for those who dare stray from the norm.

Some insurance interests aid in adding undue pressure on maverick farmers. Elmer Laird has been farming near Davidson, Saskatchewan for a number of years, and cannot collect crop insurance because he refuses to use chemicals. In 1968, when a surplus of grain developed in Canada, Laird decided it was necessary to cut the costs of production. Chemical fertilizers and weed control chemicals add substantially to the operation of any farm and prices of the products are constantly on the rise. Laird decided to try farming without them. In 1973 when the surplus broke, Laird says the sprayer was "long gone" and with it the idea of chemicals. He had changed farm practices to deal with weed and pest control and had studied the controversy over occupational and environmental damage created by chemicals. In 1978, his crop production was reduced substantially, and he applied for compensation under the Saskatchewan Crop Insurance Corporation's all-risk crop insurance. Adjusters told him he would not be able to collect since his crop failure was due to not using chemicals. Laird appealed the decision of the provincial insurance organ, but to no avail. As a consequence he no longer buys crop insurance. There is no sense paying into what you cannot collect from. Laird, however, is confident enough to continue farming without chemicals despite the pressure imposed by the insurance corporations. He says his production has not been substantially affected. Although dockage (a deduction from the grain grade for impurities, such as weed seeds) on his grain runs to about 7 or 8 per cent, it is minimal as compared to the costs—both financial and environmental—of using chemicals. Laird says the tide is now shifting and a number of farm operators are "quietly" forsaking the use of chemicals. The Saskatchewan Crop Insurance Corporation, however, has not changed its policy on organic farming.

Meanwhile, Laird is forced to farm with only hail protection because the myth of the necessity of chemicals is so pervasive.[16]

How reliable are drug manufacturers and sellers in their research? A recent case suggests that some industry research is "the best results industry can buy." In the summer of 1980 it was revealed that one of the largest "independent" toxicology lab contractors in the United States, Industrial Bio-Test, was suspected of presenting fraudulent test data. A Chicago subsidiary of Nalco Chemical Company, Industrial Bio-Test services many of the major chemical manufacturers, including Chevron, in their development and registration of pesticides.[17] Industrial Bio-Test Laboratories (IBT) was accused in 1978 by United States federal investigators of doctoring data and conducting haphazard research for a decade. Subsequently, criminal indictments of IBT were sought by government agencies.[18] The Newsletter of the National Farmers' Union put out the following warnings:

> CAUTION: Chemicals
>
> Regional Office has recently received a letter from the federal Dept. of Health and Welfare which states that three years ago, it was found that some of the tests conducted by Industrial Bio-test Laboratories Incorporated (IBT) of Northbrook, Ill., were considered invalid. The letter goes on to say that there are 97 pesticides involved. 405 IBT studies have been examined; of these 157 were declared valid, 15 partially usable and 233 are invalid. There are 410 studies yet to be examined; it is expected to take a further two years of verification.
>
> The chemicals are listed by brand name so a word of caution on any other brand containing the same active ingredients will have the same unverified test. The chemicals are:

Acephate
Alachlor
Alanap
Alar
Allidochlor
Ametryn
Antor
Atrazine
Azodrin
B. Thuringiensis
Barban
Bifenox
Binapacryl
Bromofenoxim
Bux
Captan
Captafol
Carbofuran

Chlorobrouron
Chlorpropham
Chlorothalonil
Chlorpyrifos
Ciodrin
Cyanazine
Cyprazine
Dacthal
Delnav
Desmedipham
Dialifor
Diallate
Diazinon
Dibrom
Dichlobenil
Difenzoquat
Dinitramine
Dinoseb

Diquat
Disulfoton
Dynap
Edifenphos
Embard
Endosulfan
Endothall
Ethiolate
Ethion
Fenamiphos
Fenitrothion
Fensulfothion
Fentin Hydroxide
Fenvalerate
Folpet
Formetanate hydrochloride
Glyphosate
Glyphosine
Harvade
Metobromuron
Methamidophos
Methidathion
Methiocarb
Methoprene
Metolachlor
Metribuzin
Norea
Nicotine Sulphate
Omite
Oxydemeton methyl
Paraquat
Penncap E
Penncap M
Permethrin
Phenmedipham
Phosphamidon
Picloram
Polyram
Profenofos
Propham
Profluralin
Propachlor
Propoxur
Prowl
Pyrethrins
Simazine
Sumithrin
TCMIB
Terbufos
Terbuthylazine
Terbutryn
Tedion
Tetrachlorvinphos
Thiofanox
Toxaphene
Triallate
Trivax
Vapona
Vegadex
Vendex
Vitavax

WE HAVE ASKED DR. DAVID PENMAN, THE DEPUTY MINISTER OF ENVIRONMENT, TO SPEAK TO OUR MEETING ON THIS POTENTIALLY HAZARDOUS SITUATION.

In the fall of 1980, the Alberta Federation of Labour put out the following news release:

For Immediate Release—September 4, 1980

PESTICIDES HARMFUL

The Alberta Federation of Labour wants to know if the Provincial Department of the Environment will continue to permit the sale and use of a number of agricultural chemicals whose environmental and health hazards remain in doubt.

Recently it was learned that Industrial Bio-test Laboratories of Northbrook, Illinois was under investigation for suspected fraud and incompetence in the procedures used to test such chemicals for possible long-term hazards.

Apparently, governments have generally relied on the validity of evidence submitted by such labs as a basis of registration for use.

AFL Health and Safety Director, Ray Sentes, has asked the Minister whether any chemicals manufactured, distributed or used in Alberta have been tested by Industrial Bio-test Laboratories. As well, he's asked that such a list be made public.

"Most important," said Mr. Sentes, "we want to know if our provincial government will continue to allow chemicals which have been registered on the basis of possibly fraudulent information to be sold and used in this province."

Mr. Sentes says the Federal Health Protection Branch of Health and Welfare Canada has initiated an investigation of the test results. It is important that government at the provincial level make its position known.

Pesticides, such as 2 4, 5 T, were used to devastate forests in the Vietnam War, and they also assaulted many U.S. soldiers. We might say that farmers and agricultural workers are the war veterans of domestic attacks in the fields.

In their conclusion regarding pesticide poisoning, the Environmental Defence Fund states:

At present, pesticide sales continue to skyrocket at the same time that the EPA (U.S. Environment Protection Agency) and other regulatory authorities are permitting human exposure on a grand scale . . . Pesticides either known to be harmful or not shown to be safe will continue to be marketed and used; residues of these compounds in food and feed, if detected at all, will be approved as safe because they do not exceed questionable tolerance levels; and advertisers will continue to stimulate pesticide sales on the unfounded premise that they may be used "safely." And all of this will occur against a backdrop of federal regulatory agencies presumably servicing the public interest.[19]

Independent research suggests that the gloomy forecasts presented by pesticide and chemical interests for those who do not use their products are inaccurate. In a recent study in which all pesticides used were stopped and non-chemical pest control measures were increased, the loss was only about 9 per cent. Dr. David Pimentel, Professor of Agriculture and Life Sciences at Cornell University in Ithaca, New York, suggests that industry figures are grossly exaggerated, particularly if other non-chemical methods of pest control are instituted.[20] A recent U.S. report entitled *Pest Management Strategies In Crop Protection*, compiled by the Office of Technology Assessment in 1979, states that by using an integrated pest management program (IPM), pesticide use can be cut by 75 per cent, crop yields increased by 15 per cent, and production costs held steady.[21] While chemical interests have created a dependency among farmers for their annual fix, there are alternatives to this addiction.

The nature of chemical hazards and the intransigency of companies to comply with safety standards is evident in the following case in which a Regina magistrates' court held that the Saskatchewan Wheat Pool Farm Service Centre at Outlook came under provincial jurisdiction, and violated provincial health and safety laws. Only the opinion concerning the chemical violation is extracted:

IN THE MATTER OF THE OCCUPATIONAL HEALTH ACT, 1972

BETWEEN: HER MAJESTY THE QUEEN IN THE RIGHT OF THE PROVINCE OF SASKATCHEWAN

VS.

SASKATCHEWAN WHEAT POOL

BEFORE: J. J. FLYNN—JUDGE OF THE MAGISTRATES' COURT IN AND FOR THE PROVINCE OF SASKATCHEWAN

D. MURRAY BROWN—APPEARING FOR THE CROWN AND THE ATTORNEY GENERAL FOR SASKATCHEWAN

W. J. VANCISE—APPEARING FOR THE DEFENDANT, SASKATCHEWAN WHEAT POOL

THE ATTORNEY GENERAL FOR CANADA NOT APPEARING

JUDGMENT

The Defendant is charged that on the 18th day of May, 1976, at Farm Service Centre, Outlook, Saskatchewan, being an employer within the meaning of The Occupational Health Act, 1972, did fail to ensure, as far as is reasonably practicable, the health, safety and welfare of all its workers; contrary to Section 23A (a) of The Occupational Health Act, 1972, and being an offence under Section 24 of the said Act, when no materials were available at the site to properly clean up and decontaminate an accidental spill of toxic chemical Furadan.

The Defendant has complied with the provisions of The Constitutional Questions Act for Saskatchewan.

There are therefore two questions which the Court may have to answer:

First: Is the regulation of standards of employment of employees at the Saskatchewan Wheat Pool's Farm Service Centre at Outlook, competent to the Provincial Authorities, and

Secondly: If the answer to Question number one is in the affirmative, did the Defendant commit an offence under the said Act.

The Saskatchewan Wheat Pool, a body corporate, licensed to carry on business in the Province of Saskatchewan, has historically always been engaged in the operation of Grain Elevators. In recent years the Defendant Corporation added to its existing activities by creating a Farm Service Division to provide service to farms. In the first year of the Farm Service Division, that is, 1964, the Defendant built four Farm Service Centres. Over the years they have added to that until today there are 23 Service Centres of which the one at Outlook is one.

It appears from the evidence that in some instances there are seed and/or feed mills attached to the Service Centre. The Service Centre in Outlook, however, is not one of those with a seed or feed mill attached, nor is it attached to a rail line or to an elevator. In fact Saskatchewan Wheat Pool does not have an elevator in Outlook, Saskatchewan.

It appears that the Service Centres do some 57 million dollars of business per annum. They handle some 2,500 items which could be divided into six categories:

1. Fertilizers
2. Chemicals
3. Equipment
4. Seeds
5. Livestock supplies
6. Miscellaneous items

. . .

Having found that it is subject to the Act I must now turn to the next question.

The pertinent facts are as follows:

The Outlook, Saskatchewan Farm Service Centre is composed of a warehouse with an office attached to the front of the building. Immediately behind the office area and separated by a wall is the heated storage area. Immediately behind the heated storage area is the cold storage area or general warehouse area.

Inside the heated storage area on May 18, 1976, there were stored 3,200 gallons of Furadan which were there for approximately one year. The Furadan was stored in one gallon plastic containers packed in cardboard cartons. Furadan is a highly toxic insecticide of the carbamate type which can enter the human body by respiration, ingestion or absorption through the skin only with prolonged exposure and large amounts being used. Its effect within the body is to inhibit the production of the blood enzyme cholinesterase and thus interfere with the normal control of the organs and muscles by the nervous system.

The hot storage area in which the Furadan was kept at the Outlook Farm Service Centre has ventilation provided by two four inch ventilators, which are installed in the ceiling of the area.

The heated area where the Furadan is stored is an inactive area in terms of the movement of goods within the warehouse. Further, this area is not used for the shipping or receiving of products. However, stock must be moved into and out of the area from time to time.

There is no dispensing or mixing of chemicals taking place anywhere within the warehouse.

May 18, 1976 was a busy day, and in order to meet customers' demands, some products had to be moved to get at others. This resulted in disarrangement of product location and some crowding of the travel aisle in the general warehouse area.

Towards the end of the day of May 18, 1976, the warehouse area had become disorganized with goods, thus narrowing the travel aisle, and as a result of this shuffling of products a pallet of Furadan was left by an employee at the side of the travel aisle.

While in the process of routine cleaning of the warehouse at the end of the day's operations and during the placement of products, a forklift truck driven by Mr.

Ken Wilda, an employee of the Defendant, Saskatchewan Wheat Pool at the Farm Service Centre in Outlook, struck the pallet of Furadan which was left at the side of the travel aisle of the warehouse area resulting in a spill of this highly toxic liquid chemical. Mr. Ken Wilda had made several trips past the pallet before he struck a corner of a carton thereon, rupturing a one gallon plastic container of Furadan and spilling approximately two cups of the toxic chemical onto the warehouse floor.

Mr. Gordon Mantei, Manager of the Outlook Farm Service Centre had provided Mr. Kim Trew, Senior Workhouseman, with pamphlets and manuals concerning the safe handling of agricultural chemicals and had discussed these matters with him.

Mr. Ken Wilda, operator of the forklift truck, had previously been instructed by Gordon Mantei, Manager of the Farm Service Centre, and Kim Trew, Senior Warehouseman, to vacate the area immediately in the event of spillage of any chemicals.

Mr. Ken Wilda left the area and informed his supervisor, Mr. Kim Trew, of the spillage. Mr. Trew put on a half-fact cartridge respirator and rubber gloves and removed the damaged carton from the warehouse. There was one pair of rubber boots available. Mr. Mantei was not present at the Farm Service Centre at this time. Though the manuals were available and Mr. Trew knew their location, he was not aware of the proper procedures for cleaning up a Furadan spill and made several phone calls in an effort to secure such information. One of these was to a Federal Department of Environment National Emergency Control Centre, Vancouver, who were not able to provide the desired information immediately. Mr. Trew thereupon spread sand over the spilled material and went home. Several hours later, a Mr. Weir from the Vancouver Control Centre telephoned Mr. Trew at his home with the requested information. Mr. Trew and Mr. Wilda then returned to the warehouse and undertook the cleanup, using their own rubber boots on hand at the Farm Service Centre. They also used the rubber gloves, goggles and respirators available at the Farm Service Centre. No bleach, hydrated lime or caustic soda were available for decontaminating the area of the spill, so Mr. Trew and Mr. Wilda used Spic and Span which was available at the Farm Service Centre along with vinegar and water.

After completing this part of the cleanup, Mr. Trew's vision became became blurred and he suffered from increased salivation. He was taken by Mr. Wilda to the hospital in Outlook where he was administered with Antopen which is used as an antidote for many chemical toxins including Furadan. After the prescribed antidote was administered the symptoms quickly disappeared.

The recommended clean-up procedures for Furadan spills as stated by the manufacturer are as follows:

FMC of Canada Limited
Agricultural Chemical Division
Regina, Saskatchewan
DECONTAMINATION OF FURADAN
CLEAN UP OF SPILLED FURADAN 4.8 FLOWABLE

1. Put on a respirator, goggles, rubber gloves and protective clothing.
2. Apply about 4 pounds of hydrated lime OR caustic soda OR ½ gallon of bleach on each gallon of spilled product. Leave it untouched for 5 minutes to allow for reaction between chemicals.
3. Scatter sawdust (if not available, use fine dry soil) to absorb liquid. Sweep up and

dispose of this waste together with broken containers by burying at least 18 inches away from any water supply.

4. Floor areas should then be washed with bleach, baking soda or hydrated lime and water.

Employees of the Outlook Farm Service Centre of the Saskatchewan Wheat Pool did not have access to hydrated lime, caustic soda, bleach, or protective clothing such as coveralls and smocks as recommended by the manufacturer.

After the spill was cleaned up the Farm Service Centre Manager, Gordon Mantei, on the 19th day of May, supervised the removal of the contaminated material to a sanitary landfill where he insured that it was properly buried.

The Saskatchewan Wheat Pool provides to its employees a Safety Manual which describes proper procedures for clean-up of chemical spills. This Safety Manual was issued in November of 1974. The manual is available to all employees and is situated within the office area of the Outlook Farm Service Centre.

I find that the facts disclose a state of affairs where one would reasonably expect that sooner or later a spill would in all likelihood occur. The chemical in question has to be moved to and fro through a long travel aisle. The amount and variety of produce that must be moved on a busy day all tend to increase the risk of spillage. I am of the opinion that the failure to have the material on hand to decontaminate a spill constituted an offence under Section 24 of the said Act.

I find the Defendant—Guilty as charged, and I impose a fine of $200.00

DATED at the City of Regina, in the Province of Saskatchewan, this 17th day of December, A.D. 1976.

While the decision was well received by the Saskatchewan Federation of Labour and Grain Services Union, the impact of a $200 fine is probably negligible. More recent information suggests the chemical assault continues. In the following memo from a representative of the Grain Services Union to the Saskatchewan Occupational Health and Safety Office, safety practices at the Saskatchewan Wheat Pool Agricultural Technical Centre in Watrous are criticized.

Health and Safety

The heated work area, approximately 50′ x 50′ is as indicated, not divided into specific work areas. Above the offices (which are self contained) and are located along the side of the heated area, there is a stair case leading up to open storage area. Chemicals and other supplies are stored in this area, chemicals are both Registered and Non-registered. On one occasion a metal container containing chemical corroded to the extent that a leak developed, the chemical subsequently came through the ceiling of the Manager's Office causing evacuation of same.

[A worker] contacted the manufacturer as to why the corrosion, the Company responded by saying they didn't know why the chemical corroded the container, they never knew it would do that.

On the opposite side of the heated work area are a machine work bench and two fairly large storage cabinets. In these cabinets are stored dozens of what appear to be approximately ½ litre and smaller bottles, both glass and plastic, containing both registered and unregistered chemicals to be used by themselves and/or in combination with each other for experimental research on the grain plots as to their effectiveness.

The test chemicals are apparently supplied by most of the major chemical companies under contract with Saskatchewan Wheat Pool. Interprovincial Co-operatives is included in the list of suppliers.

The non-registered chemicals are only indentifiable by letter and number, and contain no other information, such as base, formula, safety precautions, or treatment (antidote) in case of accident, *nothing*!

The mixing, bottling etc., in other words the lab work, is carried out on top of the storage cabinets completely exposed to the rest of the work area. There are no washing facilities (sink) in the immediate vicinity, and no disposal facilities.

On the day in question, there were numerous machines in the immediate area with workmen performing repairs. The machines included a small plot Combine Grain Auger, and test plot field Sprayer, which one had to manoeuver around on a tour of the work area.

Obviously these crowded conditions in themselves could cause an accident in the lab area and further if such accident does occur the release of toxic fumes etc. would be free to contaminate all workmen in the area, with no immediate water supply at hand, and no shower facilities available on the premises.

A fume hood is apparently on order, the function of which would be to expel the chemical fumes into the atmosphere released by the mixing activity, also a sink has been requested in the lab area so that the chemical containers could be rinsed and washed.

Safety, Decontamination, Clean-up and Notification

During course of my discussions with employees I inquired as to whether the following required notification procedures had been followed:

1. Notification to the nearest Poison Control Centre of the existence of the Research Centre and a list of chemicals and/or substances in use.
2. Notification to the local Fire Department along with a list of chemicals in use.
3. Notification to the R.C.M.P. along with a list of chemicals and/or substances in use.

The reply to my inquiry was no, the above 3 authorities have not been notified and further that it would be impossible from their point of view on 2 counts:

1. Technicians are apparently required by Sask. Pool and bound by swearing to keep chemical information CONFIDENTIAL.
2. It would be virtually impossible to supply the required information as the chemical formulae and/or treatment procedures, in the event of contamination, are unavailable on location for the unregistered chemicals in use.

Further, even if the above information was available, the very fact that there is a continuous mixing of chemicals, the degree etc. of toxicity of such mixtures quite possibly is unknown, therefore treatment would be extremely difficult if not impossible.

Safety Inspections (Sask. Pool)

Employee conceded that Sask. Pool Safety Office had visited farm on occasion, however, the impression I got from the discussion was that [the safety officer] appeared to either not grasp the gravity of the situation or was not interested.

Conclusion

Employees advise that in their struggle to improve conditions (including the Manager's efforts) the central and main obstacle thrown up by Sask. Pool is that the present location and structure is a "*temporary*" facility, yet to employees' knowledge no proposed alternative is in the works at this time.

Our concerns with the Health and Safety aspect must not only be directed to the working conditions in the quonset work area, but also to the environment which the Field Workers and Technicians are exposed to while working in the test plots.

For example—the degree of exposure and contamination of employees to the chemicals being applied to the test plots.

Also I was shown one bottle of chemical that is used on grains for the treatment of Ergot and Smut, which by the chemical company's own instruction the treated grain must be destroyed.

The toxicity of this chemical is so great that I was advised that in Alberta last year grain treated with 1 ounce of the chemical and consumed by cattle caused 50 of them to die.

ADDENDUM TO HEALTH AND SAFETY PORTION

Employees at the Ag. Tech. Centre also apply both Aqua and Anhydrous fertilizer. These are supplied from the Pool's liquid fertilizer depot in Humboldt. When questioned as to whether they had received any instructions on the safety precautions and equipment necessary in handling of either the Aqua or Anhydrous Ammonia products the answer was NO, NOTHING!

The above observations were made in March, 1980. On April 9, 1980 an occupational health officer visited the research farm and wrote up eight violations of the Occupational Health and Safety Act of 1977, including one involving Imminent Risk of Serious Personal Injury. The officer also noted other recommendations which should be given consideration.

Assault on Grain Workers

While most of us enjoy our daily bread, cereal or other grain-based food, we generally have little knowledge of the human toll exacted from workers in delivering such products. The storage and handling of grain affects the health and life-chances of farmers, grain elevator operators, transporters, warehousemen, and processors. In discussing the health hazards of grain storage, one researcher notes:

> As the need for storage has become more apparent and storage itself more sophisticated, new hazards to health have been demonstrated which relate to the mechanisms of and the chemicals utilized in the storage process; moreover, injurious properties of grain and its biological contaminants have a potentially greater opportunity of causing ill health.[22]

The most dramatic health hazard of grain storage is explosions. For example, on October 3, 1975, an explosion at the Burrard Terminal Elevator in Vancouver killed five workers. Subsequently, Dr. W. D. Finn of the University of British Columbia headed a full-scale inquiry into the Burrard explosion and related health and safety hazards. Labelled the Finn Commission Report, it claims that the failure of government and industry to put into effect many of the earlier recommendations of the 1960 Ontario McAndrew Commission investigation into grain elevator safety may have caused the Burrard explosion and subsequent fire.[23] Lack of adequate inspections and non-enforcement of health and safety regulations were indicated as contributing to such violence against terminal workers.

While Finn, an engineering professor, was critical of the Federal Department of Labour and terminal owners' operations, for lax, unsafe, and illegal actions, management saw it differently. The assistant general manager of Pioneer Grain Company, Claude Cruickshank, said the accident was caused by workers, not unsafe conditions.

> People caused the explosion, not machines. It would never have happened if there had been some communication between people at the top of the terminal and those at the bottom. The fire was caused basically because of a lack of communication.[24]

By blaming the victims (workers), management is not accepting culpability. While the Grain Workers' Union was pleased with the 35 recommendations, grain executives were not readily accepting them.[25] Undoubtedly, the cozy relationship between government and the grain industry was being threatened by this report. Furthermore, the cost of changes to make the workplace safer would be lost capital for business. Much of the expense would be for controlling grain dust, which can be not only highly combustible, but also lethal and disabling if inhaled.

Grain Dust: Farmers' Asbestos

The managers of the grain industry have been waging a long-term battle against unions of grain workers who want the hazards of grain dust recognized, compensated for, and, they hope, eliminated. An example of management's attempt to blame the worker is the following circular concerning grain dust and smoking:

> SASKATCHEWAN WHEAT POOL
> Country Elevator Division
> Saskatchewan Wheat Pool Bldg.
> Regina, Sask.
>
> December 22, 1977
>
> CIRCULAR NO. 31"A" 1977-78
> GRAIN DUST AND SMOKING
> This circular is being forwarded to all employees in C.E.D. to outline some concerns regarding the hazards involved in working in grain dust. This topic has re-

ceived considerable discussion in the news in the past and many wrong impressions have been left with the public as well as with employees who work in grain dust.

At an International Symposium on Grain Dust and Health, held in Saskatoon in November, medical scientists from all over the world gathered to discuss the findings of studies completed to determine the effects of grain dust on lungs. It appears that they cannot identify the disease or the process of damage, if any, that takes place in the lungs of the grain workers.

In a report entitled "The Health Consequences of Smoking," the Surgeon General of the United States states: "Cigarette smoking is the most important cause of Chronic Obstructive Pulmonary Disease (COPD). Cigarette smokers have higher death rates from chronic bronchitis and emphysema, more frequently report symptoms of pulmonary disease, and have poorer performance in pulmonary function tests than do non-smokers. If an increased risk of COPD due to air pollution exists, it is small compared to that due to cigarette smoking under conditions of air pollution to which the average person is exposed. The possibility remains that the two different kinds of exposure may interact to increase the total effect beyond that contributed by each exposure."

In all studies completed to date, there has been a higher incidence of abnormal pulmonary function among grain handlers who smoke than among the non-smoking grain handlers. In fact, some studies have shown that the lung function of grain handlers who do not smoke is no different from that of the general public.

Circular 41 "A", forwarded to all agents on March 2, 1976, outlined a study being conducted by Dr. Gerrard in Saskatoon and asked for your cooperation in attending for medical examinations if requested. Part of these examinations have been completed; the balance will be completed in the new year. All employees who have been examined to date have been non-smokers. The next group to be examined will be employees who are smokers. We quote from Dr. Gerrard: "All those who were working whom we studied were, we are glad to say, strong and healthy." We will have a further report when the study is completed with a comparison between smokers and non-smokers; grain handlers and a professional group can also be compared.

Personal decisions and habits that are bad from a health point of view create self-imposed risks. We, therefore, encourage all employees to stop smoking.

H. R. Cobb
Safety Coordinator

While it is well established that smoking creates numerous health hazards, by blaming the worker the company fails to acknowledge its role in creating health risks. The following response in the Grain Services Union *Facts and Comments*, 1978 by Bill Gilbey of the Grain Services Union in Regina points out the long history of grain dust disease recognition:

OVERWHELMING RECOGNITION
OF GRAIN DUST DISEASE

Members in Country Elevator Division have no doubt received and read Company

Circular No. 31 "A" 1977/78, dated December 22, 1977, and put out under the signature of H. R. Cobb, Safety Co-ordinator, entitled "Grain Dust and Smoking."

In the Circular No. 31 "A", the Company says: "At an International Symposium on Grain Dust and Health held in Saskatoon in November, medical scientists from all over the world gathered to discuss the findings of studies completed to determine the effects of grain dust on lungs. It appears that they cannot identify the disease or the process of damage, if any, that takes place in the lungs of grain workers."

What kind of games are being played with those two words "if any" in the above paragraph? Not one of the dozens of the medical scientists present made any statement which could possibly be interpreted to mean that they were in doubt—they all agree that grain dust causes damage and disease to the lungs. Many also agree that more research should take place to determine exactly what element of the dust causes the real damage and etc. None of them said "if any."

If the Company is genuinely concerned with the health of all its employees, then a good starting point to prove that would be to get off the "if any" type of distortion of facts.

Given the completely one-sided content and tone of the circular, we trust that Mr. Cobb or whomever will feel obliged to come forth with a Circular No. 31 "A-1" which will deal with a few facts instead of vague generalizations. After all, they are playing around with your health.

Maybe the Company would want to include in such a circular a few examples of what is really being said in sum total about occupational health by renowned international specialists. Part-quotes and discussing a portion of a problem out of context can be very misleading; sometimes more destructive and harmful than silence.

In 1713, 265 years ago, Ramazzini observed that grain dust, damp and stored grain, caused respiratory health problems in mill workers. (Note: Darn few smokers among grain workers in those days.)

In 1964, Dr. J. E. Merriman, Associate Professor of Medicine, University of Saskatchewan, Dr. N. Williams, Director, Occupational Health Branch, Saskatchewan Department of Public Health, Regina, and Dr. A. Skoulas, Research Fellow, Department of Medicine, University of Saskatchewan, Saskatoon, completed a survey of 502 Saskatchewan elevator agents and recommended the following: "The objective must be to prevent the inhalation of grain dust. This can be achieved to an extent by the installation of grain dust control equipment in the elevators."

In April, 1977, Dr. J. Waggoner, research specialist at the National Institute of Occupational Health and Safety, Cincinnati, Ohio, speaking to the same meeting at Madison stated, "The typical reaction from industry is, eliminate smoking and you will eliminate the respiratory condition," but he further stated, "the whole smoking issue is an attempt at subterfuge by industry."

On December 14, 1977, the Free Press Report on Farming, reporting on the same International Symposium on Grain Dust, Saskatoon, in November, 1977 (the same meeting referred to in Mr. Cobb's Circular No. 31 "A"), stated that medical experts had reported that from 16-20 per cent of non-smoking grain workers develop chronic cough and abnormal lung function, compared to 4-8 per cent of the non-smoking general population.

On February 13, 1978, Dr. C. P. Warren, respiratory specialist at the St.

Boniface Hospital, Winnipeg, was interviewed on the CBC morning program "Saskatchewan Today" concerning his upcoming Grain Dust Survey of 2,400 rural residents of Manitoba. When queried about the relationship of smoking to grain dust disease, Dr. Warren commented that, although smoking can aggravate grain dust disease as it aggravates most industrial diseases, anyone who suggests that non-smokers are safe from the effects of grain dust are wrong. Dr. Warren clearly stated that grain dust is a definite health problem.

Nobody would argue that smoking does not have an adverse effect on many parts of the body, aggravating existing conditions including hereditary lung weakness, cancer, dust ingestion, etc. This is not a matter of arguing against those who say smoking is harmful to anyone's health. It is not a question of opposing any campaign to discourage smoking. But it is an attempt to describe the whole problem of grain dust as it actually is, and try to persuade the grain industry to quit playing wordbending games and put consideration of health and life up front, where it belongs.

More recent findings provide added evidence of the violence of grain dust. A study of lifetime non-smoking grain elevator workers in the eastern half of Saskatchewan found that they had a higher prevalence of chronic bronchitis and airflow obstruction than a control group of non-smokers.[26] Both smoking and non-smoking grain elevator agents in Manitoba were found to have a higher prevalence of cough, phlegm, dysphen and grain fever than local males in the community.[27] It has also been verified that besides grain elevator workers, farmers have higher rates of respiratory problems than the general population due to grain dust, even if they don't smoke.[28]

The Finn Commission recommendations included upgrading dust control systems. However, both the government and industry warn of the economic costs involved. For example, in 1977 at an international symposium on grain dust and health in Saskatoon, former Federal Transport Minister Otto Lang opened the conference by reminding people that those calling for clean air should not forget about costs.[29] Industry spokesmen estimated the costs of adapting elevators to new safety standards to be as high as $50-60 million. The *Western Producer* reported the following:

Mr. Lang, *who said he was speaking as a representative of the grain industry*, told the symposium he is concerned over the costs to the industry of "achieving a level of protection at which we won't know if we're overspending or overprotecting."[30]

Subsequently, Lang said he anticipated a relaxation of announced labour department regulations concerning working conditions in elevators, including dust levels.[31]

A major argument of producers is that workers' health involves a large capital outlay without any economic return. For example, the *Regina Leader-Post* of November 17, 1976 reported that the Saskatchewan Wheat Pool board of directors objected to the mounting costs of workers' health, particularly since there is no return on investment. Alarmed by such an attitude, Robert Sass, Saskatchewan Director of Occupational Health and Safety, wrote the following letter to the President of the Saskatchewan Wheat Pool:

December 6, 1976.

Mr. J. K. Turner,
President,
Saskatchewan Wheat Pool,
Wheat Pool Building,
Albert & Victoria,
Regina, Saskatchewan.

Dear Mr. Turner:

I am writing this personal letter to you as a result of a report in the *Leader Post* of November 17, 1976 (attached) which maintains that the Wheat Pool Board of Directors "objected to the mounting costs in both time and capital involved in . . . meeting pollution, environmental and safety regulations, *particularly since there is no return on investment*" (emphasis mine). I am quite disturbed that the Wheat Pool, in light of its origins and history, see all good in terms of a profit-loss statement. Can the above quote from the *Leader Post* actually reflect the sentiments of Wheat Pool management?

I can understand and appreciate the frustration emanating from "bureaucracy" and the "encroachment of useless and sometimes frightening controls of not worthwhile purpose" as expressed in the same article by Pool General Manager Ira Mumford. At the same time let us not forget that bureaucrats carry out the law and do not make law. Nonetheless, I would hope that we would agree that legislation designed to protect the health and safety of workers is a necessary government responsibility in a competitive market economy, even though the cost of corrective measures may indeed lessen the total profit picture. Must we argue that a safe and healthy workplace is also a profitable one? Is not the well-being of human life worthwhile and a good! I should think we have no choice but to do whatever necessary to protect human life since it is the proper ethical task for both business and government.

My concern about judging the health and safety of our workers in light of "return on investment" is similar to arguing with Torquemada, the first inquisitor general of Spain, that the success of the inquisition could best be obtained by not burning Jews at the stake in order to save their souls. Civilized men, regardless of political or religious belief, surely must agree that the inquisition was not in the best interests of mankind. We need not be guided by any philosophy to save a drowning child.

My fear about the *Leader Post* article of November 17th is that it may have the effect of discouraging government, no matter what party, from passing regulations which would improve existing working conditions for the working people in Saskatchewan, while at the same time indicating dissatisfaction with possible costs necessary to reduce the concentration of dust in grain elevators. I am assured by our Chief Occupational Medical Officer, Dr. L. E. Euinton, who has reviewed existing scientific studies on the effects of grain dust on the health of grain buyers, that a serious health problem exists. He is in full agreement with the contents of the "Report on National Conference on Grain Dust and Health" August 27, 1976, sponsored by the Canada Department of Labour. I would hope that you would make an effort from your most busy schedule to note the extent of this disease and do whatever you can to correct the problem.

I hope and believe that we do share the same concerns. If I have over-reacted and am incorrect in my fears, I would be most grateful to you if you would take the time to put right my thinking regarding my expressed perceptions. I assure you I do not write to you for motives other than those expressed.

With gratitude,

Respectfully,

ROBERT SASS,
Associate Deputy Minister of Labour &
Director, Occupational Health & Safety Division.

Company officials of Manitoba Pool Elevators complained at their 52nd annual meeting that costs to comply with new government regulations could be twice the $5 million they had already spent, without returning a penny in increased revenue.[32] In addressing the possible extension of more stringent dust control standards at the country elevator level, the *Manitoba Co-Operator* concludes its editorial on the need to "exercise caution" in bringing in new standards with the following:

> Men and women have been breathing grain dust for centuries from the days of the wooden threshing flails. The alternative was to die of starvation. Farmers live with it all their lives. It is an essential hazard to man's survival.
>
> Let us hope that the lawmakers in their zeal to achieve 100 per cent purity of the air we breathe—when such an objective is impossible—do not create an even greater danger to those working in the industry. Good works sometimes must be approached with caution lest the risks outweigh the benefits.[33]

While the grain industry has complained of rising compensation costs and other workers' health costs,[34] the following (see Table 6-2) assessment rates for the grain industry per $100 of salary show a sharp decline in recent years.

When the House of Commons Standing Committee on Labour was receiving briefs on Bill C-8—An Act to Amend the Canada Labour Code, the Canadian Grain Handling Industry[35] attacked the workers' right to refuse work in the face of imminent danger and the creation of safety committees. The Grain Industry believes the right to refuse imminent danger will be used against them.

> It is submitted that, far more often than an employer orders an employee to work in an unsafe situation, an employee seeking leverage over an employer, either in a negotiation context or one which involves the resolution of outstanding grievances, will find unsafe what he has never complained about before.[36]

Therefore, the Grain Industry views its employees as not really concerned with safety and health, but as manipulative and greedy, looking for another bargaining tool.

Table 6-2

Grain Industry Assessment Rates*

	Year	Rate		Amount
	1969	$1.00		
	1970	$1.00		
	1971	$1.50		
Respiratory	1972	$1.75	—Bal. Deficit	$1,042,212.00
	1973	$4.00		
	1974	$6.00		
	1975	$6.00		
	1976	$6.00		
	1977	$6.00	—Expense—	$1,074,000.00
	1978	$5.50	—Expense—	$949,000.00
	1979	$2.50	—Expense—	$627,000.00
	1980	$1.35	—Surplus—	$2,500,000.00

* Provided by Bill Gilbey, Grain Services Union.

Regarding safety committees, the brief states:

> In collective bargaining, employers usually resist safety and health committees wherever possible on the basis that the employer has the legal and managerial responsibility to ensure proper safety and health conditions in the plant and if derelict in his obligations to do so, is subject to sanctions both legal and otherwise. The artificial injection by statute of employees or employee groups into what is essentially a management concern is unwarranted in the light of the existing known facts especially the absence of proof that employers have exhibited indifference or negligence where safety and health of their employees has been concerned.[37]

As will be shown in Chapter 10, the sanctions are few and far between and don't act as a deterrent. Employers' indifference and/or negligence is evident in the Finn Commission Report, Grain Services Union Briefs, previous Grain Industry statements concerning costs of workers' health, and the annual violence evident in deaths and injuries in the grain industry.

Possibly of most concern to employers is the idea of worker participation in decision-making.

> To institutionalize a procedure whereby employees participate in this aspect of the life of the enterprise is a first step towards co-management, which can also be distorted for purposes beyond the stated issue at hand.[38]

According to the grain industry, regulations should be enforced and, in particular, careless workers should be prosecuted.

> Hundreds of regulations already imposed by government already exist to ensure maximum health and safety at the work place and if these were properly enforced there would be no necessity for sections such as those proposed. Under the present

safety sections of the Labour Code not one employee has ever been prosecuted for failure to ensure his own safety.[39]

Given the above attitudes and actions among employers, the Grain Services Union and other unions of farmers have a continuous struggle on their hands. While the federal government has developed guidelines for helping to ensure a relatively safe dust level in the grain industry, the extent of their implementation and impact will largely be determined through the struggles of grain workers.[40]

Farm Workers Unite

The history of agricultural workers has been the history of exploitation of primarily immigrant labour, including women and children. Few attempts at organizing them have been documented in Canada, and those have ended in failure. Farmers who own their farm view themselves as small businessmen and thus identify more with the companies buying their produce than the workers in their fields. For example, the Beet Workers International Union which emerged in the 1930s was defeated by the combined efforts of growers and processors. As is noted by two historical researchers: "Ironically, the agitation by the beet workers designed ostensibly to unite grower and worker, drew the company and the growers closer together."[41] Farm workers and farmers have more in common in terms of health hazards than do farmers and the grain executives to whom they sell their commodity.

The fact that most agricultural workers still experience assault on the job is evident in the recent deaths of workers' children. On July 16, 1980, a seven-month-old girl, Sukhdeep Madhar, rolled off a cot and drowned in a bucket of water in a migrant work camp in British Columbia. The coroner's jury called for immediate action to clean up the squalid living conditions of Fraser Valley farm workers. Matsqui fire commissioner Ernest Templeton was "amazed" when he inspected the building August 13, 1980 and found no fire extinguishers, inadequate fire exits, and hazardous material used in the construction of the building. Building inspector Harold Neuman rated the building as much below the standards required for human habitation. Canadian Farmworkers' Union president Ray Chouder told the jury there were many camps worse than the one investigated. "And the farm workers are forced to live in such house barns, or hay barns, as we saw yesterday. *They have no choice because they are not paid enough to choose where or how they can live.*"[42]

Three young boys aged, 8, 9, and 10 drowned July 25, 1980, while their parents picked in the fields. These victims were also of East Indian origin. The racism and oppressive conditions of farmwork can only be adequately addressed by organizing. However, given the problems of language, immigration status, length of season, hours of work, and resistance of growers, organizing is difficult. Furthermore, government has not provided assistance. Farm workers are not covered by labour legislation in British Columbia, and were denied the basic right to form a union until 1975.[43] Nonetheless, due to the violent conditions of agricultural workers, the Canadian Farmworkers Union was formed in the spring of 1980. An important demand of farmworkers is day care until they earn enough to pay for it themselves. This would help to avert the above-noted atrocities. The demand has not been met.

Farmer managers and agribusiness respond to demands for better pay, childcare facilities, and improved living conditions with the cry that it will cost too much money—i.e., they will go out of business. But this was not the case in California when farmworkers organized and would not be the case in British Columbia. Only about 5-7 per cent of the retail price of food is labour, with the rest going to processing and profit. Of course the farmer gets only a share, with the rest going to agribusiness.

> While the politics and economics of the food industry are still being hotly debated, one crystal-clear fact remains: farmworkers, who supply our most basic human need, food, are beginning a bitter struggle to gain a decent wage, healthy working conditions, and society's respect and admiration for the job they have.
>
> They could get more money living in the poverty of welfare, yet they choose to work in pitiful conditions to do an essential job. It is our responsibility—farmworkers, farmers, contractors, government, all of us—to ensure that these conditions are changed.[44]

PROFILE: "You Think You Have a Cold . . ."

Grain elevators—the mark of the West, and particularly of Saskatchewan. For years these pillars, icons of the grain industry, have adorned major highways and sideroads criss-crossing the prairies. Regional postcards stress that the prairies "feed the world." The breadbasket theme expressed on postcards has run the gamut from photos of grain fields, to grain storage bins, to grain elevators. But never is there a mention of grain dust or the faltering lung capacity of those who have worked in it for years.

Until recently grain dust disease didn't even exist—not officially. When a grain elevator worker applied for compensation, excuses abounded. Farmers are not mandatorily covered by compensation for grain dust or diseases and accidents. Probably most never even realize the source of their respiratory problems.

Then, after a battle, Wilbert F. Chambers, an elevator agent from Outlook, Saskatchewan, broke through the barrier. Chambers, after working for more than 15 years as an elevator agent, received compensation from the Saskatchewan Workers' Compensation Board for 25 per cent lung disability in 1971.

Saskatchewan has become the most progressive province in terms of recognizing grain dust as an occupational hazard. Chambers was the first person in Canada to win a compensation award for what was recognized as a clear-cut case of grain dust disease. His success opened the gates. Since that initial victory in 1971, an estimated 100 workers in Saskatchewan have received payment for respiratory problems due to grain dust.

Rupert Berscht is one. In 1969 he began working with the Saskatchewan Wheat Pool in maintenance, repairing and renovating elevators. Often the crew worked on the lower shafts of a grain elevator repairing bins. One knock against the ancient wooden walls, and billows of grain dust would waft downward, vestiges of the tonnes of grain which had been weighted, graded and shipped off to markets. Sometimes, says Rupert, the dust was so thick "you couldn't see the guy standing next to you."

"You'd get the dust in your lungs and it would bother you. But I don't know when it [the respiratory problem] started . . . you'd think you had a cold and it would slowly develop."

Rupert says that there was so-called "protective gear" around. But grain dust particles are small and seep through minute cracks. The face masks provided would clog up. "They're useless."

In addition to working with grain dust all day, Rupert recalls the inadequate living accommodation provided by the Saskatchewan Wheat Pool for maintenance workers out on the road. He often spent five working days away from home, living in a trailer which served as the crew's bunkhouse. The trailer did not include washing facilities. It was left up to workers to pay the additional cost of a hotel room if they wanted to bathe or shower, and often hotels weren't accessible.

A few years after beginning to work on elevators, Rupert quit. "I just couldn't take it anymore." The dust was hindering his breathing. Shortly after his resignation it was discovered that he had cancer of the scrotum and an operation was scheduled. Rupert maintains that his doctor verbally noted that his cancer was likely caused by the grain dust harbored in his work clothes. The operation, according to Rupert, arrested the cancer.

Shortly afterward, in April of 1973, Rupert decided to apply for compensation due to lung damage caused by grain dust. After a three-year battle, throughout which his respiratory problems were attributed to smoking, Rupert received an award from the workers' compensation board for 25 per cent reduction in lung capacity due to grain dust. Today, he receives $113.80 a month.

At 63, Rupert is unable to work. "Sometimes I can walk for a block, a block and a half, and it doesn't bother me. Sometimes, though, I walk two feet and I have to stop for a little bit." Dust of any sort makes him choke and gives him severe allergy symptoms such as welts.

In Saskatchewan, the standard procedure for determining whether grain dust is the culprit behind a respiratory problem is to give allergy tests. Grain dust is injected under the skin and if the reaction is a bad rash the worker is deemed susceptible.

Often, however, the allergy is seen as only a temporary problem and often those afflicted are compensated for loss of earning power, rather than for permanent lung damage. In other words, the board believes that if the environment is changed, the respiratory problem will disappear.

As a consequence of that attitude, the Saskatchewan Workers' Compensa-

Rupert Berscht

tion Board will only compensate Rupert for 25 per cent disability until he reaches the age of 65. One of the factors in Rupert's winning his case is that, with only a grade eight education, retraining for other employment was difficult. But, when retirement age arrives, the Saskatchewan WCB has decided that his earning power can no longer be taken into consideration, since most people beyond the age of 65 don't work full time. Never mind whether the problem is permanent or not.

Despite the WCB decision, Rupert says: "It won't get better, that's for sure . . . I'll have to live it out."

He is considering appealing the WCB's decision to cut off his compensation at 65, but admits that he is "so fed-up that I don't give a darn."

Frustration shows in Rupert's voice as he explains that the compensation board is wary of paying out money. "They're (the WCB) a different bunch altogether."

Frank Ziegler, a former elevator agent, senses much the same attitude within the compensation board in Saskatchewan, as well as the Saskatchewan Wheat Pool.

"I figured I owned those pools," says Frank. For years he echoed the belief that the wheat pools were formed by the people for the people. These days, Frank will tell you that just isn't so. Time has changed the once co-operative pools. Like other profit-oriented corporations, the Wheat Pool management is not keen on installing equipment that will not benefit the accumulation of capital.

In 1954, Frank began work as an elevator agent in Holdfast, Saskatchewan. And in 1966 he became another name on the Saskatchewan Wheat Pool's casualty list.

Frank first noticed his respiratory problems after seven years with the Pool. He quit smoking thinking his problem might be due to cigarettes. But the wheezing did not disappear and his condition deteriorated. "I worked twelve years and never took a day off," he recalls. But in 1966 the Wheat Pool thought he should take a leave of absence because of "bad" nerves. "I thought I was taking a little holiday," says Frank. He had stored up six months sick leave during twelve years and agreed to leave but only for a respite. According to Frank, it was understood that he would resume his job as an elevator agent. "But when I wanted to come back the company doctor wouldn't pass me in my physical. They just said, 'So long, it's been good to know you' and then they give you a two-bit pen."

The Saskatchewan Wheat Pool had decided that Frank was not fit for work. Frank in turn decided that if he was not fit for work, his work had likely made him unfit. He applied for workers' compensation and his local doctor stood behind him supporting his claim for work-related respiratory problems. The WCB, however, decided his ill-health was in fact a hereditary respiratory disability. "Then I figured I was beat."

For years, Frank was forced to accept the judgment. Then in 1976 he began hearing about successful claims for grain dust disease and decided to appeal the decision the WCB had made against him in the 1960s. After allergy tests, Frank won his case in 1977.

Today, at 63, he receives 75 per cent compensation. And while that may seem like a generous sum, the percentage is based on his wage in 1954—an outdated $150 a month. Frank's claim was retroactive to 1954. He received a lump sum totalling $27,000, the sum of accumulated monthly payments prior to 1977.

Is it fair? "What would you call fair?" questions Frank. How can you measure the cost of health?

"These days my temper rises a little faster . . . there's just something that bothers me. I couldn't run across the street and I can't golf or skate . . . I'm afraid I might choke up." In cold damp weather, Frank has difficulty breathing and dust, which trails along many Saskatchewan roads, bothers him.

While he insists that more care must be taken to protect grain handlers, Frank has no pat solutions to the problem. He knows that masks are useless since they block frequently. Dust eliminators and proper ventilation are being suggested, and Frank feels that while they would be a definite improvement in reducing exposure to grain dust, such equipment is not a panacea. He voices a new fear as well: with the constant use of chemicals in farming, the passage of time may well bring new diseases to those handling chemically treated grains. How to prevent that problem? Frank takes a tough, but logical stand: "I think we have to farm without chemicals." Grain dust is a serious problem, but while working to get rid of that health hazard is important, Frank also warns that we should be wary of creating new ones.

Even more important than prevention is presentiment. Historically, prevention has only come after the fact—after diseases have been recognized by using workers as guinea pigs. Frank emphasizes that what is needed is foresight—and lots of it.

NOTES

1. Dr. Fayek Kelada, *Report for Minister's Advisory Council on Occupational Health and Safety Regarding Farm Safety and Related Health Matters* (Regina: Saskatchewan Labour, June 6, 1980), p. 1.
2. John Herd Thompson and Allen Seager, "Workers, Growers and Monopolists: The 'Labour Problem' in the Alberta Beet Sugar Industry During the 1930's," *Labour/Le Travailleur*, 1978, pp. 153-74.
3. For a discussion of rural depopulation and multinational corporations' impact upon Canada's food policy see Gurcharn S. Basran, "The Rural Depopulation of the Prairies," in John Allan Fry (ed.), *Economy, Class and Social Reality: Issues In Contemporary Canadian Society* (Toronto: Butterworths, 1979), pp. 391-410; and Harold E. Bronson, "Multinational Corporations and Canadian Food Policy," in Fry, pp. 364-90.

4. Statistics Canada, *Workmen's/Workers' Compensation*, Cat. #86-501 (Ottawa: Ministry of Supply and Services Canada, 1980), p. 25.
5. These data are reported in Kelada, *Regarding Farm Safety*, pp. 1-2.
6. Ibid.
7. Material from Mr. Jack Gilbey, Grain Services Union.
8. Ibid. The "Crow Rates" are the freight rates established by agreement between CPR and the government in 1897 for transporting grain. These rates were to be frozen forever since the federal government gave away so much money and land to the CPR. Now the CPR is fighting to have them raised to derive a profit.
9. "Safety Dictated By Cost," *U.T.U. News Canada*, 11 (March-April, 1980), p. 1.
10. Ibid., p. 6.
11. Environmental Defence Fund and Robert H. Boyle, *Malignant Neglect* (New York: Vintage Books, 1979), pp. 117-36.
12. Ibid., p. 117.
13. John Twigg, *Regina Leader-Post*, August 1980.
14. Peter Von Stockelberg, "Chemicals in Food Said Failing Society, Making People Sick," *Regina Leader-Post*, November 15, 1980. Also affected by contamination are the consumers of farm products. It has recently been discovered that Ontario wheats were infected by vomitoxin (a substance which causes vomiting). "Health Department Found Toxin In Wheat By Accident," *Calgary Herald*, November 19, 1980.
15. Peter Von Stockelberg, "Chemical Industry's Figures Questioned," *Regina Leader-Post*, November 13, 1980.
16. For further information on farming without chemicals, see David Pimental and John H. Perkins, (eds.), *Pest Control: Cultural and Environmental Aspects* (Westview Press, 5500 Central Avenue, Boulder, Colorado, 1979).
17. Ronald B. Taylor, "The Pesticide Crisis—2: Safety Standards Are Based on Scientific Tests Riddled with Outdated, Even Spurious Data," *The Calgary Herald*, September 18, 1980.
18. This is only one case documented by criminologists Marshall B. Clinard and Peter Yeager in *Corporate Crime*. (New York, The Free Press, 1980, pp. 266-71.) They also note that a U.S. federal grand jury indicated in 1979 another "independent" laboratory, Biometric Testing, its chairman, and four former officers on charges of falsifying research reports on animal tests for cancer risks and toxicity of certain new drugs. Two of the former executives pleaded guilty in federal court to conspiring to falsify research reports on animal tests so they could show that certain drugs were harmless even though they had not tested them! Clinard and Yeager's comprehensive study of corporate crime found pharmaceutically-related companies one of the most criminal industries.
19. Environmental Defence Fund and Boyle, *Malignant Neglect*, p. 136.
20. Von Stockelberg, "Chemical Industry's Figures Questioned," p. 61.
21. Ibid.
22. C. A. R. Dennis, "Health Hazards of Grain Storage," in R. N. Sinha and W. E. Muir (eds.), *Grain Storage: Part of A System* (Westport, Connecticut: Avi Publishing, 1973).
23. *Free Press Report on Farming*, Vol. 47 (April 27, 1977), pp. 1-3.
24. "Many Already See Action on Finn's Recommendations," *Western Producer*, May 12, 1977.

25. "Grain Executives 'Don't Buy' Some Criticism," *The Vancouver Sun*, April 30, 1977. Also see "Grain Terminal Probe Blasts Labour Canada," *The Vancouver Sun*, April 30, 1977.

26. James A. Dosmar et al., "Chronic Bronchitis and Decreased Forced Expiratory Flow Rates In Lifetime Nonsmoking Grain Workers," *American Review of Respiratory Disease* 121 (1980): 11-16.

27. C. P. W. Warren and J. Manfreda, "Respiratory Abnormalities In Grain Workers 1971-1977: A Preliminary Analysis," in *Occupational Pulmonary Disease* (New York, Academic Press, 1980), pp. 297-304.

28. C. P. W. Warren and J. Manfreda, "Respiratory Symptoms In Manitoba Farmers: Association With Grain and Hay Handling," *Canadian Medical Association Journal* 122 (June 7, 1980): 1259-64.

29. Marc Lisac, "Dust Symposium Calls For Research," *Free Press Report on Farming* 197 (November 16, 1977): 1, 27.

30. "Economic Pressures Won't Go Away," *Western Producer*, November 17, 1977 (emphasis added).

31. "Lang Says Feds to Relent on Tough New Regulations for Grain Dust and Labour," *Free Press Report on Farming*, November 23, 1977, p. 28.

32. "Grain Uncertainty Ahead," *Winnipeg Tribune*, November 9, 1977.

33. "Exercising Caution," *The Manitoba Co-Operator* 35 (January 12, 1978).

34. For example, see the *Western Grain Elevator Association Brief to the Saskatchewan Workers' Compensation Act Review Committee Respecting the Operation of and Amendment to the Workers' Compensation (Accident Fund) Act of Saskatchewan, 1978.*

35. The Canadian Grain Handling Industry includes: (1) Western Grain Elevator Association—Alberta Wheat Pool, Manitoba Pool Elevators, Cargil Grain Co. Ltd., Parrish & Heinbecker Ltd., N. M. Paterson & Sons, Pioneer Grain Ltd., Saskatchewan Wheat Pool, United Grain Growers Ltd.; (2) Eastern Elevator Association of Canada—Collingwood Terminals Limited, Canada Steamship Lines Limited, Midland Simcoe Elevator Co. Ltd., Great Lakes Elevator Co. Ltd., Marathon Realty Co. Ltd., Goderich Elevator & Transit Co. Ltd., Maple Leaf Mills Ltd.; (3) Saint-Lawrence & Atlantic Elevator Association—Burge du Canada Limitée, La Compagnie des Cereales Cargill Limitée, Part Cartier Elevateurs Compagnie, Les Elevateurs de Sorel Limitée, Les Elevateurs des Trois-Rivières Limitée.

36. *A Submission By the Canadian Grain Handling Industry to the House of Commons Standing Committee On Labour On Bill C-8—An Act to Amend the Canada Labour Code*, February 23, 1978, p. 23.

37. Ibid., p. 25.

38. Ibid.

39. Ibid., p. 26.

40. Labour Canada, Occupational Safety and Health Branch. *Guidelines For An Environmental and Medical Surveillance Program In the Grain Industry*, 2nd ed. (Ottawa: June 15, 1979).

41. Thompson and Seager, "Workers, Growers and Monopolists," p. 174.

42. Michael Bocking, "Jurors Rap Workers' Living Conditions," *Vancouver Sun*, August 22, 1980.

43. Ron Labonte, "The Plight of the Farmworkers," *Vancouver Sun*, August 25, 1980.

44. Ibid.

Part III

Current Solutions

Chapter 7

The "Dumb Worker": Blaming the Victim

To say that some of these workers died from accidents due to their own carelessness is about as helpful as saying that some of those who died at the hands of murderers asked for it. It overlooks the fact that where workers are careless, it is not because they love to live dangerously. They have production quotas to meet, quotas they themselves do not set. If quotas were set with an eye to keeping work at a safe pace rather than to keeping the production-to-wages ratio as high as possible, it might be more reasonable to expect workers to take the time to be careful. Beyond this, we should bear in mind that the vast majority of occupational deaths result from disease, not accidents, and disease is generally a function of conditions outside a workers' control, such as the level of coal dust in the air . . . .[1]

The assumption held by those in power about what causes a problem are ultimately expressed in attempts to deal with the problem. The Chief Executive Officer for Alberta Workers' Health, Safety and Compensation, Dr. Herbert Buchwald, was at first cautious and questioning of my approach to the topic.[2] I told him that I was interested in learning about their operation and philosophy and was open to hearing "their side" of the picture. He then began to outline the provincial thrust towards health and safety matters and its underlying philosophy. According to Mr. Buchwald, 70-80 per cent of accidents and fatalities in the workplace are caused by "careless workers." He believes the emphasis should be upon changing the attitudes of workers and management in order to reduce the level of deaths and injuries. When I asked what studies he was basing this approach upon he simply said it was his observation after working several years in the area.

Explaining Health Hazards

By focusing upon the worker as the cause of accidents, we then look for solutions to violence in the workplace by somehow changing the worker. The victim is thus set up as the culprit, freeing the company or work environment from blame. By blaming the victim, attention is turned to certain "kinds of people" theories of the causes of accidents. Accident researchers may try to determine whether certain biological, psychological or social traits are more evident among accident victims than among non-accident victims. Such differences are assumed to be the cause of accidents. If certain people are believed to be "accident prone," then all we need do is use pre-employment screening or training to deal with the problem. If violence in the workplace can be explained as due to certain "kinds of workers," management is left with clean hands. However, if certain "kinds of environments"[3] are viewed as causing accidents then the onus is on the employer to change the environment. For example, if piece-work and bonus incentives lead to speedups and more accidents, these policies, not the workers, need to be changed. Likewise, if poor equipment design or poor ventilation leads to violence against the worker, studying the characteristics of the worker is futile.

If you view certain "kinds of environments" as more violent than others, the focus will be upon changing the workplace, not the worker. However, since management has historically had the power to define "acceptable" risks which workers will be subject to, the degree of violence in the workplace reflects differences in power between management and workers. The conflict between maximization of profits and minimization of violence in the workplace becomes part of the power struggle between workers and management. This "power/conflict" explanation suggests the need for a shift of power from owners to workers in order to adequately address the problem.

While all three of the above-mentioned explanations of workplace violence are to be found today (kinds of people, kinds of environment, and power/conflict) the "kinds of people" approach tends to prevail in management and government attempts to "solve" the problem. This generally takes the form of blaming the worker for his or her injury, illness and/or death. This leads to the initiation of a variety of programs, such as educational and safety training, without changing the structure, nature or process of work.

The "blaming the victim" approach is evident in some traditional crimes of violence. For example, in the violent crime of rape the victim is often viewed as the criminal, or at least as a willing participant in the violence—if she didn't struggle and/or wore "suggestive" clothing, she is said to have been "asking for it." The same kind of victim blaming occurs in violence in the workplace. Like the rape myth that "she was really looking for it" and "anyone who wanted to could avoid being raped," there is the workplace myth that "any worker can avoid a violent accident or death" and "it's only those who are dumb and/or careless who are hurt." In rape, the onus is on the woman to prove she did not "consent," and in workplace violence, it is on the victim to prove the harm was caused by work. Diseases and stress are particularly hard to "prove" to the satisfaction of the Workers' Compensation Board, especially as the worker's lifestyle is often used against him or her. For example, smoking habits have been used to disallow claims for disease. Even in the case of obvious violent accidents, workers may have difficulty getting compensation, particularly when they are claiming permanent disability.

The Political Ideology of Being Safe: "Accident Proneness"

In health and safety research, the kinds of questions asked and the methods of obtaining answers will indicate the assumptions of the causes of health and safety problems. For example, researchers can look at the nature and characteristics of the work force, such as age, marital status, experience, sex, nature of industry, type of injury, or other factors. Traditionally students of accident research have approached the accident as a "chain of multiple events" which are described in order, with no single key cause identified. Another, more recent, way to analyse accidents is the "epidemiological model" adapted from disease studies which have a host (accident victim), agent (injury deliverer), and supporting environment. From this perspective one must look at all three factors in explaining accidents. The "host" may be described in terms of age, sex, economic status, and intelligence, while the "agent" may be analysed in terms of potential hazard, method of use, mode of injury, and type of agent, with the "environment" viewed in terms of effects upon the host and/or agent, e.g., temperature, noise, social climate, and normal work procedures. This approach is largely apolitical; however, it may lead to the identification of significant political factors in the area of health and safety. For example, the "host" is affected by the "agent" and the working "environment" and the changing of the environment brings the power relationship between management and labour to the fore.

In a comprehensive review of accident research, Surry states that:

> Before discussion of the material, it should be pointed out that care should be taken to avoid the human failing of blaming all faults, misfortunes, or, in this case, accidents, on those who do not "fit" with the social group. Such "pointing the finger" without objective evidence can be needlessly very damaging. However, with the meager amount of careful and objective works available, the evidence suggests *the industrial accident rate is a function of social discontent and conflict at work.*[4]

In spite of the above caution, "blaming the victim" has been a major method of explaining occupational health and safety problems. One of the dominant theories used to explain industrial accidents has been "accident proneness." The term was coined by Eric Farmer following a study in 1919 which directed students of accident research away from a focus upon the work environment to a study of individual and personal characteristics. It was thought that a worker's chance of having an accident was due to personal qualities such as "carelessness" or "light-heartedness" and that accidents could be prevented by the use of proper care and thoughtfulness. One early writer in the field of industrial safety, for example, identified the following psychological factors as significant in causing accidents:

(1) lack of awareness of potential accident hazards
(2) excitability of temperament
(3) a sluggish temperament
(4) deficiency of intellect
(5) inattention
(6) psychomotor retardation
(7) a deficiency of English.[5]

"Accident proneness" is a classic example of blaming the victim. It leaves the employer without any culpability and thus without reason to change the working environment. The term "accident proneness" came to be defined as "a personal idiosyncracy of relative permanence predisposing the individual to a higher rate of accidents." In a devastating critique of the concept, Surry states that " 'Proneness' is a no more useful concept than that of 'fate'—no one stable personality characteristic associated with proneness has been found during the last fifty years of research."[6] However, she goes on to point out that despite its scientific uselessness as an explanation of accidents, it persists.

> Doctors and psychologists, *particularly those in industry*, seemed to have avidly accepted the concept of accident proneness as an innate stable characteristic, presumably because it gave them something concrete to search for while treating the many accident victims.[7]

This ideology of the "deficient worker" makes little scientific sense but supports the dominant corporate ideology which emphasizes blaming the victim so that the organization remains free from blame. Management may identify the accident repeater as having a "poor social background," being "socially maladjusted," "emotionally unstable," hyperactive if young or evidencing suppressed aggression if older, "insecure," "frustrated," or a number of other "disturbing" qualities. This can be used to not hire workers, fire them, change their jobs, force "treatment" upon them, and other forms of harassment.

> A related and particularly dangerous misuse of psychological approaches is to justify in a logically circular fashion administrative actions against individuals who, for whatever reason, have been in repeated accidents. In the present state of our knowledge, we cannot reliably attribute an individual's accident history to his psychological characteristics and hence there are no grounds for basing administrative action upon psychological theory, or for attempting to validate psychological hypotheses on the basis of administratively accumulated accident histories.[8]

The use of the blaming the victim ideology is evident in a recent promotional letter sent out to health and safety personnel from Equifax Services:

> October 14, 1980
>
> Dear Safety/Security Director:
>
> Your company can now *slow the growth of worker's compensation costs.*

> A new Workmen's Compensation Records checking service is now available! Mail the enclosed card today to find out how this important new service from Equifax can help you.
>
> Worker's comp costs are growing by leaps and bounds. They are now a major cost of doing business. Even today's best safety programs can't protect you completely. Risk reduction through careful selection and placement of personnel is a natural place to start *reducing your injury rate*. Awareness of an applicant's previous injuries is essential for lowering the chances of re-injury.
>
> Equifax's WORKMEN'S COMPENSATION RECORDS services can help your company achieve that goal. While an employer cannot discriminate against a person because of a handicap, careful selection and the use of the Worker's Compensation Records Report can, *without discriminating*, (1) provide information to assist employers in placing a disabled or partially disabled individual in a suitable job, (2) help screen out the professional habitual worker's compensation claimant, and (3) verify application information.
>
> The new WORKMEN'S COMPENSATION RECORDS report from Equifax provides information on a job applicant's previous worker's compensation claims. (You may request that information be obtained from the Workmen's Compensation Board in the Province of Quebec or through former employers in other provinces). The report covers the nature of an injury/accident, the type and percentage of disability, the date and amount of any compensation or settlement, and current status. . . .
>
> It's our job to know and use all legal sources and means of information to give you the best employment reports possible. . . .
>
> We have offices in over 1,100 locations. That puts Equifax (and you) in *a better position (time and cost-wise)* than your staff can to know and use local information sources. Our people live and work where the information is. They know where to find those scattered references, people who have moved, and *records from the courts* and *credit bureaus, traffic violation records*, etc. . . .

The letter concludes with an invitation to the reader to send in the enclosed card to find out more about their services. Equifax Inc. is an Atlanta, Georgia-based multinational corporation, with about 13,000 employees and an annual revenue of over $300 million. It has two divisions and eleven affiliates, including two Canadian affiliates. The Credit Bureau of Montreal Ltd. is an Equifax affiliate dealing with credit reports, collection services, and credit and promotions, while the other Canadian affiliate, Equifax Services Ltd. of Toronto, deals in insurance, employment and financial control information for Business Decisions in Canada. While 1984 is still a few years away, the information and services provided by Equifax suggest that nothing gets by "big brother." The attempt by Equifax to capitalize on the scientifically discredited "accident proneness" theory is another example of how money can be made from the blood, pain and suffering of workers.

Doing a Number on the Worker

Many contemporary studies still attempt to find the cause of accidents in the character of the worker. Mr. Keith Mason, statistician in the Actuarial and Research Department, Workers' Compensation Board of British Columbia, has produced a number of studies focusing upon attributes of the worker. For example, he tested the hypothesis that fathers of young children have a higher fatality rate than that of all married men in the same age group and found support for the hypothesis. However, he cautions the reader:

> As a final note, it is worth emphasizing that studies of this type do not establish causation. It is quite conceivable that married men who have children are *fundamentally different*, in terms of some other characteristic, from married men that don't; and that this characteristic would be more directly related to fatality rates.[9]

Of course, innumerable relationships may exist between fatherhood and fatality rates: married men with children might be more "virile," that is, they might have a greater sex drive or more male hormones . . . married men with children might be under more work stress due to the fact of family obligations . . . etc. However, why focus upon children as a "cause" of fatalities? In other studies Mason found that married men 35-54 years old whose wives are pregnant have more accidents;[10] eating breakfast (blood sugar levels) had no effect on reducing accident rates; the change in sleeping patterns while off work affected accidents;[11] critical periods in workers' biorhythm patterns do not contribute to accidents;[12] back strains occur disproportionately on Monday mornings.[13]

One of Mason's studies looked at the rate of unemployment and accident rates in British Columbia from 1947 to 1968. He found that the lower the unemployment rate, the higher the accident rate. In discussing this he states:

> The intuitive reasoning that caused us to consider this hypothesis is as follows: as the unemployment rate varies, those workers with marginal skills will be entering and leaving employment. As this shifting is taking place, the average level of skill and experience for employed workers as a whole is consequently shifting, which would thus be affecting the accident rate. For example, as the unemployment rate drops and the demand for labour increases, workers with less skill and experience will find employment. Intuitively this would translate into a higher accident rate.[14]

The implications of this finding would seem to be that higher unemployment is good for the health and safety of workers! Such analysis is absurd in not considering environmental factors such as health and safety standards, their enforcement, training practices, etc. The reasoning is not much better in research findings which note that younger and less experienced workers have more accidents.

Nicholas Ashford, in his study of occupational health and safety, points out that blaming the young and inexperienced fails to get at the structural causes of their excessive accident rates.

> The identification of aging and inexperience as significant contributory causes for

accidents does not mean that the "worker is to blame" or that work conditions are safe. Accidents are the result of man-environment interactions, and in that sense most accidents are the result of an "unsafe act." If work conditions were made safer and accounted for normal human deficiencies, including aging or inexperience, the unsafe act might not have a chance to occur. A fashionable modern-day version of accident proneness states that *unsafe acts* rather than *unsafe conditions* are responsible for 90% of industrial injuries.[15]

Unsafe Acts: Doing Violence To Workers

The assumption that 90 per cent of accidents are due to unsafe acts was exposed as a myth in Ashford's study, which showed that a third or less of accidental injuries or deaths were caused by unsafe acts, while over half were caused by unsafe and/or illegal conditions.[16] Nonetheless, identifying unsafe acts is often crucial to accident investigations. For example, in one province, government inspectors are given the following guide listing causes of accidents. While we have listed only the major subheadings, it gives one an idea of the orientation.

DIRECT CAUSES OF ACCIDENTS

Direct causes of accidents may be attributed to unsafe acts, unsafe conditions, or an Act of God (e.g., earthquake, extraordinary rainfall, etc.) Examples of unsafe acts and unsafe conditions are listed below and may be used as a *guide* by the investigator.

UNSAFE ACTS

1. Operating without authority, failure to secure or warn.
2. Operating or working at unsafe speed.
3. Making safety devices inoperative.
4. Using unsafe equipment, hands instead of equipment for equipment safety.
5. Unsafe loading, placing, mixing, combining, etc.
6. Taking unsafe position or posture.
7. Working on moving or dangerous equipment.
8. Distracting, teasing, abusing, startling, etc. (horseplay).
9. Failure to use safe attire or personal protective devices.

UNSAFE CONDITIONS

10. Improperly guarded.
11. Hazardous arrangement, procedure, etc.
12. Improper illumination.
13. Improper ventilation.
14. Unsafe dress or apparel.
15. Unsafe design or construction.
16. Unguarded.

The complete listing takes up about two and one-half pages for Unsafe Acts and one page for Unsafe Conditions. The major thrust of the instructions and their actual operation is to emphasize unsafe acts as primary causes. Unfortunately, this approach ignores the context of work. For example, a worker may be killed from a fall off a highrise construction, the direct cause being the "unsafe act" of not wearing a safety belt. However, safety belts may not be readily available, management may ignore their non-use, speedup to complete the project may produce lax standards, etc. Nonetheless, an "unsafe act" can be labelled as the most immediate cause. This protects the company and provides an easy means of identifying "causes" for accident reports but does not get to the root of the problem. W. T. Singleton, in an *Introduction to Ergonomics*, makes the following observation:

> Human errors are an important source of information about equipment design fault. . . . *The only real solution is to design in such a way that safety devices and procedures are an inherent and necessary part of machines and tasks, as well as being emphasized in instructions and training schemes*—for example, a fuse box so designed that it is physically impossible to open it without switching off the power is obviously safer than one that merely has a note saying "switch off power before opening box."[17]

The Victim's Perspective

We often consult "experts" to tell us why accidents occur, but what do the *workers* think? A survey of injured workers was conducted in one of Mason's studies.[18] In the survey, 618 claimants of the B.C. Workers' Compensation Board were asked: "Is there anything you feel the Compensation Board should (or should not) be doing in the field of accident prevention?" (See Table 7-1.) There were 192 comments to the question and 70 per cent of them concerned more and better safety inspections and safety procedures. Approximately 22 per cent called for more safety instruction, with only one person asking for more WCB advertising. A major thrust of many WCBs is safety instruction and advertising, but workers identify the problem as one of establishing and enforcing rules, rather than just education.

In answer to the more specific question "Do you think there is any particular thing that could be done where you work to prevent accidents?" (see Table 7-2) seventy per cent of the responses concerned machinery and equipment, working environment, and production. The workers gave relatively little emphasis to instruction and personal safety equipment, which are emphasized by employers and government.

Those closest to the reality of the workplace—workers—largely reject the "kinds of people" explanation of accidents and emphasize "kinds of environment" factors such as machinery and "power/conflict" factors such as policing and enforcement as the appropriate means to deal with the problem. Those with the most power define the way the problem will be examined and the remedies which will be used to deal with it. Unfortunately, management and government have tended to view health and safety problems as essentially education and training problems. Therefore, major campaigns are instituted to educate and train workers in order to overcome *their deficiencies*. However, no matter how

Table 7-1

What Injured Workers Believe the Compensation Board Should Do

Specified Comments			
Safety Inspections	103	More inspections	88
		Inspect small employers	10
		Unannounced inspections	2
		Safety committee members accompany inspectors	2
		Stop pleasing employers	1
Safety Instruction	42	Talks by WCB to workmen	24
		Distribute more signs, posters and pamphlets	9
		More instruction from employers	7
		Seminars for handicapped	2
Safety Procedures	30	Enforcement of safety rules	16
		Provision of proper clothing, equipment by employers	8
		Stretchers, first aid kits	4
		Two or more men working together	2
Specific Hazards	11	Lifting too much weight	7
		Dust, lighting	4
Miscellaneous	6	Hire WCB staff from working ranks	2
		Rewards for safe shops	2
		Require knowledge of English	1
		More WCB advertising	1
Total	192		

educated and trained workers are, if hazards exist in the work environment there will be injuries and deaths. The four workers who fell 36 storeys in Vancouver on January 7, 1981 from faulty scaffolding would not have lived if they had been more properly trained. The four men were killed due to apparent defects in the scaffolding.[19] This is not to say that such programs are totally useless; however, they should not be the major focus of prevention programs.

Hypersusceptibility: The New "Hype"

Another example of the "blaming the victim" approach relates to the use of chemicals in the workplace. In this kind of approach "hypersusceptible" employees are "blamed" for their health problems. This leads to screening out

Table 7-2

What Injured Workers Believe Should Be Done to Prevent Accidents

		Specified Comments	
Machinery, Equipment	54	New equipment, machinery	30
		Better maintenance of machinery	12
		Better safety features on machinery	11
		Machines for left-handers	1
Working Environment	48	Better housekeeping	25
		Ventilation, lighting, heating	12
		Chemical fumes	4
		Nails in logs	4
		Too much noise	3
Production	26	Reduce pace of production	14
		More staff	12
Instruction	23	Better job training	21
		More warning signs	2
Safety Procedures	17	Hire qualified employees	5
		Competent safety officers	4
		Reduce lifting loads	4
		Two or more men working together	4
Personal Safety Equipment	14	Compulsory hard hats, safety boots	6
		Safety glasses, shields (grinders)	4
		General safety equipment	4
Miscellaneous	2	Reduce boredom, routine	1
		Design safety outfit, tight but not restricting	1
Total	184		

certain employees and essentially finding the problem in the employees' "makeup" rather than in the workplace environment. In a critical analysis of the term "hypersusceptibility," Ashford points out its ideological and political uses.

> The term is abused in precisely the same way as the term accident proneness. By pursuing a policy of detecting the hypersusceptible worker for his own good, an industrial physician may perpetrate a "blame the worker" attitude on the part of management. Unfortunately, to many industrial physicians, "preventative medi-

cine" constitutes identifying the hypersusceptible worker and recommending him for a job transfer—or, in the case of pre-employment examination, for no job at all. *The removal of the health hazards, rather than hypersusceptible persons, should be the goal of preventative medicine.*[20]

The use of hypersusceptibility may allow the screening out or firing of pregnant or potentially pregnant women, smokers, heavy eaters, diabetics, etc. The possibilities are endless for determining which "kinds of people" are more susceptible to hazards in the workplace. This policy provides a convenient, "scientific" way for management to save money without changing a hazardous environment. The example of smoking and cancer is instructive.

As we noted in Chapter 3, asbestos workers who don't smoke have an eight times greater risk of developing lung cancer than an unexposed population, but asbestos workers who smoked had a 92 times greater chance of developing lung cancer. For years, compensation boards and employers argued against compensation to workers who smoked, assuming that the workers' lifestyle, specifically smoking, was the cause of their cancer. Reluctantly, the boards ultimately recognized the synergistic effect and now sometimes give partial compensation. However, there is a movement afoot to go back to blaming the victim totally for his or her health problem. It is now being argued by some that asbestos is not a general carcinogen. In a lecture to the Lambton Industrial Society in Sarnia, Ontario, Dr. Harry Demopoulous, "expert" on environmental disease, stated that under current controls and standards, asbestos poses no health hazards. In speaking to the business-oriented audience, Dr. Demopoulous said cancer is caused mainly by personal habits such as poor diet and excessive smoking and drinking rather than asbestos, nuclear power plants or air and water pollution.[21] Management's position is clear—if workers joined Participaction and quit their personal vices cancer would disappear.

How is this perspective translated into practice? In the spring of 1980, it was revealed by the Canadian Chemical Workers Union that 43 employees of Johns-Manville Canada had died of asbestos-related diseases during the previous 12 years. Unions urged action to investigate and deal with the crisis.[22] In the fall of 1980 Johns-Manville announced it was instituting a ban on smoking in all Johns-Manville facilities that use asbestos fibres. Workers found smoking on company property ran the risk of losing their jobs.[23] What about eliminating or reducing the asbestos hazard? Nothing was mentioned regarding this approach. While smoking is hazardous to one's health, wherever one works, focusing upon it in terms of addressing the problem of cancer leaves the work environment, and thus management, free from culpability. The need to clean up the environment, to lower levels of dust, and to perform other potentially expensive chores is sidestepped, and once again the victim is blamed on the basis of his or her personal habits. But while smoking is a carcinogen, what of its combined effect with asbestos? What about the non-smokers exposed to the same levels? These and many other issues are ignored. Health and safety education becomes merely a ploy to avoid responsibility for establishing an inherently healthy work environment. A theory of the causes of cancer which blames the victim is sure to gain adherents in industry. The November 27th, 1978 issue of *Dow Canadian*, a newsletter put out by Dow Chemical of Canada, Ltd., had an article entitled "Cancerphobia—Forget it . . . ." Written by Dr. Elizabeth Whelan of the Harvard School of Public Health, it essentially identifies smoking and "imprudent lifestyles," not food additives, drugs, pollution, or the workplace, as the causes of cancer. According to this, workers are their own worst enemies, and have only to change their thinking and lifestyles to be safe. The message is that we really should not create "artificial" causes and issues, but attack the "real" problem. The following worker was the victim of such theories.

Alexander Borisenko

PROFILE: "The Company Says 'Get Out' "

He's cheery, stubborn and has a working-class sense of justice. Once he believed the adage that loyalty breeds justice. If you're faithful to your employer and do assigned tasks efficiently, then when somthing goes amiss—such as an on-the-job accident—you will receive just compensation.

Instead, "cost-benefit" is the company's buzzword, and an injured or diseased worker costs but doesn't produce.

Alexander Borisenko has learned that when it comes to health and safety issues the employer and employee's philosophies diverge. "If you're healthy and do your work then you are a good worker. But, if you get sick and have trouble working then the company says 'get out,' " explains Alex.

Alex has logged a total of thirty years in the coalmines. These days he's winded, his lung capacity diminished by as much as 50 per cent—yet another victim of black lung or coal-dust disease.

Alex sits in his living room, looking through the picture window which offers a view of the Rocky Mountains. But that's the extent to which he can enjoy their majesty. Hiking trips or strolls through the surrounding forests are out of the question, since even a walk around the block is exhausting. Alex sleeps long hours and spends waking ones relaxing. At 66, he has been prematurely relegated to his easy chair, with only an occasional foray outdoors. Yet, despite his occupational illness, Alex does not disparage his lifestyle in Canada. This country has offered his wife and four children freedoms they might never have known otherwise.

In broken English, Alex relives history. He was born in eastern Europe, lived in Germany, then in Belgium, where he first worked in the coalmines, then moved on to Canada in 1951. With the promise of work, he, like many other Europeans, transplanted his roots to this country.

Alex gets up to retrieve a well-used machete, as he talks about the fields of sugar beets he and his wife worked to harvest during their first few years in Canada and southern Alberta. It was honest work, says Alex, but it was only seasonal. In an effort to find a full-time, year-round occupation, Alex sought out jobs in the coalmines of Alberta, finally settling in Canmore to live out 27 years of work with Canmore Mines Ltd.

Today, the buildings used to house shafts and processing equipment are indelibly etched into the side of a mountain near Canmore. A locked gateway announces that trespassers will be prosecuted. The hum of industry has been silenced. The mine was closed because it couldn't fill the requirements of economic feasibility. The jobs are gone with it. But many of the former workers are left behind to breathe through the layers of coal dust which have permeated their lungs.

Alex is one. After years of work for Canmore Mines Ltd. he began having chest problems. Alex recalls the pain and puzzling over the cause. He had never had any serious physical ailments, and though he smoked, he considered his consumption of cigarettes to be moderate. In 1974, he began to miss work, and noticed a marked decrease in his energy level. After a trip to the local doctor he was told that there was "a bit of coal dust" in his lungs. In retrospect Alex is convinced that he wasn't told the entire truth. "I think he knew that I had black lung." In a town whose main industry is coal, Alex believes it would not be difficult to pressure or buy a doctor into avoiding the health issue.

There are usually periodic checks for illness among miners, and after one of these, during which Alex vocalized his health concerns, it was suggested he take a trip to Edmonton to have a complete physical. The visit didn't determine the cause, but as his health continued to deteriorate Alex was encouraged by his local of the United Mineworkers of America to apply for Workers' Compensation on the grounds of lung damage due to coal dust.

In 1976 he did. The board's decision was handed down in the fall of that year noting "there is no measurable functional impairment and the little you do have is likely related to cigarette smoking." Alex was forced to continue working. If he had not, without recognition of black lung he would have lost all seniority and retirement benefits. For the time being he was forced to accept the verdict.

In 1977 he decided once again to file for compensation. But, much to the discouragement of Alex and the union, the decision handed down was much the same as the initial response from the WCB—"no functional impairment." Yet, in a contradictory move, the board suggested that he cease working underground and take a surface job. Experienced coalminers were scarce at that time, and the company adamantly opposed Alex's request to be moved above ground. It was underground or nothing. Ironically, the compensation board intervened and pressured the company into giving Alex a surface position. But, according to Alex, the above-ground job was even dirtier than the underground work. Though he worked outside, the air was laden with coal dust from the dumping of coal cars.

During his numerous tests, several records had been compiled on lung capacity. In 1978, an independent physician and a specialist in internal medicine compared new x-rays to those taken a year before by board doctors. They confirmed that Alex's condition had deteriorated substantially in a 12-month span. But still Alex was not able to convince the WCB that he had black lung and that the rapid progression of the disease was evidence of it.

One of the barriers in Alex's compensation application, and applications made by diseased coalminers in general, is that Alberta, lagging behind a number of countries, has not officially recognized black lung disease. For instance, the United Kingdom has realized since 1943 that coalminers are subject to this occupational hazard. The United States officially admitted to the existence of black lung in 1969. Since this province has not conceded the problem, it has also not instituted preventive measures such as dust controls. Although standards have been in the works for years, they have yet to be legislated. In Australia black lung has nearly been eliminated through monitoring of dust, with only an estimated six per cent of the coal mining population contracting the disease. Canada, on the other hand, sacrifices approximately 26 per cent of its coalminers to black lung.

Besides those stumbling blocks, Alex also had to prove that his lung problem was not the result of smoking. In an effort to invalidate the smoking argument, the United Mineworkers local financed a trip to a pulmonary lab in Beckley, West Virginia. There, doctors have been trained in the specific science of lung disease and have the experience and knowledge necessary to determine the type of disease and its cause.

On his return to Canada, Alex held a report from specialists in West Virginia which he hoped would end his battle for compensation. The specialists had confirmed that Alex had black lung and that he had an estimated 50 per cent loss of lung capacity in both lungs. The doctors noted that the severity of his problem was due to coal dust and not to smoking.

But that diagnosis wasn't good enough for the WCB. Alex was told that the report wasn't acceptable, since the board did not recognize the American doctors. According to Alex, the only acceptable diagnosis for the board would have had to come from the WCB doctors. "The WCB plays and their doctors dance," says Alex in his broken English.

Finally the Borisenko family, frustrated with the WCB's inaction, agreed to be interviewed on the CBC's *Ombudsman* program. The case unfolded on national television and the WCB wasn't spared embarrassment. On March 22, 1979, Alex was granted partial disability for black lung. His award, however, was only for 25 per cent disability and was retroactive only to 1977 when he finished full-time work for Canmore Mines Ltd. Alex's monthly compensation check is $282.

Alex is not pleased with the board's assessment of 25 per cent. But after years of fighting, he is also tired: "I could have been left with nothing, 25 per cent is better than nothing." Alex's case was a testing ground. Few workers have received similar awards for black lung in Alberta. Most miners who discover they have the disease do not have the stamina to wrangle through the hoops. Some do not have the time: the disease is progressive and a miner is never quite sure how much longer he has to live. How many people are willing to accept bureaucratic conflict in the face of death? Alex says that most of his friends did not. One he recalls fought long and hard for compensation, "but by the time he received it, he had no time to live."

It's All in Your Head

At a conference on *Stress In the Workplace*, two of the authors viewed a cartoon financed by Upjohn and produced by Walt Disney emphasizing that stress in the workplace is often due to paranoia among workers and is thus self-induced. The scenario involves an employee who believes that the boss has it in for him. According to the cartoon, such an "irrational belief" produces unnecessary stress. However, as one popular contemporary poster points out, "Just Because You're Paranoid Doesn't Mean They Are Not Out To Get You!" One's beliefs are real and have a consequence upon oneself and others. Blaming the victim does not get at the source of the beliefs.

Stress will not be made to disappear by psychologizing about the "kinds of people" who are susceptible to it. A. E. Kowalski, director of the Canadian Stress Institute, noted at the 63rd annual conference of the Industrial Accident Prevention Association (an industry organization) that "Attitudes are the worst stressors in our society."[24] He further stated that people who constantly anticipate problems will experience the effects of stress. After identifying a number of stressors, he advised management to beware of the effects of unrelieved stress, which can produce increased hostility and bring harm to the work environment.

At the same business-oriented conference, Dr. Robert Webb, Ergonomics Unit, University of Guelph, argued for an approach to health and safety emphasizing human error. He observed that errors do not always result in an accident but accidents are always the result of error. "Inattention, incorrect expectations, tiredness, boredom, stress or information overload (when one person has too much to cope with at one time) often results in mistakes."[25]

The above approach exemplifies blaming the victim for accidents, disease, and stress-related health problems. Only the failings and deficiencies of workers, not those of management, are addressed. It is not surprising that workers are opposed to many of the official programs of health problem prevention and identify other causes of the problem.

"Compensation Cadillac"

The ultimate insult to workers' dignity and sense of justice is to view them as out to get something for nothing. In a speech presented at the University of Calgary medical school on June 2, 1980, Dr. Keith Morgan, a professor at the University of Western Ontario and formerly of the University of West Virginia and the Appalachia Centre for Occupational Lung Disease, claimed that in the United States it becomes "financially rewarding" for workers to "exaggerate" symptoms of ill health. In presenting his observations on compensation for black lung disease in the United States, Dr. Morgan presented a "welfare cadillac" image of coal miners receiving large amounts of money for their illness. The message he presented is that if workers have a powerful union they will benefit, even though cigarette smoking is the major cause of cancer. When asked by a member of the audience about the inhalation of aluminum dust as a "cure" for silicosis he believed it didn't make sense.[26] However, he said his comment was "off the record" since he was seeking research funds from the mining industry in Ontario. His conclusion was that we need to change personal behaviour patterns of workers, particularly their smoking habits.

The "compensation Cadillac," like the "welfare Cadillac," is a mythology which masks the real suffering and violence which the recipient undergoes, including economic hardship. By dismissing "those people" as getting something for nothing, the rest of society can continue to ignore the basic reality of inequality and violence in the workplace. A particularly popular means of presenting the image of the "careless" and deficient worker as the cause of health and safety problems is advertising.

"Alive": The Ideology of the "Dumb Worker"

On February 5, 1979, Alberta Labour Minister Neil Crawford announced to a press conference the "Alive" campaign to attack problems of health and safety. According to the Minister, "Public information can help reduce industrial accidents in Alberta."[27] The emphasis of the program is to help workers stay alive by staying alert, through mass media advertising, posters, brochures and an educational trailer which travels throughout the province. Like many other provinces, Alberta emphasizes education of the worker as a significant, if not the most significant, aspect of preventing health hazards. This is a particularly insidious form of blaming the victim, since few people are against education and training per se. But the point is not whether workers *should* become aware of hazards and how to protect against them, but whether this should be the *major focus* of prevention strategies. No matter how educated or trained workers are, if a workplace is unsafe or unhealthy, violence will occur to workers. It is much better to eliminate the possibility of hazards rather than trying to merely reduce their likelihood through abstract calls for education and vigilance.

The ideology of blaming the victim is particularly evident in the "Alive" posters which have been distributed throughout Alberta. The following four posters are typical of the program. In Poster 1, "Lloyd's falling down on the job" [sic] because of his bad habits. Nothing is said about railings, safety straps, boots, wind, slippery conditions, or a multitude of other hazards Lloyd does not control. Hubert Maisonneuve, who fell nine floors due to unsafe conditions (see profile in Chapter 1), would not likely find this poster helpful. The message in Poster 2 is that Tom made "an ash" of himself and therefore will miss work. It is no wonder that workers generally, and unions specifically, find such accusations repulsive. The young man in Chapter 3 working without protective gear with caustic soda is being made "an ash of" by the company through their lax policies of protection. According to Poster 3, while machines maim, smart workers don't get hurt. Frank was off guard so he "gave his right arm to work." Again the message is clear: workers cause accidents and only they can prevent them! No mention is made of changing the nature of machines, pace of work, routine or structure of the workplace, etc. Finally, in Poster 4, Ken did not protect his eyes so he "won't be seeing you again." The victim is again portrayed as the culprit while management and the work environment are not implicated at all.

The message of these "Alive" posters is that workers are careless and that one should not be too sympathetic to injured workers because it's their own fault. The myth of the "dumb worker" is used to explain the increase in workplace violence by assuming that the "unsafe act" equals the "unsafe worker."

In *An Initial Review of the Alive Trailer Program*, forty interviews were conducted in July and August of 1979. This sample of visitors to the trailer, mainly

students, generally found it interesting.[28] But it is difficult to determine whether such educational programs have any real preventive impact. In one study, sixteen of the safety posters distributed by the British Columbia Workmen's Compensation Board were evaluated by 1,051 claimants.[29] There was no significant statistical relationship found between seeing a poster and avoiding certain types of accidents. In other words, if Lloyd (Poster 1) had seen that type of poster the accident probably would not have been prevented. As with other types of detached bureaucratic educational programs, the message transmitted is as much for the benefit of the organization as for that of the "target population."[30]

Tom's not going to work today.

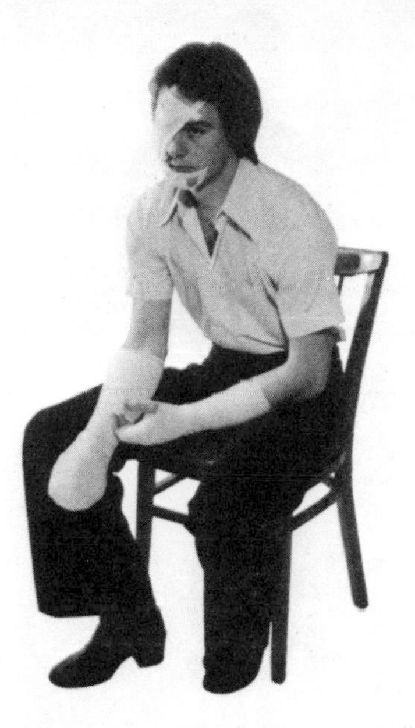

Clean up your act — don't make an ash of yourself.

DL9-78

For example, drug education programs may persist in spite of their ineffectiveness merely because they are believed to be effective by those in power.[31] Education is a popular means of addressing social problems and usually has a fair amount of support. If the philosophy of an occupational health and safety division is based upon the ideology of the "dumb worker" and the "unsafe act" as the major cause of health hazards, then education makes sense. It is also politically safe, especially among executives who recognize the costs of eliminating unhealthy and unsafe practices.

Frank gave his right arm to work.

Machines maim.
Don't be caught off guard.

DL11-78

The Buck Stops Where?

The ideology of "blaming the victim" is a convenient political weapon of busines and government which ignores the reality of health hazards in the workplace. As noted earlier in this chapter, the belief that the large majority of accidents are due to worker carelessness, accident proneness or unsafe acts is a myth masquerading as a fact. It is not the worker, but the worker's environment, shaped by the policies, practices, and procedures of management, which creates health hazards. Management creates risks which workers are subjected to and govern-

ment attempts to regulate. Since workers have no real power in defining "acceptable risk levels" these are generally taken for granted by management and government and prevention efforts are aimed at the worker, not the workplace.

The absurdity of blaming the victim is particularly apparent in the case of chemical hazards. Generally, workers are not told what hazards exist and have no control over the introduction or use of the chemicals, but are expected to "adapt" to their deleterious effects. If they happen to get burned or develop a disease it is their carelessness, hypersusceptibility, or lifestyle, such as smoking, which is blamed. Likewise, worker stress and its consequences on and off the job are often viewed as due to workers' attitudes, paranoia, temperament, or other personal failings.

The theory of the "big lie" says that if something is repeated often enough, it will be taken for a fact. The ideology of the "dumb worker" has indeed permeated health and safety approaches. It is evident not only in educational programs directed at workers, but also in the policing of the workplace. It will take concentrated effort by workers and their allies to counter this prevalent mythology.

NOTES

1. Jeffrey H. Reiman, *The Rich Get Richer and the Poor Get Prison* (New York: John Wiley & Sons, 1979), p. 68.
2. Charles Reasons met with Dr. Buchwald concerning the Alberta program.
3. The "kinds of people," "kinds of environment," and "power/conflict" explanations are taken from Charles E. Reasons, "Social Thought and Social Structure: Competing Paradigms In Criminology," *Criminology* 13 (November 1975): 335.
4. Jean Surry, *Industrial Accident Research: A Human Engineering Approach* (Toronto: Ontario Ministry of Labour, March 1979), pp. 114-15. (emphasis added).
5. Boyd Fisher, *Mental Causes of Accidents* (New York: Houghton Mifflin, 1922).
6. Surry, *Industrial Accident Research*, p. 162.
7. Ibid., p. 163.
8. W. Hadden, E. A. Suchman, and D. A. Klein, *Accident Research: Its Methods and Approaches* (New York: Harper and Row, 1964).
9. Keith Mason, *Industrial Fatalities to Fathers of Young Children* (Vancouver: Workers' Compensation Board of British Columbia, April 1972), p. 9 (emphasis added).
10. Keith Mason, *Industrial Fatalities To Husbands of Pregnant Wives* (Vancouver: Workers' Compensation Board of British Columbia, April 1972).
11. Keith Mason, *Industrial Accident Survey* (Vancouver: Workers' Compensation Board of B.C., June 1973).
12. Keith Mason, *An Investigation of the Biorhythm Theory* (Vancouver: Workers' Compensation Board of B.C., July 1971). Biorythm theory assumes that your behaviour and well-being are related to your birthdate.
13. Keith Mason, *Accident Patterns By Time-of-Day and Day-of-Week of Injury Occurrence* (Vancouver: Workers' Compensation Board, September 1975).
14. Keith Mason, *A Correlation Between the Unemployment Rate and the Industrial Accident Rate for B.C. Males, 1947-1968* (Vancouver: Workmen's Compensation Board, December 1970), p. 1.
15. Nicholas Askounes Ashford, *Crisis In The Workplace: Occupational Disease and Injury* (Cambridge, Mass.: MIT Press, 1976), p. 111.
16. Ibid., pp. 114-15.
17. Ibid., pp. 112-13.
18. Mason, *Industrial Accident Survey*, pp. 2-3.
19. "Workers' Fall Blamed on Faulty Scaffolding," *The Calgary Herald*, March 3, 1981.
20. Ashford, *Crisis In the Workplace*, p. 118 (emphasis added).

21. "Asbestos Not a General Carcinogen," *Canadian Occupational Health and Safety News*, June 13, 1980, p. 1-2.

22. "Investigation, Tighter Standards Sought," *Canadian Occupational Health and Safety News*, April 14, 1980, p. 1.

23. "Johns-Manville Implements Smoking Ban at All Its Asbestos Plants," *Canadian Occupational Health and Safety News*, August 18, 1980, p. 2.

24. "Conference Topics Reflect IAPA Theme," *Canadian Occupational Health and Safety Newsletter*, May 12, 1980.

25. Ibid., pp. 5-6.

26. Inhaling aluminum dust is a method which is used by miners to purportedly neutralize the harmful effects of silica. It has been shown to be of no worth. See Lloyd Tataryn, *Dying for a Living: The Politics of Industrial Disease* (Ottawa: Deneau and Greenberg, 1979).

27. "Minister Introduces Alive Campaign," *Alberta Occupational Health & Safety* 3, 2(April 1979): 6.

28. *An Initial Review of the Alive Trailer Program* (Edmonton: Occupational Health and Safety Division, January 1980).

29. Keith Mason, *A Survey Evaluation of Safety Posters* (Vancouver: Workers' Compensation Board, June 1973).

30. For example, see David L. Altheide and John M. Johnson, *Bureaucratic Propaganda* (Boston: Allyn and Bacon, 1980).

31. Charles E. Reasons and John Seem, "Drug Education: A Case Study of Legislative Intent and Perceived Effect," *Drug Forum* 7(2) (1978-79): 181-95.

Chapter 8

Is Workers' Compensation for the Worker?

We, however, feel confident that you, Sir, have thoroughly understood the unfairness of the proposals of the Manufacturers' representatives better than we have ourselves. True they propose a collective system of insurance, and a Compensation Board, so did we first of anyone before the Commission, but what would be the use even of that system to the workers unless the compensation to be paid be of some use in keeping them out of the hands of the charitably disposed. The social side of the legislation is to prevent the injured soldiers in industry and their dependents from being thrown on the scrap heap as objects of charity, and the dependents of the killed worker, male or female, being able to continue in existence by the aid of Government legislation in the interests of the whole people, instead of being beset with all the temptations that arise around those left to face the world without the means of a livelihood.[1]

Historical Origins

Before workers' compensation schemes were introduced, injured and disabled workers or their families would receive whatever financial or medical assistance they obtained from union or society benefit plans, from employer benevolence, from private insurance, from family or municipal charity or under the common law, from legal settlements or court awards. This might include some medical aid and hospitalization costs, but was mainly income maintenance, and limited at that.

Quite rightly, workers' compensation schemes have not been categorized as social welfare, even though they were one of the earliest forms of active government involvement in the areas of health and income policy.[2] One recent writer has described them as "Canada's first piece of social insurance."[3]

There is no easy way to describe the origins and history of workers' compensation. It is a vast subject which has been too little researched and rarely written about in any depth. This is especially true in Canada. Most of what we know publicly is contained in various government studies and documents—royal commissions, inquiries, legislative committee and task force reports, and in trade union or industry papers and submissions.

Unfortunately, most of the public government documents are not written from a workers' perspective. They treat workers' compensation as if it were solely a gratuitous benefit to workers for which they should be uncompromisingly grateful.

Compensation is, like veteran's compensation, based upon a right to reimbursement for health and income loss sustained during the course of work. It is not a benefit bestowed out of charity nor has it been based on a "means" or needs test. It is a right, like wages, borne out of the struggle between workers and business owners.

This distinction is extremely important. Arguments over the extent and quality of coverage must proceed on the basis of recognizing the right to compensation—as an established historical, social, and legal fact. Simultaneously, the improvement of workers' compensation has been and will continue to be a matter of labour-business struggle.

It is also fundamental to recognize that Canadian workers' compensation schemes were modelled after European and American schemes. They came about because of an increasingly mobilized international and domestic working-class and trade union political atmosphere and an alarming toll of industrial injuries and deaths occurring throughout the western world in the late nineteenth and early twentieth centuries.[4]

The workers' compensation schemes also were born out of the utter failure of the business-biased legal system to provide inexpensive, certain and adequate judicial remedies to injured workers. In the late nineteenth and early twentieth centuries, so many legal defences were available to employers and the cost, inefficiency, and uncertainty of the judicial process were so glaring, that the injustice of the process became a matter of common scorn and acrimony. Prevailing accident theories (some are still current) attributed fault mostly to workers. The courts adopted a similar posture. As British Columbia's Mr. Justice Sloan stated in 1942:

> Under the common law only 20 to 30 per cent of the workmen injured in industrial accidents could hope to recover damages from their employers and even then, in many instances, after protracted and expensive litigation. The 70 to 80 per cent who could not recover comprised a large class *which created grave and distressing social and economic problems.*[5]

The small percentage of workers who actually did sue and recover full damages is largely a matter of conjecture.

One can easily imagine the threats to prevailing business and political interests presented by that situation.

Industrial owners and insurance companies were threatened by the possibility of occasional, unforeseeable large damage awards. The legal system was open to massive working-class cynicism because of its unresponsiveness. Workers had mobilized and would continue to mobilize through trade unions and political parties around the material injustice of workplace danger. Skilled workers would be lost to industry unless compensatory medical and rehabilitative measures and preventive inducements were found.

Beginning in Ontario circa 1886, provincial governments introduced statutes to attempt to ameliorate the compensation situation through improving the common law, apparently following the example of the English Employers' Liability Acts of 1880 and 1897. This approach predominated until 1915. There is a pattern of organized labour involvement in these legislative changes, but there was disenchantment with the results.

According to trade union historian H. A. Logan, the Trades and Labour Congress (TLC), a national trade union body, and the railway unions agitated for revision.[6] Logan cites this agitation as a major force contributing to the eventual appointment of Sir William Meredith by Ontario in 1910 to study the employer's liability legislation. Meredith, a former Conservative party leader, was Ontario's Chief Justice and his appointment suggested the political importance of the task. Canada's judges have always performed political as well as judicial tasks.

Again according to Logan, the reformed Nova Scotia legislation of 1910 was still so inadequate that miners often favoured their own relief funds over the courts.[7]

But these legal changes posed new threats to business and the insurance industry:

> These changes in the common law faced the employer with the greater likelihood of large damage suits as well as the expense of court actions. The labour-management bitterness that ensued from legal battles was another cost to be reckoned with. The number of workers who took their employers to court began to escalate both as a result of their improved chances of winning their cases and because of the growing strength of unions and fraternal societies which assisted their members in carrying their claims for compensation through the courts. Insurance companies, with greater frequency, settled claims for damages out of court rather than face the possibility of more costly judgments awarded by the courts. This in turn raised accident liability insurance rates. Employers began to realize that a pooling of risks from accident claims would increase their business costs by a modest but predictable amount; this was to be preferred to the existing arrangement which left the individual employer open to large and unpredictable costs arising out of accident liability suits.[8]

Eventually, a massive study and hands-on process of labour-management negotiation was undertaken by Chief Justice William Meredith in Ontario between 1910 and 1914. His interim and final reports are a classic in Canadian social and labour history.[9]

From the beginning, and as is still the case today, the Canadian Manufacturers' Association played a leading role in the question of the nature and extent of a state-administered compensation scheme.[10]

The CMA actually submitted an entire draft statute to Meredith, complete with marginal notes, of seventy-nine sections. It was based on the underlying principles of the German system with amended use of the statute then in force in the U.S. state of Washington.

The CMA wanted a "current cost plan," as in Germany, under which employers would only be assessed for the amount of an injured worker's costs to be paid in the current year, not for all future costs arising from accidents occurring in that year. They also wanted a seven-day "waiting period" during which no benefits at all would be paid. Further, they initially requested that workers contribute directly to the mutual insurance fund, along with employers. Later, they relented somewhat and proposed in their final draft bill that the workers pay for any increased benefits beyond what was initially proposed. They also opposed application of the Act to any employer with less than three workers, and did not want industrial diseases to be covered.

The Canadian Manufacturers' Association has also played a leading role in opposing social insurance welfare programs, such as unemployment insurance, even in its contributory form.[11]

Eventually, a compulsory, state-administered, "no-fault" scheme emerged based on a mix of the German, English, and U.S. schemes. The CMA had wanted some direct financial contribution from workers. That was lost, but in return, workers gave up all rights to sue the employer directly and a provision remained which disentitled any worker (except in cases of death or serious injury) who was seriously and wilfully negligent. According to some sources, labour representatives were bullied by a vigorous CMA attack on Meredith's proposals and did not press demands for increased benefit levels as fully as possible.[12] The seven-day "waiting period" was introduced and industrial diseases covered but, as we shall see, in a special form, designed to limit their coverage.

Ontario's scheme came into force on January 1, 1915, followed by Nova Scotia's on April 23, 1915.

Meanwhile, a separate Commission with labour representation was established in British Columbia. The Pineo Committee, reflecting the active superior political power of British Columbia's labour and working-class political movements, won British Columbia legislation which improved upon the Ontario precedent.

A substantial concession, with mixed benefits, was won for workers in regard to medical aid. In an improvement upon the Ontario and Nova Scotia schemes, medical aid (including first aid, hospitalization, transportation and medical services) was provided to all workers coming within the Act's coverage. And this medical aid, unlike wage-loss, was payable from the date of injury. Between 1917 and 1940, this medical aid payment to workers amounted to \$5.8 million, approximately 45 per cent of the total medical aid cost over those years.[13]

Significantly, the British Columbia Compensation Board was also given jurisdiction over occupational health and safety prevention in industry. According to the Pineo Report, this was for the purpose of ensuring that compensation served the needs of prevention and that prevention efforts would predominate over time.[14]

The British Columbia legislation, in force from January 1, 1917, was, like that of Ontario, heavily influenced by the Washington state scheme which had been in effect since 1911 and which excluded all private casualty insurance companies. Pineo reports that the U.S. insurance industry had lobbied heavily to stop the spread of a government "no-fault" insurance scheme.[15] It is worth wondering to what extent private insurance was kept out of the Canadian schemes at least partly because the companies were nearly all foreign-owned.[16]

Similar schemes were subsequently introduced in Manitoba (1917), Alberta (1918), New Brunswick (1919), Saskatchewan (1929), Quebec (1931), Prince Edward Island (1949), Newfoundland (1951), the Yukon (1973), and the Northwest Territories (1977). The late emergence of a scheme in Quebec is of some interest.

According to one labour historian, the Trades and Labour Congress rejected a 1928 Quebec scheme because it failed to provide for compulsory collective liability of all industries and left insurance in the hands of private companies.[17]

> The Congress executive therefore advised the convention . . . that the act was not in harmony with the demands of organized labour and advised continuance of the effort to get legislation that would "guarantee a maximum of protection to employees at a minimum cost to industry."[18]

WCBs as Contemporary Bureaucracies

WCB-bashing has been forced upon disabled workers and trade unions across Canada and has become almost a national preoccupation. But it would be a mistake to think that all WCBs are staffed by unthinking bureaucrats who care little for workers. Insensitive and unresponsive government ministers are partly responsible, and there is a great distinction to be made between senior management staff and the line staff who make up WCBs. Often the problem is the compensation law or the internal organization of the Board. And two overriding problems have been the general Canadian law itself: secrecy as a way of life in government,[19] and the principle that a government body is not really legally accountable for omissions, only for gross errors when it finally does something.

Given the huge volume of claims and the importance of WCB decisions for workers' economic and medical future, it is inevitable that there will be both system failures and complaints. However, it has become almost inevitable to hear senior WCB administrators respond to criticism from workers, trade unionists, Members of Parliament, and ombudsmen with statements which question the legitimacy of the complainer, are overly defensive or run something like "over 95 per cent of our claims are successfully handled with no dispute."

It is often forgotten that most workers' compensation claims are for medical aid only, with no lost time from work. For example, in Ontario for the years 1976-78, approximately 60 per cent of all claims were for medical aid only.[20]

Statistics Canada estimates that about 56 per cent of all claims across Canada are for medical aid only.[21] Medical expenses constitute about 20 per cent of all WCB payouts. (This helps to explain why the medical profession has so much interest in and influence over workers' compensation. The interest and influence is privately, not publicly, exercised).

Medical aid only claims are rarely contentious. Therefore, when WCBs defend against criticism by arguing, as they often do, that the vast majority of their claims are not disputed, the reality is somewhat different. If only the serious cases are considered—wage-loss cases beyond two weeks, industrial disease cases, and pension cases—the percentage of disputed cases is much higher. There is also a question, of course, about what constitutes a disputed claim. Thousands of workers unhappy with their decisions have just given up, perhaps unaware of appeal rights or methods, or without resources or proper advice to pursue their cases. This is especially true with non-unionized immigrant workers.

Generally there is no appeal to the courts from WCB decisions on the merits of a claim, unless the Board has acted illegally. However, it is expensive to pursue a claim through the courts. Consequently, it is very important to have some truly independent appeal system outside of the courts for both medical and general issues. This has been slow to develop across Canada.

The single most contentious area of disputes is with WCB-employed physicians whose decisions are all-important and whose reports are generally withheld from the very workers whose lives are most affected by them. This secrecy has much to do with the bureaucracy problem. Unfortunately, the organized medical profession does not generally support the right of the patient or worker to access to medical files. This legacy of professional medical paternalism is a stumbling-block to progressive change within the WCBs.

Complaints Mount

It is virtually impossible to count accurately how many complaints are handled by people and agencies outside the WCB. Members of the provincial legislatures, private lawyers, publicly-paid staff legal aid lawyers, law student and community worker clinics, groups like Toronto's Union of Injured Workers, trade union shop stewards, business agents and officers, social workers, welfare agencies, ministers, newspaper and radio journalists, open-line shows and complaint columns, provincial ombudsmen's offices, and others all continuously get many complaints about workers' compensation. All of these types of people are involved in listening to complaints, investigating, and representing or otherwise assisting workers before the Boards.

In its first three months of operation the office of the British Columbia Ombudsman received more complaints about workers' compensation than about any other single British Columbia government agency. Between October and

December 1979, 74 complaints out of a total of 580—approximately 13 per cent—concerned WCB matters. That total exceeded complaints about the compulsory provincial motor vehicle insurance scheme and welfare.[22]

Even making allowances for a flood of old WCB complaints coming forward to the ombudsman in the first three months in British Columbia, the picture across Canada is fairly consistent. All provinces except Newfoundland have an ombudsman office; four provinces have had them for ten years or more.

Across the country, WCB complaints are consistently among the leading categories of complaints received by the ombudsman. For example, in Alberta from 1977 to 1979 inclusive, approximate totals of 518 WCB complaints were exceeded only by social welfare (751 approximately) and prisoners (753 approximately).[23]

In New Brunswick from 1976 to 1979 inclusive, WCB complaints were matched or exceeded only by complaints about social welfare, highways and licensing, municipalities, and prison issues.[24]

In Manitoba from 1973 to 1977 inclusive, 32 WCB complaints were found to be "not supported" by the ombudsman's office, whereas some 92 WCB complaints were either "rectified" or some other form of assistance or information was supplied.[25]

According to Dr. Karl Friedmann, British Columbia's Ombudsman and a leading intellectual analyst of the historical operation of Canadian and international Ombudsmen's offices, the high numbers of WCB complaints alone do not tell the whole story.

For one thing, he says, across the country, WCB complaints are generally more difficult to investigate and resolve. Files are thicker and more complex, investigation takes longer and access to internal regulations and policy precedents is often more inconsistent and difficult than with other government agencies.

Importantly, he says, the general Canadian experience is that Workers' Compensation Boards are the most difficult single agency to deal with when it comes to gaining acceptance for changing administrative policies or making sensitive policies where none existed. He cites excessive rigidity in procedures and outlooks and lack of responsiveness to recommendations as major problems. He also says he does not understand exactly why this should be the case.

By October 1980, the British Columbia Ombudsman's office had received 300 WCB complaints and, because of the difficulty of the cases, few were being closed. Additional staff had to be hired. And already, the British Columbia WCB Chairman had taken exception to the Ombudsman's involvement and was refusing access to files without a written complaint in each instance.

Canadian Ombudsmen's difficulties with WCB claims have reached such a level that a two-day informal seminar was held early in 1980 in Alberta, involving Canadian Ombudsmen representatives, centered on this issue alone. No formal published proceedings have yet been issued. Nor is it clear what general action or recommendations will follow. Over the years, WCB claims issues have regularly generated discussion at annual Canadian Ombudsman Conferences.

A major study of WCB claims problems was launched within the Ontario Ombudsman's office in 1980. This study was a result of long-standing difficulties experienced by both the Ontario Ombudsman and by the Ontario legislature in having recommendations listened to and acted upon by the Ontario WCB.

So long has been the history of WCB secrecy and defensiveness in Canada that when British Columbia began to publish its adjudication policies and major decisions around 1973, it was the first province to do so since 1915.[26] Remarkably, it is still the only province to have a regular decision reporting service, while most provinces still do not have a published, comprehensive adjudication manual available. In some provinces, there do not even appear to be comprehensive adjudication policies written for consistent internal use.

The Politics of the WCB

The various Workers' Compensation Boards across Canada form a substantial economic, social and political dimension in Canadian life.

Senior WCB personnel—in medical, legal, claims, rehabilitation, statistics, education, and financial departments—sit on a variety of provincial and national policy-making bodies. They have input into issues of manpower and employment, private and public disability policies, health care services and medical research, workplace health and safety, social and vocational rehabilitation, first aid services, education, and a wide variety of important social issues and services, including labour relations matters and industrial and financial policies. Their viewpoints are influential in determining whether government policies are worker-sensitive across large areas of Canadian society.

Taken together, the Canadian WCBs directly employ many thousands of workers. The WCB staffs in Ontario and British Columbia combined exceed 4,000 people. Indirect employment includes services and supplies, vehicles, equipment, construction, enormous medical and hospital services, business and union representation and consultation services, and other related programs in manpower, labour, welfare, health, and business.

The British Columbia WCB sends or receives over 6 million pieces of mail each year; the figure is over 10 million in Ontario. This volume of mail alone employs many workers in the envelope, paper and postage manufacturing, secretarial and delivery services industries.

One reason for lack of WCB reform from within has undoubtedly been that the WCBs, like other government agencies, were operated on a cozy, low-key, paternalistic staff management system for many decades,[27] finally shifting to an employee's association, and unionizing in the mid-1970s. Even when WCB employees unionized in B.C., the British Columbia Labour Relations Board carefully ruled out organization into separate unions, and a union developed which was not affiliated within a larger union or the British Columbia Federation of Labour. Instead, a union was certified only for the employees at the B.C. WCB—the B.C. WCB Employees Union. This history of management paternalism and isolation from the unionized mainstream are not the only factors contributing to internal difficulties. Inadequate staffing, salaries, and resources; lack of research and policy planning; a passive, defensive posture; "crisis management," and a bad public image have also contributed. Combined, these circumstances have added to the inability of the good WCB staff to generate constant, worker-biased WCB reforms over the years.

There has also been a historical failure to provide services in languages other than English and to aggressively hire or promote minority group members for staff positions.

Despite these odds, the British Columbia WCB Employees Union in 1976-77 contributed progressive submissions to a Departmental Inquiry in a political context which required some initiative and determination on the union's part. Informal links with the British Columbia labour movement were strengthened.

This type of history may be typical, in some respects at least, throughout Canada. For instance, a public inquiry was held in Newfoundland in 1972-73 concerning the relationship between the WCB and its employees and the effectiveness of the Board. The complaints focused upon delinquent or arbitrary management practices. The report is somewhat flawed by its stated overview that "the Workmen's Compensation Board operates on the same principles as any privately owned insurance company."[28]

A glaring difficulty has been the overall failure of WCB commissioners to consistently generate worker-oriented reforms. Much of this has been due to a recurring tendency to appoint Commissioners who are inexperienced with occupational health or workers' compensation, or who are appointed primarily for patronage reasons, at the behest of the ruling party or in response to some particular business or labour connection. Workers' compensation boards have also been a tripartite structure, to little obvious worker advantage, if any. The B.C. Board, by custom, has had one "labour" representative out of three commissioners.

Organized labour in British Columbia has put this "responsiveness" issue to the WCB, and to Royal Commissions, over the years. For instance, at the British Columbia 1942 Sloan Royal Commission, Harold Winch (former CCF MP) complained that "having noted the injustices done to workers excluded from benefits of the Act, they [WCB senior personnel] have failed to take the initiative to ask for legislative amendments that would correct the injustices."[29]

The WCB Chairman (Winn) of the time answered in the transcript:

> The Trades and Labour Council . . . and the Railway Brotherhood both raised the point, but we don't feel it is our job to advise the Government with regard to changes under the Act, *and that is the attitude of associated Boards in Canada* . . . We are administrative bodies, and shouldn't put the Government in that position by urging a lot of things that cost money. Those who seek to get these things advanced—some of them we might call an extremist body—I can mention a hundred and one things that would treble the Workmen's Compensation in a few months—easily more than treble.[30]

The Commissioner generally agreed, saying "the responsibility of initiating remedial legislation is not within the ambit of his authority but lies in other hands."[31] But he went on to say that he was "quite certain" that Board members would bring "palpable injustice . . . to the attention of the Minister of Labour for his consideration and action."[32] It is nearly impossible to know the record on that point.

This exchange reveals many interconnected points explaining the historical injustice of Canadian WCB law and administration. It is always labour or working-class interests who lobby for progressive changes and they include "extremist" elements. This is used as a reason to refuse to act on the recommendations. Recommendations are dismissed because of those who make them or because the Act does not absolutely require the Boards to make such recommendations. The lowest common denominator and passive approach of all Canadian WCB administrators is used as a defence.

And one notices that Mr. Winn argues that it is not part of his job at all. Such a theory plays right into business hands. Mr. Winn was Chairman of the British Columbia WCB from 1917 until 1946, almost 30 years.

Cabinet ministers generally know nothing about the actual details of the WCB legislation and administration. They must rely strongly on WCB administrators. This is even more the case as Canadian WCBs generally do not come under the direct departmental line responsibility of a Cabinet Ministry. They are all akin to independent Crown corporations. Thus, the Ministers have not had the direct intelligence, resources, and constitutional responsibility to be meaning fully accountable to provincial legislatures for WCB policy. The usual reason given for this insulation is that it would be inappropriate for governments of the day to influence individual case decisions by political pressures. Fair enough, but that does not answer the question of general policies or the statute itself.

This scenario is combined with the legal reality that the Canadian courts have played a less than significant—if not downright negative—role in checking WCB policy interpretations of their Acts. The hiatus created in progressive, continuous legislative and policy rejuvenation marks the system as one of inertia and passivity combined with externally-inspired "crisis" management via periodic political explosions. At various points, Royal Commissions, Task Forces and so on have to be called in to deflate political pressures and smooth the process of reform, offering a few improvements to workers to forestall the next crisis. The 1980-81 Weiler inquiry in Ontario is the latest example. It is no wonder WCBs have always been used as kicking cans. Sadly, such theories of the WCB administration continue to prevail. In a letter to a British Columbia worker's lawyer on a case where it was pointed out that the WCB Act did not allow for extensions to appeal medical decisions to a medical review panel (whereas all other appeals can be extended), the Board Secretary said:

> Any suggestion you may have for a statutory revision on this subject should be directed to the Minister of Labour or to your own M.L.A. rather than to the Board.[33]

This is an indefensible rejection of competence, interest and initiative.

The Saskatchewan Report of the Task Force on Workmen's Compensation in March 1973 stated:

> [W]e would suggest that the annual report . . . could be a very useful tool for the Board if it made an effort to point out deficiencies in its programs, rather than just outlining the functions that have worked well in the preceding year. Deficiencies in financing, in legislation or in facilities could be brought to the attention of the public and the government through the mechanism of the annual report.[34]

WCBs Are Big Business

The significance of workers' compensation must also be assessed in terms of the size and nature of the money generated and provided for investment. As taxing authorities, circulators of capital and investors of capital, the Canadian WCBs have a considerable economic impact.

As of the end of 1977, all twelve Canadian WCBs together had approximately $2.4 billion in investments, $90.6 million in fixed assets and $382.8 million in cash.[35]

Billions of dollars are presently circulated and invested. Each of the WCBs maintains short-term and long-term investment portfolios. As outlined below, the three WCBs in Alberta, British Columbia and Ontario presently have a combined investment portfolio well in excess of $2 billion. The type of securities which may be purchased and the administration of these funds vary somewhat under the workers' compensation provisions of each province. They also vary with the financial administration and political policies of each provincial government.

On December 31, 1978, the Alberta WCB had in excess of $260 million invested in securities. Approximately $80 million or 30 per cent was invested in Government of Canada bonds; approximately $120 million or 46 per cent was invested in provincially-guaranteed securities (telephone, hydro and municipal bonds, etc.); approximately $53 million or 20 per cent was invested in corporate securities (A.E.C. Power Ltd., C.I.L., Stelco and Thunder Bay Terminals Ltd. being the largest). The remainder, approximately $10 million, was in National Housing Association guaranteed mortgages. Alberta's Annual Report for 1978 states that the average yield on the book value of the entire 1978 investment portfolio was 8.59 per cent. There is a wide variation in the security interest rates, running from 3.75 per cent to 9.75 per cent for Government of Canada securities, from 5.25 per cent to 10.75 per cent for provincially-guaranteed hydro, telephone and municipal securities and from 9.5 per cent to 11.5 per cent for corporate securities.

Ontario's investment portfolio totalled in excess of $1.3 billion in September 1979, earning $105 million in interest in 1978 alone, 16.3 per cent of all Ontario Board revenues. In 1971, only 4 per cent of all Ontario WCB income was from investment. The long-term investment portfolio yielded 9.18 per cent in 1978. No breakdowns are given except to state that 70.2 per cent of investments were in long-term bonds, 18.5 per cent in mortgages and 11.3 per cent in short-term securities.

A recent public relations publication of the Board, *WCB Report*, puts it this way: "The Workmen's Compensation Board (of Ontario) is the 31st largest financial institution in Canada. Excluding banks and insurance companies, it operates one of the top half-dozen investment funds."[36]

As of December 1979, the British Columbia WCB had over $570 million invested in securities. Over $316 million, approximately 55 per cent, was invested solely in B.C. Hydro and Power Authority securities. In 1975-76 B.C. Hydro investments had represented 44 per cent of the WCB portfolio. Practically all investments in recent years have been in B.C. Hydro and Power Authority and British Columbia Railway bonds. The former institution is constantly under attack by environmentalists, native people, trade unions and other citizen groups opposed to its various massive energy development policies, many on the grounds of environmental pollution and resource giveaway. The British Columbia Railway has recently been the subject of a British Columbia Royal Commission which doubted its entire financial viability. Apparently, no corporate securities are held by the British Columbia WCB, with other investments in British Columbia provincial highways, schools, hospitals, railways, or municipal securities. The British Columbia WCB, unlike Alberta, does not publish a breakdown of the list of maturity dates and interest rates for each security. They do give the general yield on the average book value of their long-term securities as 8.24 per cent for 1979.

What is clear from these figures is that business — especially the large resource and manufacturing industries dependent upon hydro, roads and railways — have been well served by the available WCB invested funds. What is not clear is whether these WCB investments have been uniformly sound, across Canada, in terms of proper management for secure and high interest yields. Political or business influence over investment policies is another concern. This aspect of WCB financial administration has seldom received public scrutiny. A September 1976 Eckler, Brown, Segal & Co. Ltd. Report on the Actuarial Aspects of the British Columbia WCB stated that higher yields could be obtained from mortgage and high-grade corporate bonds "involving minimal added risks" and "from the intensive management of the overall portfolio"[37] (Eckler has also been the Ontario Board's consulting actuary). It went on to argue that if improvement in investment policies did not occur, British Columbia employers should be saved the necessary costs resulting from such failure by the government paying the WCB "an amount equivalent to the additional revenue that might have accrued from such a policy."[38] This is a classic business strategy: to try to make taxpayers—that is, workers—pay instead of business.

Thus, it cannot be said that compensation assessments are "lost" to industry, particularly since they are income-tax-deductible! Not only are the collected funds invested in enterprise which benefits overall economic development but the increased returns on investments are used to keep assessment rates down.

As was said by the Ontario Federation of Labour in their June 1980 submission to a provincial study:

> In 1979 the W.C.B. reported to the Standing Resource Development Committee of the Ontario Legislature that it had assets well in excess of two billion dollars. They also announced that the massive W.C.B. investment portfolio was directed by executives from four multi-national corporations. It is sadly ironic to note that these affairs of a purportedly worker-oriented crown corporation had absolutely no worker participation. However, the W.C.B. announced that all its investments were profitable. Also, the W.C.B. has implemented an average reduction of 8.5% in its 1980 assessment rates for 150,000 Ontario companies because of "the stable level of new claims and benefit payments."[39]

Before leaving the subject of the WCBs' massive capital pools, it must be noted that very little research into ill-health prevention has been sponsored by WCBs, despite the huge funds at their disposal. For example, the British Columbia WCB has only recently provided funding or sponsorship for health impact studies. Remarkably, the Board has never had an epidemiologist on staff who conducts studies into the frequency and severity of death or illness in selected industries or occupations. If anything, this is the Canadian pattern.

These capital pools could also be used productively by pursuing other health- and safety-related matters. For example, the capital could be used to stimulate investment into businesses which themselves develop accident prevention products, healthier technologies, machinery and equipment. Canadians must take a lead in this area, particularly those industries which are key to our economy and have unacceptable health risks for their workers, such as forestry, pulp and paper, metal manufacturing, mining, and petro-chemicals. Canada has been an occupational health and safety "colony," importing technologies developed elsewhere and relying on other countries, notably the U.S., for both pollution standards and abatement techniques.

Assessments on Employers—Promoting Safety and Health?

An oft-heard business complaint is that workers' compensation assessments upon employers must be kept low so as not to unduly burden industry. Taken in isolation and without supporting data, this complaint means nothing. In addition, it is based upon a fallacy and works against promoting healthier workplaces. WCB assessments were meant to be a lever to promote prevention. Yet no case has ever been shown of overall WCB assessments being excessive. In fact, as Table 8-1 indicates, for all Canadian industry in 1976, WCB assessments represent approximately 1.5 points out of a total employer labour cost of 132.3 points. If all capital and business costs were also considered, not just labour costs, WCB assessments probably constitute a financial drain on Canadian business of something well under .5 per cent of all costs. *In other words, much more money is probably spent by Canadian business on executive fringe benefits, expensive office decors, landscaping, advertising, entertainment and political donations than on compensation.*

Table 8-1

Workers' Compensation Payments as a Percentage of Average Total Compensation for all Industries and Selected Industries, Canada (1976)*

	All Industries	Manufacturing	Construction	Transportation & Communications	Trade	Education, Health & Welfare	Commercial Services	Public Administration
Direct Payment to Employees								
Basic pay—actual	$10,845	$10,498	$14,242	$11,888	$ 9,970	$11,659	$ 9,009	$10,929
—percentage	100.0	100.0	100.0	100.0	100.0	100.0	100.0	100.0
Commissions, incentives	2.4	2.3	0.8	0.5	6.7	0.0	3.8	0.0
Overtime & premium pay	4.5	6.3	6.0	7.2	1.8	1.4	3.1	4.8
Paid holidays, vacation, sick leave & other pay	12.6	11.9	10.0	13.3	10.5	14.1	11.3	15.2
Bonuses, severance pay, other benefits	2.2	2.6	2.7	2.4	2.5	1.6	2.7	1.6
Total Gross Payroll	121.7	123.0	120.2	123.6	121.6	117.1	120.7	121.6
Employer Contributions								
Workmen's Compensation	1.5	2.1	2.9	1.4	1.0	0.4	0.8	0.8
Unemployment insurance	1.6	1.7	1.4	1.6	1.7	1.5	1.6	1.7
Canada or Quebec pension plan	1.2	1.3	0.9	1.1	1.3	1.1	1.3	1.2
Private pension plans	4.4	3.6	2.2	9.1	2.4	3.5	2.2	8.4
Other life, health & other plans	1.9	2.7	1.5	2.4	2.0	1.0	1.7	1.2
Total Compensation	132.3	134.4	129.1	139.1	129.9	124.6	128.3	134.8
Relative Earnings (Industry Average as Percentage of All Industry Average)								
Basis pay	100	97	131	110	92	108	83	101
Gross payroll	100	98	130	111	92	103	82	101
Total compensation	100	98	128	115	90	101	81	103

* Statistics Canada, *Labour Costs in Canada—All Industry* (Cat. #72-618).

Unfortunately, government commissions, inquiries and task forces into workers' compensation and WCBs themselves seldom, if ever, examine this economic reality. Instead, they generally give credence to these types of abstract employer concerns as a reason for keeping WCB benefits and services to a minimum.

Mutual insurance is the cheapest form of insurance and in this, business secured a very great advantage from workers' compensation. This is particularly so for small- to medium-sized employers operating a hazardous business or employers with large payrolls relative to other costs.

Because of workers' compensation, employers can budget their insurance costs in advance and pay them on an orderly basis. No employer will be hit by a large damage award—such as in a civil court system award—to disrupt their business financial structure.

Because Canadian workers' compensation is a compulsory and collective system, taking in thousands of employers, assessment rates can be kept as low as politically possible. And they have been.

But the assessment rates are supposed to be set at a level which corresponds to the demonstrated hazard of the employer's business, as revealed by the medical aid, wage loss, pension and fatal claims made by workers of that employer and in that industry.

This is the fundamental importance of workers' compensation when it comes to promoting safe and healthy workplaces. Unless compensation assessment rates and penalty assessments accurately reflect the real cost of workplace ill-health, there will be no real economic incentive upon employers to operate as safely as possible. That is the theory of the system. Therefore, inadequate compensation—such as the massive historical failure to recognize and compensate for a variety of industrial diseases—actually contributes to negligence at the same time as it works an economic injustice on the disabled workers.

The conventional wisdom is that the experience or merit-rating system of setting WCB assessment rates has not had an overall proven impact upon accident prevention and accident rates. Whether this is true in all provinces for all industries has not been studied. Admittedly, it is not easy to prove one way or the other in all cases. One of the few published studies recently suggested that the Ontario system *may* lead to lower accident rates, based upon the accident record of Ontario metalworking industries between 1966 and 1972.[40]

It is also debatable whether the problem has been a failure to adequately apply the merit-rating system or that the system itself cannot produce results, no matter how well worked. We think it is the former. The labour viewpoint most commonly heard is that the WCBs have not set the general assessment rates high enough nor have they been adjusted adequately to seriously impact upon individual industries or employers so as to generate improved performance. Furthermore, from a workers' perspective, the WCBs have shown insufficient interest in evaluating and improving upon the merit-rating principle.

In many provinces, large numbers of employers and whole industries are allowed to operate on a self-insuring basis, simply paying as they go. Across Canada, government bodies and major sections of the transportation industry usually fall into this category.

The general picture has been that WCBs have rarely adopted a determined approach to imposing penalty assessments. Only political pressure, overt or implied, can explain that situation. For instance, the British Columbia WCB, under a reformist NDP government, radically stepped up its use of penalty assessments, both in number and amount, between 1972 and 1975. The Cominco smelter at Trail, British Columbia, was slapped with what became approximately a $30,000 per month penalty assessment. Since Social Credit returned in late 1975, the relative use of penalty assessments has declined noticeably and the general relative assessment rates were not increased from 1976-79 despite a Social Credit government commissioned study—the Eckler, Brown Report (1976)—which said that they should be. Cominco's assessment was also reduced substantially, but after trade union pressure, again increased. Nevertheless, Cominco still finds it economically advantageous to pay the penalty assessment rather than to act quickly and spend money on the changes required for a cleanup. Obviously, the assessment is not high enough to have the impact required. This situation is made worse by a potential 80 per cent rebate plan, with interest, offered by the Board.[41]

A serious failure has been that workers' compensation and occupational health and safety have been addressed in Canada as if they were separate and mutually exclusive areas. Only in British Columbia and Prince Edward Island are they now both administered within one government body.

Compensation should serve the needs of prevention. The level and use of compensation assessment rates should be a major focus for improvement if we are ever to make serious inroads upon the toll of industrial injury, disease and death.

NOTES

1. Fred Bancroft and Joseph Gibbons, *Memorandum of the Trades and Labour Congress of Canada* to Sir William R. Meredith, Chief Justice of Ontario, Commissioner on Workmen's Compensation, Toronto, 25 March 1913. See *Final Report on Laws Relating to the Liability of Employers* (Toronto: King's Printer, 1913), Appendix XII, pp. 694-95.
2. See, for example, M. K. Strong, *Public Welfare Administration in Canada* (Chicago: University of Chicago Press, 1930), which contains only three brief references to workers' compensation.
3. Dennis Guest, *The Emergence of Social Security in Canada* (Vancouver: University of British Columbia Press, 1980), p. 39.
4. Michael Piva, "The Workers' Compensation Movement in Ontario," *Ontario History* 67 (1975): 39-56.

5. *Report of the Commissioner re: Workmen's Compensation Board* (Mr. Justice Gordon McG. Sloan) (Victoria, B.C.: King's Printer, 1942), p. DD12 (emphasis added) (hereafter cited as *Sloan Report*).
6. H. A. Logan, *Trade Unions in Canada* (Toronto: Macmillan, 1948), p. 501.
7. Ibid., pp. 182-83.
8. Guest, *The Emergence of Social Security in Canada*, pp. 40-41.
9. William Meredith, *First Interim Report*, Ontario Sessional Papers #65 (Toronto: King's Printer, March 27, 1912.); *Second Interim Report*, Ontario Sessional Papers #85 (Toronto: King's Printer, April 1, 1913); *Final Report*, Ontario Sessional Papers #53 (Toronto: King's Printer, October 31, 1913).
10. See, for example, *Canadian Manufacturers' Association (Ontario Division) Brief to Weiler Task Force on Ontario Workmen's Compensation* (Toronto, 1980).
11. Carl Cuneo, "State Mediation of Class Contradictions in Canadian Unemployment Insurance, 1930-35." *Studies in Political Economy*, No. 3 (Spring 1980): 45-46.
12. Piva, "Workers' Compensation Movement in Ontario," and Guest, *Emergence of Social Security in Canada*, p. 43.
13. *Sloan Report*, p. DD73.
14. *Report of the Committee of Investigation on Workmen's Compensation Laws* (Victoria, B.C.: King's Printer, March 1, 1916), p. 21 (hereafter cited as *Pineo Report*).
15. Ibid., p. 9.
16. See, for example, G. W. Taylor, *Timber: History of the Forest Industry in British Columbia* (Vancouver: J. J. Douglas Ltd., 1975), pp. 113-14.
17. Logan, *Trade Unions in Canada*, pp. 501-2.
18. Ibid., p. 502 citing *Proceedings*, 44th Annual Convention, T.L.C., p. 87.
19. T. G. Ison, Research Publication #4, *Information Access and the Workmen's Compensation Board* (Toronto: Ontario Commission on Freedom of Information and Individual Privacy, January 1979).
20. *Ontario W.C.B. Annual Report*, 1978, p. 12.
21. Statistics Canada, *Workmen's/Workers' Compensation*, Cat. #86-501 (Ottawa: Ministry of Supply and Services Canada, 1980), p. 27.
22. Karl A. Friedmann, *First Annual Report, British Columbia Ombudsman* (Victoria, British Columbia, May 1980).
23. See *Alberta Annual Reports*.
24. See *New Brunswick Annual Reports*.
25. See *Manitoba Annual Reports*.
26. See *W.C.B. Reporter Series Decisions* (Vancouver: B.C. WCB, 1973 to date), and *Claims Adjudication Manual*.
27. *Oral History Project*, Interviews with former WCB Staff, 8 volumes (Vancouver: B.C. WCB Library), preface.
28. *Report of the Royal Commission on Matters Pertaining to the Relationships of the Workmen's Compensation Board with the Employees* (Hugh O'Neill, Chairman) (St. John's, n.d.), p. 31.
29. *Sloan Report*, p. DD104.
30. Ibid., p. DD105 (emphasis added).
31. Ibid.
32. Ibid.
33. B.C. WCB #XC78058893, August 1, 1980 file letter.
34. *Report* (Alastair J. Muir, Chairman) (Regina, March 1973), p. 71.

35. Statistics Canada, *Workers' Compensation*, Cat. #86-501, Table 13, pp. 58-59.

36. *Will Injured Workers Get a Fair Hearing?* (Toronto: Committee on the Weiler Study, June 1980), p. 35.

37. Eckler, Brown, Segal & Co. Ltd., *Report on Acturial Aspects of the Workers' Compensation Board of British Columbia* (Victoria, B.C., 1976), p. 53.

38. Ibid., p. 54.

39. Ontario Federation of Labour Submission to the Paul C. Weiler Task Force on Workmen's Compensation in Ontario (Toronto: June 1980), p. 7.

40. Report of the *Royal Commission on Civil Liability and Compensation for Personal Injury* (Pearson Report), Vol. II (London, England: March 1978), pp. 187-89.

41. For Cominco penalty assessments see *B.C. WCB Reporter Series Decisions* #15, 19, 36, 167, 186, 192, 234, 268, 274, and 317.

Chapter 9

Workers' Compensation: Too Few, Too Late, Too Little

Sion is thirty-eight
used to work the steel gang, used to run
bent double under the rebar.
now he cannot overload his tray
and must be careful to get help when throwing
seventy-year-old drunks out of the bar.

he never figured in the statistics
of those disabled by industrial accidents,
yet another ten years' degeneration of his spine
will see him on the welfare rolls,
one of those bums too lazy to get a job.
in twenty years, should he live that long,
i shall probably be asking for help
to throw an old workmate out of the bar.[1]

—in 1977 alone, about 10 per cent of Canadian workers had claims before a compensation board;

—in 1977 alone, about 44 per cent of all claims involved wage-loss;

—in 1977 alone, over 1 million compensation claims were settled;

—by 1977, an estimated 147,000 Canadians were receiving workers' compensation pensions;

—in 1977 alone, compensation costs totalled nearly $900 million, half of 1 per cent of all Canadian personal income.[2]

Lack of Comprehensive Coverage

Not all workers are covered by workers' compensation. The percentage of the adult work force which is covered varies from province to province. Most estimates place it at 70-90 per cent of the full-time work force.[3] It was much lower in earlier years. Groups which have traditionally been excluded from compulsory coverage include agricultural workers, fishermen, domestic workers, artistic and cultural performers, athletes, and "independent contractors." This latter category has included large numbers of workers, for example, taxi drivers and casual construction or labour workers. Over the years, some of the provinces have been slowly extending coverage, either by legislative change (e.g., agricultural workers in Ontario) or by WCB interpretations of the phrase "independent contractors" (e.g., taxi-cab drivers in British Columbia). It is no mere coincidence that those workers not covered are generally non-union, non-English-speaking, immigrant, lower-paid, or female. Unfortunately, the various boards do not seem very concerned to know exactly how many workers are not covered and to take measures to ensure such coverage. Outdated legal fictions and political bargaining have often controlled which workers are covered and which are not.

This is best demonstrated with agricultural workers, who work in a traditionally dangerous occupation.

Ontario's Chief Justice Meredith in 1913 had difficulty justifying why farming and domestic service should be excluded—". . . there is, I admit, no logical reason why, if any, all should not be included, but I greatly doubt whether the state of public opinion is such as to justify such a comprehensive scheme. . . ."[4] Agricultural workers made up a substantial proportion of the adult labour force in Canada at that time.

Furthermore, the British legislation of the time covered both farming and domestic servants. Germany also had a special Agricultural Accidents Insurance Law.

According to one former senior Ontario WCB administrator, the "public opinion" of the time was based on the farming interests in the Ontario legislature circa 1913-15 who threatened to block any compensation statutes coming out of Meredith's report if it included coverage of agricultural workers.[5]

Agricultural workers are presently covered on a compulsory basis only in Ontario, Newfoundland and the Territories. In the rest of the provinces, coverage is optional and must be applied for.

As of 1978 in Saskatchewan, there were over 420 employers recognized in the agricultural area—ranching, grain, dairy or mixed farming—and over 65,000 farmers, with an estimated 20,000 farmers employing casual or full-time workers. Agricultural workers made up 24.5 per cent of the adult labour force in Saskatchewan in 1978. For Canada as a whole in 1978, the percentage was 4.5 per cent with some provinces having much higher percentages: Prince Edward Island (10.0 per cent), Manitoba (9.3 per cent), and Alberta (8.8 per cent).[6]

The Canadian Farmworkers' Union in British Columbia has recently demanded compulsory workers' compensation coverage as part of a demand for general labour standards protection for agricultural workers.[7] Interestingly, even the Chief Justice of British Columbia, back in 1952, recommended such coverage.[8]

The benefit of extending compensation coverage for athletes (hockey players) was recently advocated by former Supreme Court Justice Emmett Hall as a means of shifting medical costs away from the general medical care scheme and onto the employer and as a potential lever for cutting down on violence in the sport.[9]

Waiting Periods: Be Patient

A "waiting period" is an initial injury period during which no compensation is paid, even for covered workers. These waiting periods have been a feature of every Canadian WCB scheme and have saved business hundreds of millions of dollars. As the 1942 Sloan Royal Commission Report noted, "It is a form of contribution by employees to the fund."[10]

At the time the original acts were introduced in 1915-1917, evidence from many countries indicated that only about 30 per cent of all accidents resulted in a disability which extended beyond 14 days.[11]

> It is thus quite apparent to anyone who considers this fact that a waiting period of two weeks, or even of seven days, withholds a very large amount of money in the aggregate from injured workmen, and may result in a distinct hardship to the lower-waged workman.[12]

This is an understatement of tragic proportions. The political and economic compromise established in British Columbia was that there would be a "waiting period" of three days for all wage-loss payments during which no wage-loss compensation was payable at all, no matter how long you were disabled. (In 1925, an amendment was added in British Columbia to pay for the first three days, but only if the disability went beyond 14 days.) No estimates were given as to the number and percentage of accidents which fell entirely into the three-day waiting period. It can safely be assumed that no less than 10 per cent of all workers' time-loss accidents would be included, given the economic and employer incentives to shrug off "minor" injuries and get back to work or stay at work.

That three-day waiting period existed in British Columbia's law until March 30, 1972.

Five to six thousand claims fell into the three-day waiting period in British Columbia in 1963. A cost of $124,000 was estimated to cover such claims.[13]

Mr. Justice Tysoe was not convinced "that the elimination of the three-day waiting period would result in no extra cost to industry, either by way of compensation payments or by way of administrative expenses."[14] He also was not convinced that "its existence works an injustice on workmen and that its exclusion will not work an injustice on industry."[15]

Note this thinking: an injustice to industry means increased expenditures; all industry is equated with all workers, as if they have equal capacity to absorb loss—collectively and individually; no economic analysis has been done of industry's profit picture or of its capability to absorb increased assessments.

The original Ontario Act, along with other provinces such as Prince Edward Island, Quebec and Nova Scotia, provided for an incredible seven-day waiting period. In Ontario, this lasted 37 years, up to January 1, 1952, when it was reduced to five days. On April 3, 1963, this was reduced to three days. Even this record did not satisfy certain business interests, since there was continual opposition to the reduction in the waiting period. Additionally, various business interests were upset that the Ontario WCB included the day of the accident in the calculation of the waiting period. As late as 1967, at the McGillvray Royal Commission, some business interests even argued for an increase in the waiting period.[16] This is truly remarkable, since "one recent study estimated the proportion of time-loss claims for less than one week at 39% in Prince Edward Island, 31% in New Brunswick, and 50% in Manitoba!"[17]

The business view was that the "short" (!) waiting period "encouraged workmen to stay off work long enough to qualify for compensation, something which might not occur with a longer waiting period."[18]

This thinking is truly bizarre, as well as inhumane. Obviously what business wanted was the longest possible waiting period in order to reduce compensation assessments or to encourage under-reporting.

Compensation Ceilings and Payment Limits

Compensation statutes have always had a "ceiling," above which they will not pay for workers' lost income, no matter how much the injured worker actually earned at the time of injury or actually lost after the injury.

Astoundingly, even to Chief Justice Meredith in 1913, the Canadian Manufacturers' Association originally opposed any compensation payment at all unless more than 50 per cent of earnings were lost, and set rigid, maximum amounts for all payments. In fact, their proposed maximum would have meant this: a locomotive engineer earning $150 per month who became permanently and totally disabled and so severely injured that he would be "completely helpless" requiring "constant personal attendance" the rest of his life, would receive a pension of $40 per month! Meredith called these "extraordinary propositions."[19]

Maximum wage rates have always been kept as low as politically possible, to the economic benefit of Canadian business. The maximum wage rate sets an absolute ceiling upon the amount of wage-loss or pension benefits a worker can receive. Importantly, too, it also limits the amount that WCBs can assess employers in order to pay those workers who are injured, killed, or diseased, since WCBs are financed by a tax on the employers. Therefore, the WCB maximum wage rate is a crucial economic issue, making a difference as to whether hundreds of millions of dollars go to workers or to business. A business is only taxed up to the wage ceiling set by the compensation act.

When Mr. Justice Meredith drafted the original Ontario Act, he set the maximum wage rate at a level intended to cover the earnings of the highest-paid worker in Ontario in 1914. Even the business-biased 1978 Ontario Wyatt Report has recognized that principle.[20] Meredith actually used these words: "I propose $2,000.00 as the limit because that sum is probably the maximum amount earned in a year by the highest paid wage earner."[21]

In 1913-14, $2,000 was a very substantial amount, easily covering all workers' incomes. But we shall see how this principle was subsequently abandoned.

Two major justifications are usually given for WCB wage ceilings: that workers should contribute something to the compensation schemes, and that there must be a financial incentive to return to work. The former idea is at odds with the original Meredith principle and is obviously a penalty imposed upon higher wage earners, many of whom are being paid higher wages largely because they work in extremely unhealthy jobs—in forestry, steel, foundries, mining, and construction. The idea that all workers must be given a financial incentive to return to work is a cynical and unwelcome view of human motivation, and it interferes with proper medical rehabilitation.

Taking British Columbia as an example, let us look at the historical record. Following the Meredith principle, the original British Columbia WCB maximum annual wage rate commencing January 1, 1917 was set at $2,000. Remarkably, as if wages, profits, and prices increased not at all for the next 26 years, that $2,000 maximum was the law until March 1943. The maximum wage rate was then increased to $2,500 where it stayed until March 1952. As late as June 30, 1974, the maximum wage rate was $9,600. It was only after twice-yearly, statutory cost-of-living indexing was introduced in British Columbia in 1974 that the maximum wage rate achieved some closer proximity to the range of workers' actual wage rates. Since January 1, 1974, the British Columbia maximum WCB wage rate has gone from $9,600 to over $20,000 per year. Even then, a substantial number of workers have wage rates well in excess of the ceiling. But the Canadian compensation boards do not seem to be concerned to know how many workers are actually above the ceiling and to amend the statutes accordingly.

A study for the 1967 Ontario McGillvray Commission indicated that over 10 per cent of all workers receiving permanent disability awards had earnings above the ceiling and that over 18 per cent of all workers receiving temporary total disability awards had earnings above the ceiling.[22]

Clearly, in the interests of justice and fair compensation, wage ceilings should be completely abolished, if compensation is to relate to human needs and prevailing market conditions. If an employee is sick, it is now an accepted principle that sick-leave provisions should cover full wages, including benefits.

Furthermore, when the maximum wage rates have been changed, as in British Columbia in 1943 and 1952, they were not changed because of the original Meredith principle or by a built-in statutory provision. They were changed by the ruling elements in British Columbia's provincial legislature, for expedient political reasons. As one political historian has commented:

> The shining new coalition (Liberal-Conservative) face was bared at the 1943 session of the Legislature which passed a host of welfare and labour bills. Rising union pressures were reflected in amendments of the Workmen's Compensation Act, providing for increased benefits as recommended by the recent Sloan Commission. . . .[23]

The same pattern was followed in 1952 but apparently not to the same successful political result. Martin Robin offers the opinion that the failure of the British Columbia Liberal-Conservative coalition government to introduce "sharply increased benefits under the Workmen's Compensation laws" in 1952, as well as the failure to provide a wider progressive social platform led to many workers deserting the Liberals and the subsequent collapse of the coalition, giving way to the rise of W. A. C. Bennett and Socred (Social Credit) rule for the next two decades.[24]

This massive historical injustice has been compounded by the fact that the maximum rates of compensation have never been 100 per cent of all earnings and benefits.

While compensation payments are non-taxable, the compensation "percentage" was originally set at only 55 per cent of all wages across Canada. It was increased gradually over the years to 60 per cent, 66.66 per cent, and finally 75 per cent of wages. For example, it became 66.66 per cent in Ontario in 1920 but was not raised to 75 per cent until January 1, 1950 in that province.

In British Columbia, it was not until April 1954 that the wage-loss and pension payments reached 75 per cent of wages up to the low maximum wage rates. That is now the Canadian standard, except for Quebec, which has now adopted 90 per cent of net wages. As the percentage rates move upward, some business and government representatives will probably urge taxation of all WCB benefits as with family allowances. This has already been projected as a likely scenario.[25]

The reasons which have always been given for paying less than 100 per cent of net wages are entirely anti-working class and pro-business: they are projected to save employers money, and they express an extremely cynical view of workers which employers label "human nature."

The 1942 British Columbia Sloan Report expresses it in graphic splendour:

> To assess industry for the 100-per-cent loss arising out of (practically) 100-per-cent of injuries suffered, is to charge industry—especially the hazardous ones—with too great a burden . . . .

> It is partial because of the great number of workmen now entitled to be indemnified against loss as compared with the few who could successfully maintain an action under the common law. It is partial, too, because if full compensation be paid, human nature being what it is, there would be few of us who would rather work hard for a wage when by successfully malingering we could receive the same amount by way of compensation.[26]

Would judges assume that most judges would malinger whenever they could get away with it? Obviously not.

It is even now taken for granted that the use of a "75 per cent of wages" formula provides workers with wage-loss and pensions quite close to the after-tax income of a typical worker. But even this assumption has not been conclusively demonstrated to be true. Furthermore, as even a business-biased British Columbia study stated:

> However, it should be noted that the pension payable to a low income worker or a worker with many dependants is a smaller percentage of take-home pay than for a worker earning close to the maximum covered earnings or a single worker, while the low income worker is less likely to be able to absorb a reduction in income.[27]

If this analysis were extended across Canada, it would reveal that incalculable millions, if not billions, of dollars have been stolen from workers by Canadian business over the period 1915 to date.

Inadequate Compensation—Earnings

The loss of all non-wage benefits by an injured worker, whether economic or otherwise, is seriously overlooked by the WCB. This is even more unjust since collective agreements negotiated by unionized workers' bargained contracts—the price at which they sell their labour—have increasingly been made up of non-wage benefits.

Neither workers' compensation legislation nor any other public laws require employers to keep all non-wage benefits going for the period of the worker's work-related disability. Whether any or all of such benefits continue will depend upon the collective agreement (if workers are unionized) and on the terms of life insurance, medical and dental, and other such plans.

In the past two decades, employee benefits have increased from 15 per cent to 31 per cent of the gross annual payroll in Canada.[28] This varies between occupations, for example, from 21 per cent in the construction industry to 38 per cent in mining.

Such fringe benefits include paid holidays, vacation, sick leave and other pay, overtime and premium pay, commissions and incentives, bonuses, severance pay and benefits such as pensions, life insurance, long-term disability and so on.

Another recent private study indicated that the average cost of a full fringe benefits package is now $6,000 per year, up 20 per cent between 1978 and 1980.[29]

These established trends beg the following questions: Why are maximum compensation ceilings primarily based only upon wage rates? Are all fringe benefits taken into account in establishing compensation rates in individual cases? Why are provisions not made by law to ensure either WCB payment for the value of all fringe benefits or employer maintenance of all fringe benefits?

Depending upon the particular statute and the interpretation policy in each province or territory, some fringe benefits such as premium pay, overtime, bonuses and commissions *may* be taken into account in setting wage-loss or pension payments. The comprehensiveness and consistency of such inclusions is questionable and for higher-income-earning workers, it will be irrelevant since their wages alone will exceed the maximum ceilings. But it will matter significantly for pension purposes, since a fully or significantly disabled worker loses not only the job and the wage, but a legally bargained series of fringe benefits, including pensions, life insurance and so on.

As the Ontario Federation of Labour has stated:

> In establishing the earnings basis for compensation, all remuneration and tangible benefits should be included in the calculation, except in those cases where the accident employer continues to provide employment benefits and prerequisites to the injured worker.[30]

Job Security and Rehabilitation

A recent Labour Canada publication makes the statement that "the Canadian workers' compensation system is rehabilitation-oriented."[31]

Workers' compensation also has been cited by some writers as a major contributing factor during the late nineteenth century development of vocational rehabilitation as a service and science, together with the case approach of charity and the development of orthopedic surgery.[32]

Let us examine these propositions historically. While the Canadian WCBs have had a long involvement in rehabilitation services, there have been and continue to be extremely serious statutory shortcomings and administrative failings. A distinction must be made between physical or medical rehabilitation and vocational or social rehabilitation. Historically, most Canadian WCB rehabilitation has been of the medical variety.

In British Columbia, it was not until 1943 that any statutory provision was made for vocational rehabilitation services and retraining. It was not until 1952 that the statute allowed for such services where the injury occurred prior to 1943.[33]

The WCB statutes have always emphasized the duty "to aid in getting injured employees back to work."[34] Periodic supplement payments have been available to the injured worker "provided that he co-operates in and is available for a medical or vocational rehabilitation program which would in the opinion of the Board aid in getting him back to work, or accepts or is available for employment which is available and which in the opinion of the Board is suitable for his capabilities."[35] Medical aid is also provided as part of the scheme's benefits.

The problem, of course, is one of determining when somebody is no longer disabled from going "back to work" which is "suitable for his capabilities." Workers have no absolute legal right under Workers' Compensation Acts to return to either the job, the occupation, or the employer for whom they were working when disabled. So they may be able to go back to some kind of work, but perhaps that job or employer no longer exists; perhaps the worker is no longer capable of handling the job or occupation; perhaps the employer will not take the worker back to that job or any job; perhaps the worker has already been laid off or fired; or perhaps the worker is fit for certain types of work in which there are no openings. Any number of these things happen, especially to unskilled workers, or workers without union protection, or workers who have suffered some serious back, hand, arm, leg, knee, shoulder, foot, or head injury. Thousands of cases fall into one of these categories every year at every provincial WCB. These kinds of problems are multiplied in provinces lacking in lighter secondary manufacturing or service work. Therefore, a great strain is placed on WCB medical rehabilitation programs which are caught between treating the worker medically and ensuring that the worker gets back to some kind of work. This conflicting situation has fostered many worker complaints and created unnecessary distrust of WCB medical services.

Only a very small percentage of workers who receive vocational rehabilitation assistance are retrained to acquire new occupational skills. This percentage has been estimated at 5 per cent for British Columbia.[36] Comparable figures are not immediately available for all provinces.

Some provinces (Ontario, Alberta, British Columbia, and New Brunswick) now actually own extensive special rehabilitation clinics or facilities, and in other jurisdictions these services are purchased.

For many years in Canada, very little meaningful vocational rehabilitation has been available. The 1980 Alberta Select Committee Report put it this way:

> The (Alberta) Board's Rehabilitation Centre is presently oriented to medical treatment or medical control of problems. In Europe, the Committee found convincing evidence to support a change of emphasis from medical to a vocational role.[37]

The 1958 McKinnon Royal Commission Report in Nova Scotia found a virtual absence of rehabilitation in that province and went on to say:

> It is strongly recommended that the Board either appoint a full-time Rehabilitation Officer or make rehabilitation the principle responsibility of one of its employees."[38]

A subsequent 1968 Clarke Inquiry in Nova Scotia noted that, ten years later, not all of McKinnon's recommendations on rehabilitation had yet been implemented, and called on the Nova Scotia WCB to give "serious consideration" to establishing a rehabilitation centre.[39]

The 1967 Ontario McGillvray Royal Commission Report devoted only four and one-half pages to the entire subject. It was generally supportive of the Ontario Board's medical and vocational rehabilitation services. But the Report also showed that while over $3 million had been expended in 1965 alone for maintenance of Ontario's Downsview medical centre, less than $750,000 was spent in the entire three years (1963-65) on vocational rehabilitation.[40] A section in the Compensation Act put an absolute (and low) ceiling on the total amount of monies allowable for vocational rehabilitation. Commissioner McGillvray recommended that it be deleted.

The earlier 1950 Ontario Roach Report devoted just over two pages to the subject, revealing that less than $7,000 per year had been spent on vocational rehabilitation between 1941 and 1948, even though the Act allowed for up to $100,000 per year to be so allocated. Mr. Justice Middleton's 1932 Royal Commission Report does not even mention rehabilitation.

The 1966 British Columbia Tysoe Royal Commission Report devoted 10 pages (out of 442 pages) to rehabilitation. It was extremely positive on the subject of medical rehabilitation. On the subject of vocational rehabilitation, the Commissioner was distinctly more cautious. He observed that "the Board could do quite a bit more than it has been doing" regarding industry and trade union co-operation.[41] Vocational rehabilitation cost figures for 1951 to 1963 inclusive showed that approximately 47 per cent of all expenditures were for staff salaries and expenses; that actual training allowances and expenditures for workers (beyond oral counselling) averaged approximately $50,000 per year on a referral caseload averaging approximately $156 per worker per year. Furthermore, the number of workers sponsored in retraining each year showed a curious pattern. While 147 out of 306 referred workers were sponsored in retraining in 1955, only 70 out of 313 referred workers received retraining in 1961.

These quirks in medical and vocational rehabilitation still exist. The International Woodworkers of America, Western Regional Council #1—British Columbia's largest union, with over 50,000 members—made a submission to the British Columbia Labour Minister in the fall of 1979 protesting service cutbacks at the WCB. It pointed out that in 1975, the last year of NDP administration, the WCB had provided 522 workers with some form of academic, technical, or vocational training and a further 93 workers with on-the-job training. In 1978, under a Social Credit administration, the figures had been reduced to 200 and 30 respectively.

The average time-loss claims figures in the British Columbia logging industry between 1975 and 1978 generated the following table and comments from the union:

Class 0102

Logging	**1975**	**1976**	**1977**	**1978**
Total days lost	166,225	149,311	166,159	174,651
Total number of Wage Loss Cases	3,368	4,091	4,493	4,970
Average days lost per claim	49.35	36.50	36.98	35.14

> Are we to assume that injured workers are recovering faster? Or are our members correct when they tell us that they are being forced to return to work before they are ready, often against their own doctor's advice, when the Workers' Compensation Board terminates their wage loss benefits? We believe our members.[42]

A major difficulty with rehabilitation in Canadian WCBs is the fact that, legally, workers have no right to social or vocational rehabilitation. They have a legal right to compensation and pensions, but no legal right to job security.

The amount and quality of rehabilitation and the decision to provide rehabilitation is completely a discretionary power of the WCB. For instance, the British Columbia WCB has ruled that a worker cannot appeal any decision having to do with rehabilitation through the system of appeals to a Board of Review or a Medical Review Panel.[43]

It is this overall situation which helps explain why the four-point program of the Toronto-based Union of Injured Workers includes: "(1) Job Security or Full Compensation . . . (3) Abolition of the Board doctors."

This discriminatory dilemma has been one of the longest-standing criticisms of workers' compensation boards across Canada and is expressed well by this workers' song:

> When I was drawing compensation
> They'd hang any job on my neck,
> Yes, when I was drawing compensation
> They'd hang any job on my neck.
>
> But now that old rockin' chair's busted
> They won't let me past the first desk.[44]

The following case study provides a vivid portrayal of a victim of compensation policies and practices.

PROFILE: "Nothing More Than Serfs"

Fed up with trying to get justice through normal channels, James "Scotty" Anderson decided to wage his own type of publicity campaign. To publicize his cause as an injured worker, Scotty drove for months with a homemade sign riveted to the rear bumper of his car. The painted slogan named the company and said that this worker was being "screwed" by the workers' compensation board. The sign raised questions, garnered glares and brought personal satisfaction to Scotty. Some may even have thought it libellous, but Scotty wasn't sued by the company or the compensation board. A fair defence against libel is truth, and the targets of Scotty's slogan knew it.

Scotty Anderson is now 41 years old. Since his accident in 1974, he has suffered through a number of losses. After almost losing his life, he lost his mobility and his capacity to work. Eventually he lost his wife. In exchange he gained constant pain, financial problems, and years of frustration with the British Columbia Workers' Compensation Board. Scotty is one injured worker who knows the human toll all too well.

As a younger man he had travelled the world with the merchant marine. In 1959, after viewing Canada, he decided to relocate here, uprooting from his native Scotland. He met a French-Canadian woman, married and moved out to the west coast in 1964. Scotty worked as a sales representative for Weston Bakeries until 1968, when a 24-week strike by bakers left his paycheque in limbo. "That's when I got into truck driving . . . quite by accident," he recalls. He worked on a casual basis for Johnston Terminals in Vancouver until the foreman asked him to join the firm full-time. With no end in sight to the bakers' strike, Scotty switched careers.

In 1972, he moved his belongings and family to Rhodesia (now Zimbabwe) where he had the opportunity to manage a stockfeeds mill. One year later, the Andersons were back in Canada. "I could see the writing on the wall. The terrorism was starting on the border . . . when you have a family you have to think of that." Scotty wonders how life would be now had he stayed in Rhodesia. Security is not necessarily found in a seemingly safe environment, he now realizes.

The day after Scotty arrived back in Vancouver, he bumped into his former boss from Johnston Terminals. The following Monday he was back at work driving a truck for his old employer. A year later he was lying in a hospital in New Westminister, the bottom half of his body crushed.

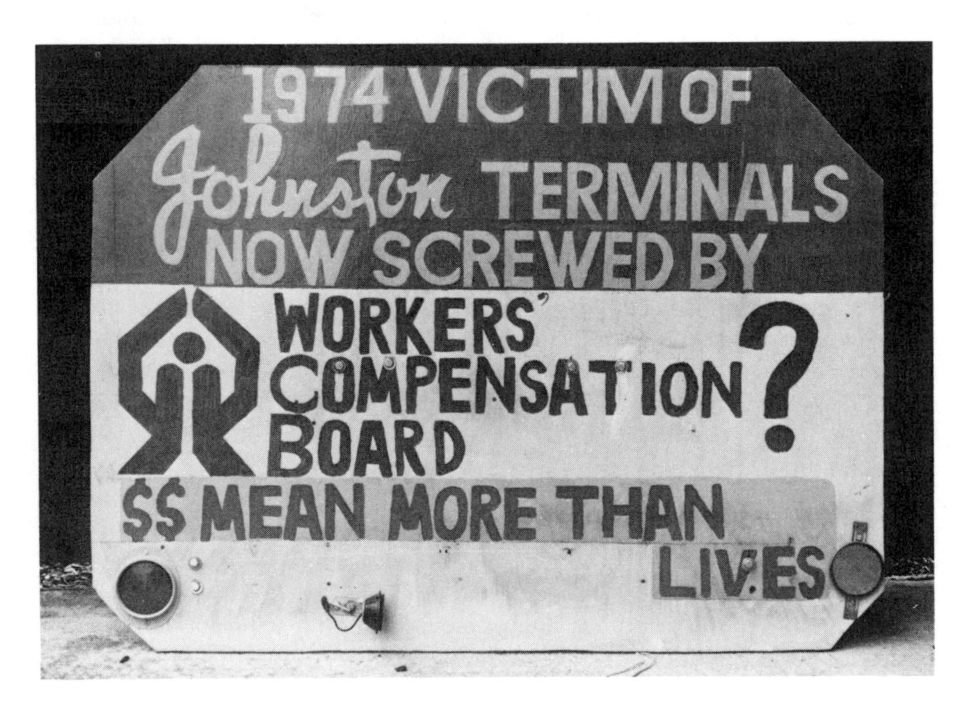

"I can still remember it you know . . . it happened in slow motion . . . these heavy things don't move fast . . . I could hear my bones smashing . . . It's a terrible crack when you hear your bones break, you know."

The day of the accident started out much the same as any other. On August 20, 1974, Scotty booked in for work and was instructed to pick up a load of hemp from a warehouse in New Westminister. He arrived at about 11:45 in the morning. A new forklift driver was on duty. The left rear tire of the forklift had a flat and its driver was anxiously awaiting someone to come and fix it before proceeding with the daily truck-loading schedule.

In the interim, the two went for lunch. "He began telling me about his problems," Scotty reminisces. "He was having problems at home and had missed a lot of days of work. The company was applying pressure and he was afraid of losing his job." In an effort to cope with the strain, the forklift driver was using tranquilizers. "I didn't give it much of a thought," notes Scotty.

When the hour-long recess was over, Scotty called his dispatcher who had lined up another job if his truck wasn't in the process of being loaded by 1:30. At about 1:10 the forklift driver decided not to wait any longer for the tire to be repaired. Since he was new on the job, and inexperienced with the layout of the warehouse, Scotty led him to the load of hemp bales. They were stacked against the wall, three high and three across. Each one weighed about 600 pounds. The loading began amid the usual "screaming around" of forklifts.

Scotty's flatbed was revving and almost full. As he was walking toward it, down a twelve-foot-wide corridor, he heard a shout from behind and was hit almost simultaneously. The forklift had been loaded with nine bales—a total of 5,600 pounds—and the driver was moving with the load suspended in the air, an action which breaches the rules. Just as the forklift was passing him, the right tire hit a bump. With the left tire flat, the uneven weight caused the load to tilt and fall. Seven of the bales came hurtling down on Scotty, pinning him up against a wall. His body from the waist down was crushed, his spine was twisted. If he had fallen flat on the ground he would have died instantly. Instead, he rested, up against the wall, minutes ticking by, until a number of men were able to remove the bales.

For the first few days he was conscious and remembers the operative procedures used to piece his bones back together. "They did what you call an open reduction. They slash you from top to bottom to expose the bone—then they drilled holes through my knees and ankles [to create joints]." A few days later blood clots began to form and Scotty's lungs filled with blood. He was on the critical list for 10 days. He spent a total of 61 days in the hospital.

Scotty was sent home on a stretcher to the care of his wife. He weighed 98 pounds, down from his regular 150. "That was when the trouble started," he recalls. "Homes are not made for wheelchairs, at least not the one we lived in at the time. My wife had to virtually pick me up like a baby and carry me to the bathroom. She had to put me to bed or move me to the sofa or to the recliner . . . I was never comfortable."

James "Scotty" Anderson

In the hospital Scotty was receiving care costing the WCB approximately $200 a day. Initially his wife received $4 a day for her efforts. The figure was eventually boosted to $7, but only after much haggling with the board. For the following five months he received in-home care from a physiotherapist.

The Anderson family's financial upheaval showed itself almost immediately. During the week of his accident, Scotty and his wife were preparing to sign mortgage papers to buy the Vancouver house they were living in. The mortgage papers fell through automatically after his accident, and he and his family were given two months to find other accommodation. Perhaps the mortgage company realized, even more than Scotty, what his financial future would be.

In 1974, his wage had been $1,350 a month. With the accident the figure dropped to $644. He had been told that he would receive 75 per cent compensation, the maximum allowed for an injury. He did. But because there is a ceiling on the maximum monthly wage—at that time $933—he was getting 75 per cent of the ceiling, which was only 54 per cent of his actual wage. "And often the checks would not come on time," says Scotty. Though his wife had been planning to return to work prior to the accident, her plans were cancelled with it. Neither Scotty nor his wife were able to work. Together they tried to cope with a handicap inflicted by the workplace. They and their three children were forced to live on $644 a month.

In January of 1975, Scotty was able to get up on crutches. His left foot had been smashed and permanently disfigured. His shoes no longer fit him. It would seem reasonable that expenses incurred because of an accident would be paid for by the WCB. But to get the board to pay for a pair of shoes, according to Scotty, was like asking for a luxury. You almost had to beg, he remarks in disgust. He had to fight for reimbursement. "I knew then that things were going to be bad."

Besides having to adjust to a new lifestyle, the Andersons were caught up daily in struggles with a government bureaucracy. It wasn't charity, but the dehumanization created by repeated requests for adequate compensation made it feel like it. Not only was Scotty learning to deal with being a physical cripple, he was struggling not to become both a financial and moral one as well.

His wife Irene didn't succeed in making the transition. In August 1976 she committed suicide. Scotty links her depression to the accident and ensuing pecuniary problems.

The following letter written by Irene Anderson was published in the *Vancouver Sun*'s "Letters to the Editor" section on April 10, 1976. It denotes the despair she felt over her husband's treatment as an injured worker.

WCB a Joke on Workers

There's much noise being made by the good old employers (all heart, you know) regarding the Workers' Compensation.

I'd like to give the side of the ungrateful recipient of such benefits. My husband was injured nearly two years ago; a case of negligence on the part of the company. Today, he's left with very little hope of ever working again, at the ripe old age of 36.

Did the nice company ever call once to ask about his condition? You've guessed it; but they make plenty of noise when it comes to the payment of compensation.

You know, cost must be kept down. After all, an injured workman is of no benefit to the company anymore, especially one so badly damaged.

In the two years of receiving Workers' Compensation, many incidents happened to make life more than unpleasant for our whole family. The occasions are just too numerous to get into all the details.

I certainly would like to see just where injured workmen are actually having the say in the running of the board. That's just a sick joke on the part of the employers. As it is now, it's hard trying to get monies and medical equipment when it is required.

Thank you for letting me get this off my chest. It's been building up for the past two years and I can't see how anything will improve in the next two or 10 or 20 years.

(Mrs.) Irene T. M. Anderson
94-45215 Wolfe Rd.
Chilliwack

"She was the last person you would ever suspect of committing suicide," says Scotty. "She was always a strong and proud person." But, she couldn't see the light at the end of the tunnel, he adds. Scotty can't say he does either. But different people have different methods of coping. He is fighting back.

Financial problems, the loss of his wife, the lack of identity and loneliness that come with being idle were important factors in leading Scotty to seek job retraining. Although he had a college education, much of the knowledge and confidence garnered in those years had become rusted with time. He took refresher courses and enrolled in a two-year program at business school in 1977. The first year was completed by only eight out of 27 students, and Scotty stood proudly among them. But when time came for the second year, the WCB decided unilaterally that Scotty would not pursue it. "I received a call from the board and the guy said 'The axe has fallen, Jim. They won't go for the second year. They figure you have enough of a good education.' " Instead, the WCB suggested that Scotty find a job.

After months of searching in Chilliwack, Scotty finally accepted a job in Vancouver in December 1978. It involved technical sales, paid relatively well, although not as well as truck driving, and supposedly involved very little mobility. Scotty was not fit for work that would force him to walk around a lot. Movement caused pain and eventually exhaustion. Every morning, Scotty left the house at 5:30, commuted to Vancouver and returned at 9:00 in the evening. "It was a real high ball job. You couldn't dictate the pace, the job dictated the pace to you." The job demanded a lot more footwork than originally thought. On his doctor's advice Scotty quit, and was instructed not to work full-time again. The never-ending financial problems caused Scotty to make a suggestion he will no doubt recall with quiet dismay for years to come. At 16, his daughter joined the labour force. "My oldest daughter had to quit school and go to work. Teenagers want things that I couldn't give. It really hurts me because she was good in school and she wanted to go on."

Scotty and his family are paying a hefty price. But things have not improved drastically. In December 1978, the board awarded Anderson a pension of permanent partial disability of 57.5 per cent—$402 a month. Scotty says that amount is 21.8 per cent of his earnings in 1973. The decision was appealed, and the figure increased to 70 per cent or $743 a month.

Scotty has been consulting with a lawyer to gain total disability benefits which would allow him the maximum pension WCB awards. A 100 per cent disability would give him $1,060 a month. In May 1979 an appeal for 100 per cent coverage won at the review level. However, the decision was overturned by the commissioner who had made the original decision. "I claim they throw dice you know . . . they set a parameter . . . this man won't get over 70 per cent. They just throw so many dice." On occasion, the board may increase your award by a bit, says Scotty and then expect disgruntled workers to be silent. "We've thrown you a few more crumbs . . . be satisfied," mocks Scotty.

But Scotty isn't satisfied. Nor should he be. For one thing, the company where Scotty worked was never thoroughly investigated to determine whether there was neglience on their part. An inquiry was held 10 days after the accident but, according to Scotty, the forklift driver was never interviewed. When Scotty began pressing for the results to the investigation, threatening phone calls to his home were the result. Eventually the RCMP nabbed a foreman from Johnston Terminals. The company, perhaps somewhat embarrassed, fired the foreman some time later.

The B.C. Workers' Compensation Board creates a maze which workers must wind through in the hopes of gaining justice. Scotty has played along so that he would not be rebuked by officials for being unco-operative. For instance, the WCB has sent him to a staff neurologist assigned to determine "whether this man is really looking for help or is in fact consciously manipulating the situation to achieve the best possible monetary results." Attributing financial woes to a psychiatric problem—a mental illusion—is a common practice which the board uses on obstinate injured workers. "Why is Anderson such a hostile man?" the board wonders. "Why can he not gratefully accept the WCB judgments handed to him?" One neurologist's report put it this way: "One might suspect that there could be an underlying paranoid disorder, but such ideas of persecution that he has seem to me to be more the result of personality immaturity than frank paranoia. His behaviour has been both manipulative and defiant and in the light of his well-within average intelligence this is obviously on a volitional basis although influenced to some extent by his tension and volatile personality."

The message behind all the jargon is this. The neurologist has reduced Scotty's problems to immaturity and a hot temper, coupled with a persecution complex. In essence, he claims that Scotty's hostility toward the board has no validity and Scotty is simply out to coerce the WCB. He disregards the fact that Scotty has given his health to a job, cannot provide a family income because of that, and cannot depend on the WCB providing support. Instead, Scotty has to haggle with the board to get a pair of shoes or a new set of crutches. His wife commits suicide in desperation. His eldest daughter has to quit school to help support the family. Nonetheless, the Board's psychic diviner casts aside these facts and chooses to believe that Scotty is the cause of his own problems.

"Everything is wearing out around me and I don't have the money to replace it. What they're going to come up with next . . . whether my back is worth five per cent or two per cent . . . who knows."

Scotty shakes his head at the reality: "We're nothing more than serfs."

Industrial Diseases: Tragic Neglect

Canadian workers' compensation law and administration has largely neglected the area of industrial disease, with tragic results both for the compensation of victims and for the identification and prevention of work-related diseases.

Terence Ison, a former B.C. Workers' Compensation Board Chairman, has pointed out that 1974 data attributed 75.6 per cent of deaths in Canada to disease and 24.4 per cent to all accidents, suicides, poisonings, and violence together.

The Canada Pension Plan's 1974 disability pension statistics attribute 95.2 per cent of disabilities to disease and only 4.8 per cent to trauma.

On the other hand, using Alberta, B.C., and Manitoba WCB statistics, he estimated that only 2-17 per cent of all WCB fatal claims paid were for disease; that only 3.4-11 per cent of all permanent disability awards were for disease and, if hearing loss pensions were excluded, the figure was only from 0.8-1.7 per cent.[45]

Furthermore, a significant percentage of industrial disease claims are cases requiring medical aid only, with no wage-loss or pension payable at all. For example, in Prince Edward Island in 1977, of a total of 125 accepted industrial disease claims, some 58, or 46.4 per cent, were for medical aid only.

The only readily available sources for information concerning industrial disease claims are the various provincial WCB Annual Reports. But the consistency and overall depth of these various reports makes analysis difficult.

Many provinces provide no breakdown at all of their industrial disease statistics. Asphyxiation; chemical inhalation, absorption, and ingestion; dermatitis; bursitis; synovitis; and poisonings are usually included in the category of industrial disease. Infections and adverse temperature conditions are not always so included.

It is virtually impossible to find any listings at all for cancers or cardiovascular (heart) disease. Pulmonary (lung) disease is similarly missing, except for the usual limited listings for respiratory poisonings, tuberculosis, silicosis, and asbestosis. Since cancer, heart, and lung disease make up the largest adult ill-health categories in Canadian society, a reading of WCB statistics would suggest that none of these conditions has much, if anything, to do with work and working conditions.

Ontario's WCB industrial disease schedule has been in the Act since 1915, when only six diseases were named. Up to 1967, only nine more disease classes had been added.

The original six Ontario listings were eventually embodied in the other Canadian statutes. The origin of these original six is traceable to the English Workmen's Compensation Act of 1906 which listed:

Anthrax	Handling of wool, hair, bristles, hides and skins
Lead Poisoning or its Sequelae	Any process involving the use of lead or its preparation or compounds
Mercury Poisoning or its Sequelae	Any process involving the use of mercury or its preparation or compounds
Phosphorus Poisoning or its Sequelae	Any process involving the use of phosphorus or its preparation or compounds
Arsenic Poisoning or its Sequelae	Any process involving the use of arsenic or its preparation or compounds
Ankylostomiasis	Mining.

From the beginning, there was business opposition to the recognition of industrial diseases as part of the compensation scheme, with the Canadian Manufacturers' Association opposed to industrial diseases being included, like injuries, as compensable accidents. However, Justice Meredith disagreed:

> It would, in my opinion, be a blot on the act if a workman who suffers from an industrial disease contracted in the course of his employment is not to be entitled to compensation. The risk of contracting disease is inherent in the occupation he follows and he is practically powerless to guard against it. A workman may to some extent guard against accidents, and it would seem not only illogical but unreasonable to compensate him in the one case and to deny him the right to compensation in the other.[46]

Cancer is only the most obvious example of the "tragic neglect" phenomenon.

The U.S. National Cancer Institute and the U.S. National Institute of Environmental Health Sciences have estimated, using conservative criteria, that at least 20 per cent of all cancers are occupationally-related.[47] Higher percentage estimates also exist.

What do we find when we examine the actual Canadian WCB cancer claims record? Let us take British Columbia as an example for the last decade, 1970-1979.

Apparently, there was an overall total of 25 cancer claims made to the B.C. WCB in the entire ten-year period of 1970 to 1979.[48]

During that same period, approximately 40,000 British Columbians died of cancer and many more thousands of British Columbians contracted some form of cancer.[49] If the 20 per cent figure is used, some 8,000 WCB claims would be projected in that decade for cancer deaths alone, as compared to the actual total of 25.

Of the 25 cancer claims made to the B.C. WCB, 17 were accepted as work-related as follows:

Lung (asbestos) —5 accepted, 7 rejected
Mesothelioma (asbestos)—10 accepted, 0 rejected
Bladder —1 accepted, 0 rejected
Leukemia —1 accepted, 1 rejected

There is no reason to think that B.C.'s situation is an inaccurate reflection of the overall national compensation picture. Indeed, B.C. may be on the liberal side, given the reformist policy and administrative changes flowing from the NDP regime in the period 1972-1975.

This is borne out by the results of a letter survey of Canadian WCBs undertaken by the Canadian Centre for Occupational Health and Safety in 1980.[50]

Manitoba has apparently recognized 13 cancer claims from 1961 to 1980. Prince Edward Island reported only one claim to date, for lung cancer related to coal tar pitch volatiles, and it was denied. New Brunswick replied "that we have not had any experiences concerning a claim for cancer at present." Nova Scotia reported a total of five cancer claims between 1975 and 1980, all for asbestos exposure, one of which was denied. Newfoundland reported no cancer claims other than for the radiation exposure of the St. Lawrence fluorspar mines, which involved 46 cases between 1975 and 1979. Saskatchewan has received 30 claims to date, 26 of which were accepted, most of which were lung cancer cases due to uranium mining radiation exposure. Ontario apparently has accepted a total of 456 cancer cases up to the end of 1979, which presumably covers a 65-year history in Canada's most populous province.

What are the costs involved in this? Who loses and who profits? For one thing, thousands upon thousands of Canadians are being denied hundreds of millions of dollars of medical aid, rehabilitation, wage-loss, and pension benefits *to which they are legally entitled*. And many of these people are widows, widowers, and children.

For another, industry owners and managers are making bonanza profits and incomes by avoiding the costs of hazardous operation. Canada's taxpayers, largely workers, pick up the bill for industry. As Robert Sass, Saskatchewan's Director of Occupational Health, has pointed out:

> Very few of the costs associated with industrial illness are absorbed by the industry that produces them. Today most of these costs are borne by the victims of industrially induced illness (loss of income and the relevant social and psychological costs) and by taxpayers in general (the cost of medical care, rehabilitation, social

> assistance and so on). As industry is allowed to engage in activities that produce illness on a relatively penalty-free or cost-free basis, it has virtually no economic incentive to prevent the health problems that it creates.[51]

How have WCBs neglected industrial disease? In a number of ways, chief of which are the following:

- —WCBs have been injury and trauma-oriented
- —WCB statutes and internal rules place procedural roadblocks in the way of industrial disease claims, e.g., time limits, conservative diagnostic criteria and assessment rules, limited lists of recognized industrial diseases
- —WCB staff, including doctors, know little of industrial diseases
- —physicians either do not know of or do not report occupational cancers to WCBs or advise their patients of same
- —WCBs do not look for claims, they only respond to claims made
- —workers and families are ignorant of possible work causations, are caught up emotionally in the death or disability and neglect claims, or are content to receive other public or private medical or income assistance
- —many diseases take years to develop and work-causation is either forgotten or impossible to reconstruct, or the worker is now retired or otherwise disabled.

In conclusion, it seems quite clear that industry and medicine will not receive any serious stimulus to identify, monitor and prevent industrial diseases until the compensation systems adequately document these diseases and levy taxes to compensate the worker victim. In the mean time, the authors certainly advocate that every worker who suffers any heart, lung, or cancer disease should file an industrial disease claim with his or her provincial WCB unless he or she receives convincing medical opinion otherwise.

NOTES

1. Mark Warrior, "Sion," in Tom Wayman (ed.), *Beaton Abbot's Got the Contract* (Edmonton: NeWest Press, n.d.).
2. See Statistics Canada, *Workmen's/Workers' Compensation*, Cat. #86-501 (Ottawa: Ministry of Supply and Services Canada, 1980).
3. Statistics Canada, *Workers' Compensation*, Cat. #86-501, p. 10, n. 1.
4. Sir William Meredith, *Final Report*, Ontario Sessional Papers #53 (Toronto: King's Printer, October 31, 1913), p. xi.
5. Ken Harding, Executive Director of the Association of WCBs of Canada, oral communication, August 29, 1980.
6. Statistics Canada, *Workers' Compensation*, Cat. #86-501 pp. 14-16, Table XI.
7. *Brief of Farmworkers' Organizing Committee to Honourable Jack Heinrich Concerning Legislative Recommendations on Matters That Affect B.C. Farm Workers*, February 22, 1980, pp. 19-22.
8. *Report of the Commissioner re: Workmen's Compensation Act and Board* (Chief Justice Gordon McG. Sloan) (Victoria, B.C.: Queen's Printer, 1952), p. 33.
9. *A Contract for Research, Canada's National-Provincial Health Program for the*

1980s (Emmett M. Hall, Special Commissioner, August 29, 1980), p. 100.

10. *Report of the Commissioner re: Workmen's Compensation Board* (Mr. Justice Gordon McG. Sloan) (Victoria, B.C.: King's Printer, 1942), p. DD34.

11. *Report of the Committee of Investigation on Workmen's Compensation Laws* (Avard Pineo, Chairman) (Victoria, B.C.: King's Printer, March 1, 1916), p. 7.

12. Ibid.

13. *Commission of Inquiry, Workers' Compensation Act, 1966, Report of the Commissioner* (The Honorable Mr. Justice Charles W. Tysoe), Victoria, B.C.: Queen's Printer, 1966, pp. 196-97 (hereafter cited as *Tysoe Report*).

14. Ibid., p. 198.

15. Ibid., p. 199.

16. *Report of the Royal Commission in the Matter of the Workmen's Compensation Act* (Commissioner: George A. McGillvray) (Toronto: Queen's Printer, 1967), pp. 51-56 (hereafter cited as *McGillvray Report*).

17. Statistics Canada, *Workers' Compensation*, Cat. #86-501 p. 28, Table 6.

18. *McGillvray Report*, p. 53.

19. Meredith, *Final Report*, p. xvi.

20. *Examination of the Financial Structure of the Workmen's Compensation Board and an Assessment of the Actuarial Deficits* (Toronto: Wyatt Company, June 1978), p. 270.

21. Meredith, *Final Report*, p. xviii.

22. *McGillvray Report*, pp. 8-9.

23. Martin Robin, *Pillars of Profit: The Company Province, 1934-72* (Toronto: McClelland and Stewart, 1973), p. 7.

24. Ibid., p. 152.

25. See *Report of Task Force on Administration of Workmen's Compensation in Ontario* (A. R. Aird, Chairman) (Toronto: August 1973), p. 116.

26. *Sloan Report*, pp. DD22-23.

27. Eckler, Brown, Segal & Co. Ltd., *Report on Actuarial Aspects of the Workers' Compensation Board of British Columbia* (Victoria, B.C., September 1976), p. 14.

28. Meltz, Noah M. and David Stager, *The Occupational Structure of Earnings in Canada, 1931-75* (Hull: Supply and Services Canada, 1979), p. 63, citing *Financial Post*, October 7, 1976 and Thorne, Riddell Associates Ltd. study *Employee Benefit Costs in Canada, 1975/76*. Report based on 600,000 workers in 155 companies. Fringe benefits do not include difficult items such as free or subsidized meals, merchandise and services, and employee stock options.

29. *Financial Times*, September 1980, citing study by Thorne, Stevenson and Kellogg, management consultants; *Vancouver Province*, September 19, 1980.

30. Submission of the Ontario Federation of Labour to the Paul C. Weiler Task Force on Workmen's Compensation in Ontario (Toronto: June 1980), p. 12.

31. *Workers' Compensation Legislation in Canada* (Labour Canada, Ottawa: 1980), p. 19.

32. J. L. Amos, "Vocational Rehabilitation During and After the War," *C.J.E.P.S.* 9(1944): 164-74, 165.

33. *B.C. W.C.B. Reporter Series Decision #21*, Vol. I (December 28, 1973), pp. 91-92.

34. Ontario W.C. Act, R.S.O. 1970, C505 as am. to December, 1979, S. 53.

35. Ibid., S. 42(5).

36. Patrick A. Tiernan, *Functions of Rehabilitation Services*, WCB Seminar Proceedings (Vancouver, 1974), pp. 61-62.
37. *Alberta Select Committee Report*, p. 19.
38. *McKinnon Report*, p. 135.
39. *Clarke Report*, pp. 108-9.
40. See *McGillvray Report*, pp. 177-78.
41. *Tysoe Report*, p. 172.
42. Submission, p. 11.
43. *W.C.B. Reporter Series Decisions* #14, #15, #55, #60, and #62, Vol. 1, *Workers' Compensation Reporter*, 1973-74.
44. Carlos Cortez, "Outa Work Blues," *I. W. W. Song Book*, 34th ed. (1973).
45. Terence G. Ison, *The Dimensions of Industrial Disease*, Industrial Relations Centre Research and Current Issues Series #35 (Kingston: Queen's University, 1978), pp. 1-2.
46. Meredith, *Final Report*, pp. v, xv.
47. U.S. Department of Health, Education and Welfare et al., *Estimates of the Fraction of Cancer Incidence in the United States Attributable to Occupational Factors* (Washington, D.C., 1978).
48. Correspondence in 1980 between author Craig Paterson and Dr. William Whitehead, Assistant Medical Director (Occupational Health), B.C. WCB.
49. This figure is a projection from the annual cancer reports of the B.C. Ministry of Health, Division of Vital Statistics. The last available Report is #155 (1980), reporting on 1977 data.
50. These provincial statistics are reported in correspondence between author Craig Paterson and the Canadian Centre for Occupational Health and Safety under C.C.O.H. & S. File Ref. #IAS-80-144,146.
51. Robert Sass, "The Underdevelopment of Occupational Health In Canada," in William Leiss (ed.), *Ecology Versus Politics in Canada* (Toronto: University of Toronto Press, 1979), p. 73.

Chapter 10

Law and Order in the Workplace

[T]o the extent that the only semblance of rights that lawmakers have given workers over the course of this century is an ability, in some circumstances, to receive medical assistance and certain forms of compensation "through workmen's compensation" acts, it may readily be perceived that the law has indeed served, and by and large continues to serve, the interests of the employer at the expense of the health of the worker . . . it is only industrial interests that have been able to influence lawmaking to date, resulting in the virtual neglect of workers' rights to a healthy environment.[1]

There Ought To Be a Law

In a democratic society the law purportedly serves the interests of all. As was noted many years ago, "both the poor and the rich are prohibited by law from sleeping under a bridge." That the law and legal system tend to reflect the interests of the rich and powerful is noted by the Law Reform Commission of Canada:

> In practice, the penalty often depends not on the nature of the crime, but on the person who commits it. Our prison population contains a quite unrepresentative proportion of poor, of disadvantaged and of native offenders; the richer you are, the better your chance of getting away with something. Is it that rich men make the laws and so what rich men do is not a crime but simply shrewd business practice? Or is it that position and wealth protect the rich against intervention? . . . *For all the respect we pay to justice and equality, we still have one law for the rich and another for the poor.*[2]

Occupational safety and health laws in Canada are regulatory laws. That is, they attempt to control the workplace in order to protect the workers' health. As Table 10-1 indicates, there are numerous agencies at both the federal and provincial levels which carry a variety of responsibilities. Former Minister of Labour John Munro noted in 1977 that there are nine departments and agencies in the federal government administering a total of 16 separate acts concerned, in part,

Table 10-1

Occupational Safety and Health in Canada
Principal Areas of Responsibility of Regulatory Authorities[1]

	Fed.	Nfld.	P.E.I.	N.S.	N.B.	Que.	Ont.	Man.	Sask.	Alta.	B.C.
General Safety											
Industrial and Commercial	LAB	L&M	WCB	LAB	L&M	L&M	LAB	LAB	LAB	WHSC	WCB
Construction	—	L&M	WCB	LAB	L&M	L&M*	LAB	LAB	LAB	WHSC	WCB
Mining	LAB	L&M	—	M	NR	NR	LAB	MNRE	LAB	WHSC	EM&PR
Transportation	TRANS/ CTC	L&M	WCB	LAB	L&M	TRANS	LAB	LAB	LAB	WHSC	WCB/ ETC
Health Protection											
Industrial Hygiene	LAB/FE	L&M	WCB	PH	L&M	ENV	LAB	LAB	LAB	WHSC	WCB
Sanitation, Occupational Environment	LAB	L&M	WCB	PH	L&M/H	ENV	LAB	LAB	LAB	WHSC	LAB
Mechanical											
Boiler and Pressure Vessels	LAB	L&M	LAB	LAB	L&M	L&M	CCR	LAB	LAB	LAB	LAB
Elevating Devices	LAB	L&M	MA	LAB	L&M	L&M	CCR	LAB	LAB	LAB	LAB
Electrical Installations	LAB	L&M	MA	LAB	L&M	L&M	CCR	LAB/MH	LAB	LAB	LAB
Gas and Oil Installations	NEB/ EMR	L&M	IC	LAB	L&M	L&M	CCR	LAB	LAB	LAB	LAB

Special Categories											
Explosives	EMR/ LAB	L&M	WCB	LAB	L&M	L&M	LAB	MR&EM/ LAB	LAB	WHSC	WCB
Radiation	AECB/ NHW	L&M	WCB	PH	L&M	ENV	PH	H	LAB	WHSC	H
Fire Prevention	LAB/PW	AG	MA	LAB	L&M	MA	SC	LAB	LAB	LAB	AG
Education and Training	LAB	L&M	WCB	WCB	ISC	WCB/ IAPA	WCB/ IAPA	LAB	LAB	WHSC	WCB

* Administered by Office de la Construction du Québec.

REGULATORY AGENCIES

AECB	Atomic Energy Control Board
AG	Attorney General
CCR	Consumer and Commercial Relations
CTC	Canadian Transport Commission
EMR	Energy, Mines and Resources
EM&PR	Energy, Mines and Petroleum Resources
ENV	Environment
ETC	Energy, Transport and Communication
FE	Fisheries and Environment
H	Health
IAPA	Industrial Accident Prevention Assn.
ISC	Industrial Safety Council
IC	Industry and Commerce
LAB	Labour
L&M	Labour and Manpower
M	Mines
MA	Municipal Affairs
MH	Manitoba Hydro
MNRE	Mines, Natural Resources and Environment
NEB	National Energy Board
NHW	National Health and Welfare
NR	Natural Resources
PH	Public Health
SA	Social Affairs
SG	Solicitor General
TRANS	Transport
WCB	Workmen's or Workers' Compensation Board
WHSC	Workers' Health, Safety and Compensation

Source: *Labour Research Bulletin*, January 1980, p. 30.

with occupational safety and health. Furthermore, some 45 departments and agencies in the provinces and territories administer 221 acts applying to workers' health. More than 400 sets of regulations setting standards and performance criteria have been issued under these acts.[3]

In the analysis of any law or set of laws aimed at regulating and controlling behaviour (whether robbery or assault in the workplace), students of the law ask two questions: What are the law's symbolic effects? and, What are its instrumental effects? The symbolic aspects of the law reflect its basic, underlying values and the groups or classes the law most apparently represents. The instrumental aspects of law concern its effectiveness in achieving these values and aims. Therefore, we could say that workers' health laws represent concern with the well-being of workers' lives. In this respect, these laws represent a victory of labour over capital, indicating that the workers' health is more important than the owner's drive for profits. However, while this may be the symbolic significance of such legislation, its specific provisions and enforcement policies may reflect other interests. More specifically, for example, provision for a fine of up to $5,000 and/or six months in jail is wholly inadequate if it is not applied. Furthermore, even if applied, it hardly acts as a deterrent if profits greatly exceed such a cost. Finally, this reflects the value of a worker's life—very cheap indeed. A man who kills another man in a drunken brawl is liable to life imprisonment for manslaughter. But what about the person who loses his life at the hands of an unsafe or unhealthy workplace? If you are buried in a trench due to violations of trenching regulations by your boss, who, for economic and/or time reasons, failed to comply, is this rational, calculated harm any less offensive than that resulting from a crime of passion? The point is that what a law says, and its penalty structure and enforcement practices, reflect on the importance given to that law in a society.

It may be that certain regulatory laws are passed largely to oppose certain interests, without really being effective subsequently. For example, Canadian competition legislation arose largely due to class conflict and subsequently has been proven largely ineffectual in maintaining, much less increasing, a competitive market place. In their study of competition law from 1890 to 1975, Goff and Reasons state:

> It is hard not to conclude that the Federal Government has protected the growth of the largest Canadian corporations, not only through its lack of effective legislation and enforcement of combines laws, but also at whom it is directing its police power. The data collected suggests that the Combines Branch has centered its attention upon the investigation, prosecution and conviction of small and medium-sized companies and corporations, leaving the very largest corporations to freely engage in their monopolistic policies.[4]

On March 5, 1981, the federal government released a report accusing major oil companies of price-fixing for ten years, thereby stealing at least $12 billion from Canadian consumers.[5] However, the government called for public hearings rather than pursuing criminal prosecution. This was undoubtedly due in part to the weak combines laws, the federal government's role in allowing such crimes, and the power of the oil industry.[6]

We need to look at the nature and enforcement of workers' health laws in order to determine whether they are really for the worker.

On Coddling Criminals

In the only national study of safety enforcement policies and practices in Canada, the Department of Labour found a wide variation in the effectiveness of safety enforcement legislation (see Table 10-2). However, it found that while penalties may be effective, they are rarely applied.

> It is reasonable to assume that the extent and degree of penalties involved influences the conduct of employers and employees in this area. Penalties should be imposed in many instances only as a last resort, but such a deterrent (within reasonable limits) should be available if everything else fails.
>
> While prosecution is the ultimate sanction in the enforcement field, where the defendant is convicted the penalty applied almost always is in the form of a fine. Conviction can lead to imprisonment in many jurisdictions, but this penalty has very rarely if ever been applied. Thus, from 1971 to 1973 inclusive, none of the parties convicted under the relevant legislation were imprisoned.[7]

While all jurisdictions allowed for the potential imprisonment of an offender, no one was ever incarcerated. In fact, we have not been able to find any case in the history of Canadian occupational safety and health laws where conviction resulted in imprisonment. Of course this cannot be said for murder, manslaughter or common assault.

In their analysis of data for 1971-73 (see Table 10-3), the Department of Labour found that only Ontario and Quebec undertook a significant number of prosecutions.

More recent evidence suggests the same type of results.[8] For example, a recent study of three provinces found little use of prosecution as a method of enforcement. In Alberta in 1977 there were 9,888 violations cited under provincial statute; however, only two prosecutions resulted. The average fine for successful prosecutions during the 1977-78 period was $200 in Alberta. Between March 1973 and December 1977, there were 49 completed prosecutions in Saskatchewan resulting in 35 employers being convicted of 47 offenses. The average fine was $186 during 1973-76, and $210 plus court costs in 1977. British Columbia prosecuted three employees in 1976 for wilful non-compliance and obtained two convictions, while it failed to prosecute any employers during 1977 for wilful non-compliance. The British Columbia Workers' Compensation Board makes use of special assessments as a "deterrent." Table 10-4 provides a picture of the use of this method. In only 8 out of 80 fines did the assessment exceed 10 per cent of the regular assessment. The average fine for all cases was $832, which works out to about three weeks' pay for the average British Columbia industrial worker. This is hardly a deterrent!

A recent example is the woman in Brandon, Manitoba who lost eight

Table 10-2

Results of Prosecutions Undertaken in the Provincial and Federal Jurisdictions*
Under the Survey Safety Enforcement Legislation, 1972-1973**

	Nfld.		P.E.I.		N.S.		N.B.		Que.		Ont.		Man.		Sask.		Alta.		B.C.		Federal Juris-diction	
	'72	'73	'72	'73	'72	'73	'72	'73	'72	'73	'72	'73	'72	'73	'72	'73	'72	'73	'72	'73	'72	'73
Conviction but sentence suspended	—	—	—	—	—	—	—	—	—	—	18	—	—	—	—	—	—	—	—	—	—	—
Fine only	4	4	—	—	5	3	9	5	250	150	232	159	—	—	—	1	—	—	4	2	—	1
Charges dismissed	—	—	—	—	—	—	3	4	79	15	34	31	—	—	—	1	—	—	—	—	—	—
Charges withdrawn	—	—	—	—	—	—	—	—	4	—	167	104	—	—	—	—	—	—	—	—	—	—
Prosecutions in process	—	—	—	—	—	—	—	—	67	365	—	—	—	—	—	—	—	—	—	3	—	—
Total	4	4	0	0	5	3	12	9	400	530	451	294	0	0	0	2	0	0	5	5	—	1

* The administering authority in Saskatchewan was not empowered to prosecute under the Workmen's Compensation Accident Fund Act, but it is empowered to prosecute under the Occupational Health Act, 1972. Prosecutions are carried out in Manitoba by the Attorney-General. No sentences of "imprisonment only" or of "fine and imprisonment" were passed in any of the provinces.

** Source: Economics & Research Branch, *Safety Enforcement Policies and Practices in Canada*. Ottawa: Canada Department of Labour, 1975.

Table 10-3

Prosecutions Undertaken in the Provincial and Federal Government Jurisdictions Under the Survey Safety Enforcement Legislation, 1971-73*

	Number of Prosecutions Undertaken		
	1971	**1972**	**1973**
Newfoundland	0	4	4
Prince Edward Island	0	0	0
Nova Scotia	0	5	3
New Brunswick	10	12	9
Quebec	200	400	530
Ontario	614	451	294
Manitoba	1	0	0
Saskatchewan[1]	n.a.	0	0
Alberta	0	0	0
British Columbia	2	5	5
Federal	0	0	1

n.a. — not applicable.

[1] The administering authority in Saskatchewan was not empowered to prosecute under the Workmen's Compensation (Accident Fund) Act, but it is empowered to prosecute under the Occupational Health Act, 1972. Prosecutions are carried out in Manitoba by the Attorney-General.

* Source: Economics and Research Branch, *Safety Enforcement Policies and Practices in Canada*. Ottawa: Canada Department of Labour, 1975.

fingers. The company was fined $500.[9] The woman, Eileen Senek, widowed mother of four, angrily said, "Pretty cheap for eight fingers." The company pleaded guilty to failing to provide necessary safety equipment on a machine she operated. In another case, a London, Ontario company, Clarke Road Building Products Ltd., was fined $1,000 in connection with the death of one of its workers. In attempting to have the fine reduced, the company's lawyer argued that it was the worker's fault. The judge found the argument objectionable because, "It is unfortunate an allegation was made here against him when he is not here to defend himself." This is the ultimate in placing money over life—even when a worker is dead the company blames him![10]

In his review of *Occupational Health and Safety in Canada*, Reschenthaler notes:

> A record high fine of $5,000 recently imposed in Alberta following three totally needless deaths due to failure of the employer to provide portable respirators makes a sham of the law. The possibility of permitting prosecution of some employers for criminal negligence should be seriously considered where fatalities result from the

Table 10-4

Special Assessments and Levies in British Columbia
1 July 1977 - 30 June 1978*

Offence	Number	Average Fine	Largest Fine	Average Fine as a Percentage of Average Assessment
Inadequate Guarding	6	$3,485	$15,548	6.8
Shoring	15	532	1,798	7.7
Scaffolding	8	880	3,596	6.8
ROPS	7	298	764	8.0
Other AP	34	616	2,893	5.8
Industrial Hygiene Offences	9	991	2,098	10.0
Noise	1	889	889	3.0

* Source: Compiled from various issues of the bi-monthly B.C. *WCB News* (Vancouver). G. B. Reschenthaler, *Occupational Health and Safety In Canada*, Montreal: Institute for Research on Public Policy, 1979, p. 122.

failure of an employer to meet standards. The view that "embarrassment" can be relied upon to induce proper behaviour where there exists the possibility of death and life-long suffering reflects either extreme naivete or callous insensitivity to the scope of the problems."[11]

Although Alberta has one of the highest workers' accident and death rates in Canada, its philosophy remains largely one of kid-glove treatment of violations of occupational health and safety laws. In 1980 only 124 stop-work orders were issued throughout the province. Alberta safety officials recommended only six prosecutions to the Attorney-General's department under the Occupational Health and Safety Act in 1980.[12]

It's a "Real" Crime

In their report concerning *Criminal Responsibility for Group Action*, the Law Reform Commission of Canada distinguishes between "real crimes" and "regulatory offenses" when discussing corporate and organizational activity.[13] Real crimes are acts which affront the basic, fundamental values of society and need to be condemned (in traditional legal language these are *mala in se*, or wrong in themselves). Taking another person's life and seriously harming another person violates our value for life. "Regulatory offenses" are deemed necessary for efficiency and convenient for the "public good", but do not violate basic values (these are called *mala prohibitar* in legalese, which means they are wrong because they intrude upon others' rights). Requirements of valid driver's license and many traffic regulations are of this nature. On the basis of this distinction, the Law Reform Commission does not recommend criminalizing corporate action. The omission is rationalized because of the purported problems of criminal intent and specific fault. A more appropriate route to follow, however, would be an analysis of the consequences of one's action or inaction. For example, failure to adequately maintain your car may bring a fine; however, if you run into someone and kill them due to this failure, criminal proceedings may be pursued. Likewise, a company's failure to maintain safe machinery may bring minimal fines, but if this failure kills a worker the company should be held criminally liable. While this may sound extreme, it is necessary in order to dramatize the magnitude of the problem and act as a deterrent.

Two Canadian legal experts, Glasbeek and Rowland, have reviewed attempts at stopping the assault on the worker through education, organization, joint worksite committees, strong regulatory agencies, and injury tax schemes. They conclude that these are all deficient mechanisms since, for the company, profit ultimately takes priority over life, particularly when the costs of such attempts are weighed against the benefits. The authors then argue for the use of the criminal law, not as a "solution" but to spotlight the problem.

> If the physical onslaught which takes place in the workplace occurred outside the employer-employee environment there is no doubt that society would use the most formidable tool it has to stop such attacks: it would use the criminal process and treat offenders as social pariahs. Prosecution under the criminal law of employers for the harm they do to workers rather than reliance on existing safety and health regulatory schemes would characterize the conduct of such employers as an unjustifiable preference for unregulated profit over the well-being of human beings who are, after all, very important in the governing of such profits. Prosecution of entrepreneurial behaviour which can inflict grievous bodily harm or even death would thus identify the kind of conduct that warrants interference and regulation by government. Expectations that such interference would be more vigorous than it is now would not be misplaced. Indeed, it may become possible to talk openly about what is a "reasonable" profit in view of the need to reduce injury and disease to an "acceptable" rate . . . .
>
> The use of the criminal process has another attraction. Because of the assumptions of the liberal state, the ideology of law requires it to claim that it punishes behaviour which has been judged unacceptable by society no matter who the perpetrator of the offensive behaviour is. It will be interesting to see how the administrators of the legal system respond when it is argued that entrepreneurs are offenders against the criminal process in much the same way as robbers of private property and people. It will provide something of an insight if the officers of justice resist the use of criminal prosecution in this context.[14]

Glasbeek and Rowland then present lengthy, legal arguments for the application of the following sections of the criminal code to violations of workers' health:

Section 202	Criminal negligence
Section 201	Duties of master to servant
Section 245(2)	Assault; unlawfully causing bodily harm
Section 380	Criminal Breach of Contract
Section 231	Traps likely to cause bodily harm
Section 387	Causing mischief
Section 176	Common nuisance
Section 243	Conspiracy
Section 212(c)	Murder

Of course, there are many problems inhibiting the use of these sections, such as how to initiate a prosecution, how to hold a corporation criminally responsible, and how to show that poor working conditions caused the alleged harm. Nonetheless, these are surmountable, as the authors point out.

They conclude by noting:

> The rather elaborate arguments presented in this article have not been made either in a spirit of malevolence based on a hatred of all employers, or to indulge ourselves in the sheer delight that academically-minded people get from engaging in abstruse, interesting theoretical exercises. We have, rather, developed the arguments herein because of our belief that the regulatory mechanisms which our society employs at present will never yield anything like the amelioration in health and safety conditions in the workplace which we would like to see. In particular, the mechanism of the so-called discipline of the market will not bring us such results. For this conclusion the proof is in a well-known pudding. Until fairly recently there had been little, if any, state regulation of health and safety in the workplace. The toll on the physical well-being of workers was terrible.[15]

The arguments presented by Glasbeek and Rowland are meant for the consumption of lawyers in hope that there will be a few brave souls eager to pursue their logic. While this is not at all a "solution" to workers' health problems, it does provide another weapon to individuals trying to publicize the massive assault on workers and deter both actual and potential offenders.

A recent Calgary case dramatizes the dual nature of justice for workers compared to others. Charges of manslaughter and assault causing bodily harm have been laid against Groveridge Imperial Construction Ltd. and the company site superintendent for failure to adequately guard an excavation site. Two men fell into the hole; one was killed and the other injured.[16] Two days earlier, a city waterworks employee only a few months from retirement died in a trench which may have been improperly shored. Criminal charges are not likely in this death.[17] We would argue that workers should have equal protection of the law when such an assault occurs. Such tactics are particularly important given the economic cost-benefit mentality which argues dollars and cents over deaths, injuries, and diseases.

Whose Cost? Whose Benefit?

In recent years there has been an increasing use of cost-benefit analysis in attempts to control government spending. These efforts have largely been made by those critical of government interference and regulation of economic institutions. The Corporate Accountability Research Group report entitled *Business War on the Law: An Analysis of the Benefits of Federal Health/Safety Enforcement* carefully describes the ideology underlying this new "economic realism" and its biases and shortcomings.[18] More specifically, they critically assess the testimony before the U.S. Senate Committee on Commerce, Science, and Transportation of Professor Murray L. Weidenbaum, former Assistant Secretary of the Treasury under Richard Nixon. A professor and director of the Center for the Study of American Business at Washington University, St. Louis, he has recently been appointed by President Reagan as chairman of the Economic Advisory Council. Weidenbaum's essential message is that government over-regulates with much economic drain and little return. His analysis is based upon much data and economic theory, therefore it has been well-received in business and some government circles as reflecting reality. However, a careful critical review of his arguments led Green and Waitzman to the following conclusion:

> In conclusion, the Weidenbaum study is shot through with methodological errors, combines uncommensurate numbers, and rhetorically attacks consumer and environmental regulation when more than two-thirds of its total is attributable to cartel regulation and paperwork. In addition, his center gets extensive funding from business grants. So he gets financial support from the business community which in turn provides an eager market for his studies that attack government regulation of business. This is surely not illegal, but neither is it independent research.[19]

The significance of his message is not in its accuaracy, but in the way it has been taken up as a "cause," particularly in business circles. Like many other ideas from down south, this message has reached Canada. A report on government regulation by the Economic Council of Canada begins with the following:

> Perhaps the greatest challenge in an empirical approach to regulation lies in assessing its benefits. Benefits must be quantified and valued, and both operations are difficult. Many of the benefits are non-economic or non-quantifiable, and it may be necessary to assess them in qualitative terms.[20]

The report goes on to cite Weidenbaum and De Finas, *The Cost of Federal Regulation of Economic Activity* as "the pioneering work which has been done in this area in the United States."[21]

In discussing Labour Canada's approach toward workers' health, the report states:

> The thrust is towards self regulation . . . the more recent period marks a clean step towards more self regulation in the establishment of the Canadian Centre for Occupational Health and Safety which will not have powers that can be relied upon in a court of law.[22]

The thrust of the message is clear: deregulation through self-regulation will be more efficient and economical. But while deregulation may be positive in some instances, for example with the establishment of effective worksite health and safety committees dominated by workers, it often amounts to industry self-regulation. This is all being done largely on the basis of presumed cost-benefit analysis.

In his study of *Occupational Health and Safety In Canada*, business professor Reschenthaler effectively argues that the cost-benefit model is erroneously applied to social regulation of such areas as occupational health and safety hazards, environmental quality, product hazards, and employment discrimination.[23] The market assumptions of a free market place with information equally available to both employee and employer, full employment opportunities, and rational weighing of workplace hazards when obtaining a job are wrong. Furthermore, how do you determine the costs "external" to business of injury and disease—such as pain and suffering, medical care, retraining, rehabilitation, care for dependents, among others?

Cost-benefit analysis tends to bias the costs and not fully recognize the benefits of regulation because it is narrowly concerned in terms of business expense and "quantifiable" factors. Things which cannot be readily measured, such as pain from social exclusion and physical suffering due to the loss of one's leg or sight, just do not appear. Cost-benefit analysis may lead us to conclude that we should not regulate industry, but just use "expendable" people. For example, in the case of trenching fatalities, proper backcutting or shoring can increase costs 30-49 per cent. It may be most economical to use only young, single persons in trenches because they only cost from $1,000-10,000 each when killed, while young married workers with dependants cost an average of $125,000 each in workmen's compensation funds.[24] The problem of calculating the expense of diseases, given the time factor, is particularly difficult. Most cost-benefit studies have been from the standpoint of business which tends to overestimate the costs of complying with health and safety regulations and underestimate the benefits. If and when cost-benefit analysis is used, it should be calculated from the standpoint of the costs incurred by workers of unsafe and unhealthy work environments and the benefits accruing from better worker health. Human life and its preservation, not profits, should be the direction of the "bias" when considering health in the workplace. Government regulation, including inspection and enforcement, should be conducted upon the assumption that human life and respect for it are the paramount priorities of society. Fortunately, the Economic Council of Canada's final report (discussed in Chapter 12) has not argued for deregulation in the area of workers' health.

Policing the Workplace

The Inspectorate

In any study of laws and their impact we must look at the issues surrounding their enforcement. As noted earlier in this section, prosecutions and convictions are relatively rare in the area of workers' health. This reflects a number of factors, including the philosophy of the WCB and ultimately the philosophy of inspectors.

the day after
    i quit
i phoned
    Workman's
Compensation
    to get them to send
a health & safety
      inspector:

"the glue gives you a rash
the glass cuts your hands
the loud crashing noises
are bad for your hearing
the heat makes you sick
pieces of metal
    get in people's eyes
someone almost cut off
    their fingers on the bar-cutter
the sand-machine
  fell down
& almost killed me
& the company won't
  buy a fan"
      i said

"Well, maybe i'll send an inspector"
  he said, grudgingly. "I'm busy checking out
a construction-site." he couldn't believe
    women's jobs were danger

      -us.[25]

Inspectors, Managers and Others

The plant manager greeted us with a smile and told the inspector to "give 'em hell." He then told us about a Chinese or Vietnamese worker (he couldn't tell the difference) who had hurt his back on the night shift and left work. The manager didn't report it because the worker didn't speak good English and just hurried off like "they" do. We then proceeded to check out the plant after coffee with the company safety supervisor. Since the inspector had called the day before notifying them I was accompanying him, they didn't really ask any questions. We went through the noisy, dirty plant periodically checking chains and other equipment and making sure workers had safety devices on. About halfway through, the shop steward met us and accompanied us for a few minutes, talking about a guy who was crushed a few months earlier when sheets of steel dumped on him from a forklift. We noted a number of violations, such as poor filters in the paint room, no screens around welders, and lack of earmuffs and goggles on some workers. When we got back to the company office only one violation was written up—a salesman without glasses on his visit. The company official persuaded the inspector that screens really are not necessary. As we drove away, the inspector explained that he normally would be accompanied by the company safety officer but he wanted to go around without him to show they are not in collusion. (It appears that word got back to the plant safety man that the workers were surprised I was with the inspector instead of him.)

We then stopped at a city construction site and spent about five minutes looking at the pipe-laying operation and 20 minutes in the construction trailer with the foreman. I sat listening attentively as the inspector and foreman badmouthed unions generally and the local leaders specifically. The anti-union talk was repeated later in the day as we sat in the office of management. While the inspector was friendly in greeting workers and engaging in casual small talk, it became evident by the end of the day that his sympathies lay with management.[26]

While the above-noted biases of inspectors are not necessarily evident in all cases, inspectors are often viewed by workers as less than independent. In reviewing several studies concerning safety and health in Canada, Joan Brown notes that labour representatives invariably spoke of the "chummy," close relationship between inspectors and management.[27]

She observes that:

> This lack of confidence in the inspectorate was strengthened by the nature and outcome of the regulatory policies adopted. The successful functioning of any self-regulation system requires a reasonable balance between education, the exercise of discretion and enforcement. Too often this reasonable balance did not exist. The weakest element almost invariably was enforcement.[28]

In part the coziness of inspectors and managers comes from recruitment patterns and enforcement philosophy. Inspectors are often recruited from supervisory, management personnel in private industry, having a special technical skill and/or trade. When asked about the qualifications of inspectors, one senior administrator responded that they "all are from industry." There appears to be a recruitment bias which favours persons with supervisory/managerial experience in private industry rather than union experience.

The recruitment pattern follows the philosophy that industry can essentially self-regulate with a little advice from inspectors. This philosophy is summed up by Brown:

> The system was founded on the assumption that the employer was legally and financially responsible for the health and safety of workers; that this was the sole responsibility of management; that industry was largely capable of regulating itself

> and willing to do so, and that the role of government (and thus the inspectorate) was to encourage and support this self-regulation. While government should set standards where necessary and have the power to enforce them, government intervention could and should be kept to the minimum, and wherever possible education should be preferred to enforcement.[29]

She then goes on to point out that this model fails to include workers in regulating workers' health, and underestimates the conflict between costs of safety and company profit motives. This approach toward enforcing laws, combined with the grossly inadequate number of inspectors considering the magnitude of the job, is a sure prescription for failure. Is the "solution" hiring more inspectors? Not necessarily.

> Just as more massive police forces cannot solve the problems of street crime, the singular enforcement of the safety laws is not a solution to crimes of safety risk in occupational settings. Where the solution lies is perhaps best illustrated by a series of studies recently presented at a conference on research into occupational accidents. Without exception, each Swedish study acknowledged: (1) the central importance of worker control and involvement in the work environment and (2) the superficiality of corrective actions of a technical or educational nature which ignore the structural underpinnings of occupational hazards.[30]

Worksite Safety Committees

One of the more recent Canadian developments in policing the workplace is the emergence of worksite safety committees made up of both workers and management. This has been particularly well-developed in Saskatchewan.

> Probably the most significant innovation pioneered by Saskatchewan was a much more substantial and effective sharing of the task of inspection and regulation between the inspectorate, the workers and the employers.[31]

In 1972 Saskatchewan law provided for mandatory joint employer-employee occupational health committees in every workplace employing ten or more workers, giving them the duty to participate in identifying and controlling workplace hazards. While five provinces have laws requiring labour-management committees (Saskatchewan, British Columbia, Ontario, Quebec and New Brunswick), the Saskatchewan experience is most revealing given its early emergence and widespread use. A recent study comparing committees in Sweden, West Germany, Austria and Saskatchewan, found the Swedish and Saskatchewan models as most responsive to the needs of workers.[32] It notes the satisfaction of John Chobaniuk, plant manager at Westeel-Rosco's steel fabricating plant in Regina, with the committees.

> The employees are the experts. They work in the plant eight hours a day, forty hours a week, so they're in the best position to know what's wrong.[33]

The report emphasizes that workers should have, individually and through their committee, the right to know about hazards, to participate in hazard prevention, and the right to refuse work in dangerous conditions. One of the problems with Saskatchewan law is that the individual right to refuse needs to be translated into the right of the committee to refuse for workers. Otherwise, the province's rights received a high rating.

Since committees in Saskatchewan have equal numbers of workers' and employers' representatives, they can be stymied by management. It is necessary, according to this report, to have at least one more worker than management representative. While in Sweden safety professionals hired by the company must be selected by the worker-dominated committee, no such provisions are found in Canada. This would go a long way toward reducing worker animosity toward the company doctor and safety expert. The recent Quebec Act, Bill 17, allows workers to participate in the selection of the physician in charge of health services.[34]

In both Sweden and Saskatchewan, workers are trained by a non-employer at the employer's expense. The importance of worker-oriented training was noted by Jennie Smyth, in charge of training in Saskatchewan, in commenting upon the separate training programs for workers and management:

> The committees are supposed to be a departure from the past, when the employer dominated whatever safety program there was. For the workers to really be able to participate, they have to build up their confidence and their independent point of view.
>
> Let's face it, workers and employers have different interests when it comes to health and safety, and the workers on the committees needed time to work with each other to understand how to advance those interests, to develop strategy and tactics of their own.[35]

Finally, the report states that the role of government must include a strong inspection program and consultation with the committee. A senior inspector in Saskatchewan trained under the old cozy management approach told how he reacted to this new approach:

> Before the act was passed, I went in and made hundreds of inspections and never talked to a worker. At first, it just scared hell out of some of the inspectors to talk to union members on the shop floor. This was a new concept.[36]

The committees in Saskatchewan fill out a simple, one-page form at each meeting listing problems discussed and decisions made. These are forwarded to the provincial health and safety division for monitoring. Of 80,000 "concerns" reported between 1973 and 1977, only 329 required government intervention, with 1,400 necessitating involvement of higher management officials.[37]

While the above picture of worksite committees may suggest they are "the" solution, we believe they must be used in conjunction with other mechanisms such as rigid enforcement, threat of criminal conviction, and penalties with teeth. As Glasbeek and Rowland point out, joint committees may be threatened by numerous techniques, including government resistance to workers' complaints.[38] Even in the Swedish model, which is held up as the epitome of workers' rights in western democratic society, the worker may not get the support of the government inspector. The following field observation from Sweden is revealing:

> What was clear, however, was the relative relationships among the safety delegate (worker-elected representative) the director and the inspector. The latter two were most observably colleagues and friends, it was the director, not the safety delegate, whom the inspector had called to arrange an interview. The safety delegate was undoubtedly the third man out, or the fourth, if one were to include the safety engineer. Sitting in that scene, it was impossible to imagine a conflict of interests in which the worker would have stood a chance against the two.[39]

Sterns concluded that the struggle for worker control cannot really come from legislation but only from political activity and consciousness-raising among workers. We agree that such action is important and, in fact, legal battles may do just that. Nonetheless, workers should continue to struggle for independent worker-controlled committees. Community organizations and community struggles may play a more significant part in future in bringing workers' health to our attention.

NOTES

1. David Estrin, "Occupational Health: Whose Health—Industry's or Workers'—Does the Law Really Protect?" *Hazards at Work: Proceedings*. A transcript of Hazards at Work: Law and the Workplace, a national seminar held in Toronto, November 16-17, 1977, p. 88.
2. Law Reform Commission of Canada, *Our Criminal Law* (Ottawa: Information Canada, 1976), p. 12 (emphasis added).
3. The Honourable John Munro, "Opening Address," *Hazards at Work: Proceedings*. A transcript of *Hazards at Work: Law and the Workplace*, a national seminar held in Toronto, November 16-17, 1977, p. 1.
4. Colin Goff and Charles Reasons, "Corporate Crime In Canada: A Study of Crime and Punishment," *Criminal Law Quarterly* 18 (August 1976): 487. A more detailed study appears in their book *Corporate Crime in Canada: A Critical Analysis of Anti-Combines Legislation* (Scarborough: Prentice-Hall, 1978).
5. Don McGillivray, "Oil Report is Pawn in Political Game," *The Calgary Herald*, March 5, 1981. James Lorimer, *Canada's Oil Monopoly* (Toronto: Lorimer, 1981).
6. Gordon Jarenko, "Ottawa Played Role in Ripoffs," *The Calgary Herald*, March 5, 1981.
7. Economics and Research Branch, *Safety Enforcement Policies and Practices In Canada* (Ottawa: Canada Department of Labour, May 1975), pp. 72-73.
8. G. B. Reschenthaler, *Occupational Health and Safety In Canada* (Montreal: Institute for Research on Public Policy, 1979).
9. "Employer's Fine Irks Factory Accident Victim," *The Calgary Herald*, October 16, 1980. In the same province, employers were ordered to repay more than $576,000 in illegally withheld wages and benefits to their employees in 1980. Cecil Rosner,

"Employers Ordered to Repay More Than $576,000," *Winnipeg Free Press*, February 17, 1981.

10. "Worker Electrocuted, Company Fined $1,000," *Canadian Occupational Health and Safety News*, September 17, 1979, p. 3.

11. Reschenthaler, *Occupational Health and Safety in Canada*, p. 142.

12. Gordon Lee, "Construction Boom Lifts Hazards Over Our Heads," *The Calgary Herald*, February 7, 1981.

13. Law Reform Commission of Canada, *Criminal Responsibility for Group Actions* (Ottawa: Information Council, 1976).

14. Harry J. Glasbeek and Susan Rowland, "Are Injuring and Killing At Work Crimes?" *Osgoode Hall Law Journal* 17 (December, 1979): 507, 522-23.

15. Ibid., p. 589.

16. Gordon Lee, "Foreman Charged In Site Death," *The Calgary Herald*, February 4, 1981. More recently, Belmoral Mines Ltd. has been charged with eight counts of manslaugher after a cave-in in Val d'Or, Quebec killed eight miners. "Calgary Firm Charged in Mine Deaths," April 11, 1981, p. 1.

17. Pat Crone, "Worker Dies In Trench," *The Calgary Herald*, February 2, 1981.

18. Mark Green and Norman Waitzman, *Business War on the Law: An Analysis of the Benefits of Federal Health/Safety Enforcement* (Washington, D.C.: The Corporate Accountability Research Group, 1979).

19. Ibid., p. 32. They noted contributors to the Center in 1976 or 1977 included James S. McDonnell, Jr., Chairman of the McDonnell-Douglas Corporation ($327,000); Olin Foundation ($316,000); J. Howard Perv Freedom Trust (Perv was the founder of Sun Oil Co.—$25,000); General Electric ($10,000), Corning Glass Works Foundation ($5,000). Who said money cannot *buy* good research!

20. Sylvia Ostry, *Regulation Reference: A Preliminary Report to First Ministers* (Ottawa: Economic Council of Canada, November 1978), p. 3.

21. Ibid., p. 8.

22. Ibid., p. 71.

23. Reschenthaler, *Occupational Health and Safety In Canada*, pp. 7-18.

24. Ibid., pp. 55-69.

25. Gwen Hauser, "The Day After I Quit," in Tom Wayman (ed.), *A Government Job At Last* (Toronto: George J. McLeod, 1976), p. 96.

26. Charles Reasons accompanied inspectors on some investigations in Alberta.

27. Joan C. Brown, "The Inspectorate: Part 1—Victims or Villains?" *Labour Gazette*, 10 (October 1978): 461-66.

28. Ibid., p. 465.

29. Ibid., p. 463.

30. L. R. Stearns, "Fact and Fiction of a Model Enforcement Bureaucracy: The Labour Inspectorate of Sweden," *British Journal of Law and Society*, Vol. 6, No. 1 (1979): 21-22.

31. Joan C. Brown, "The Inspectorate: Part 2—Change and Development," *Labour Gazette*, Vol. 78 (November/December 1978): 556.

32. American Labour Education Center, *Labour-Management Health and Safety Committees In Sweden, West Germany, Austria and Saskatchewan, Canada* (Washington, D.C.: U.S. Department of Labor, Occupational Safety and Health Administration, June 1980).

33. Ibid., p. 22.

34. Fourth Session, Thirty-First Legislative Assemblee Nationale Du Quebec, *Bill 17: An Act Respecting Occupational Health and Safety*. L'Editeur Officiel Du Quebec, 1979.
35. Ibid., p. 39.
36. Ibid., p. 45.
37. Ibid., p. 46.
38. Glasbeek and Rowland, "Are Injury and Killing at Work Crimes?"
39. Sterns, "Fact and Fiction." *British Journal of Law and Society*, 1979, p. 17.

Part IV

Alternative Approaches

MICHAEL CORCORAN
native of Kerry Ireland
killed in the Explosion
May 3 1887
Aged 46 years
Rest in Peace
Farewell dear wife my life is past
[illegible]
[illegible]
[illegible]

Chapter 11

Workers' Health and Workers' History

The workers' flag is deepest red,
It shrouded oft our martyred dead;
And ere their limbs grew stiff and cold
Their life-blood dyed its very fold.[1]

The Bakery Workers' Union has a motto:
"It Stands for Purity and Wholesomeness,
It Demands Sanitation and Justice."

Calgary, Alberta (1981)—angry steelworkers at Prudential Steel Ltd. stayed off work after one of them was killed on the job. The United Steelworkers of America held a meeting concerning safety at the plant.

Kitimat, British Columbia (1977)—comprehensive health study funded by union concerning effects of aluminum smelting on over 1,200 workers; a 91-page report followed; further studies were conducted by the B.C. WCB; "fluorosis" was added to the WCB Industrial Disease schedule in 1980.

Baie Verte, Newfoundland (1978)—strike by over 500 asbestos workers at Advocate Mines Ltd. from February to May 1978; demands involved worker dust sampling, improved safety committees, improved decontamination of workers, changes in work procedures to minimize dust exposure.

Quebec (1978)—10,000 Quebec mining and associated workers strike from March into April in part over such workers' health issues as right to refuse dangerous work, choice of doctor, noise, and air contaminant monitoring.

Canada (1981)—Canadian Union of Postal Workers strikes for health and safety issues, including paid maternity leave.

Introduction

One of the major ideas or outlooks of business and many professional and government people—often expressed publicly—is that rank and file workers don't really care about workplace safety or health and that Canadian workers are indifferent or apathetic and only really care about wages. Of course, workers without a history are workers without a future.

Business also looks at trade unions this way. Every person active in a union has heard comments from time to time, that some union or union official is "using" a workers' health issue as a smokescreen for some other economic or political point. Or, that union health and safety activists are muckrakers, opportunists or militant troublemakers bent on using workers' health as a tool to lever a future wage or other monetary benefit concession from the boss.

This kind of thinking is false and malicious: it is a reflection of general class ignorance and disdain combined with the idea that workers are an unthinking commodity to be managed by business and government elders.

In reality, there is a remarkably long and rich Canadian history of workers' health struggles—both offensive and defensive in character. There are setbacks, lapses, contradictions, and some obviously serious mistakes. But overall, the history is filled with continuing examples of workers' and trade unions' initiative, energy, and imagination. Often involving bitter and protracted strikes or walkouts, the issues have been fought out in particular workplaces and across industries, and have often reached levels of provincial, national, and international attention. Many other issues have not come to wider public view at all. Many are long forgotten. This brief chapter can only introduce some of the early elements of workers' health struggles in Canada.

Much early history is to be found in the gravestones of mining, farming, forestry, railway, construction, and fishing camps or communities across Canada.

The frightening death toll in underground mining on Vancouver Island is commemorated in such places as the Saint Peter's Church graveyard, high on a hill overlooking Nanaimo, British Columbia. The 1887 Nanaimo explosion killed at least 148 miners. Saint Peter's small plot has ten headstones remaining in testament. One example suffices.

IN MEMORY OF
My Beloved Husband
JAMES B. LYONS
Native of Ireland
Aged 44 years
Also has son
MICHAEL Aged 16 years
Native of Yorkshire, England
and both killed in the Explosion
May 3, 1887

Down the coast, at the Ladysmith, British Columbia municipal cemetery, over 25 gravestones and elaborate cairns mark the victims of mines, railways, and forestry. A sizeable cairn still stands to a 16-year-old boy, Hans Grouhel, "accidently killed at Port Alberni" on August 10, 1918 and "erected by his fellow workmen—Pacific Lumber Co."

In the same cemetery, a huge 12-foot granite obelisk erected by District 28 of the United Mine Workers of America is dedicated to Joseph Mairs—"a martyr to a noble cause—the emancipation of his fellow men." The obelisk features a plaque with two labourers' hands clasped together and the inscription "1898—8 Hours".

In these physical symbols we sense the ceremonial significance attached to work-related death by workers and their families. The obvious issues of youth employment and hours of labour emerge. Standing in the midst of the monuments, we feel the solidarity and resolution—even of future triumph—overcoming personal tragedy and despair.

Historical romanticizing was not the feature of workers' health struggles. Rank-and-file action was the key. There is a lesson in this for the present. Worker mobilization—contrary to widespread current ignorance—went far beyond mourning over physical hazards.

For example, again from Nanaimo, British Columbia, in January 1917, the Western Fuel Co.'s "Underground and Artisans' Employees Medical and Accident Relief Fund" signed an agreement with the Nanaimo Hospital Board whereby a "modern X-Ray Machine," *selected and purchased by the workers*, was placed in the Nanaimo Hospital for the use of workers and the general public."[2]

Here we see workers' own organized health committees. This is also one early example of worker initiative in the medical diagnosis and prevention field—and is related to disease rather than injury ill-health. Why didn't the hospital or the boss buy or provide the machine? Obviously, the workers at the Western Fuel Co. did not wait for the answer to that question.

Much of the history of Canadian workers' health struggles is contained in the action of trade union federations or centrals. Besides individual unions, the Knights of Labour, the IWW, the One Big Union, the Federation of Catholic Workers of Canada, the Trade Union Education League, the Workers' Unity League, the Canadian Labour Union, the Trades and Labour Congress, the Canadian CIO Committee, the Canadian Congress of Labour, the Confederation of Canadian Unions, the Canadian and Catholic Confederations of Labour, the CNTU, and the Canadian Labour Congress all have stories to tell. The stories differ because this variety of organizations has often presented quite different solutions to the economic and social issues facing the Canadian working class.

Canada's first trade union centre, the 1873 Canadian Labour Union, arose out of an issue with significant workers' health implications—the fight for a 9-hour day. One major Canadian labour historian, Charles Lipton, identifies that struggle as the focus for the first demonstration of Canadian workers' solidarity as a class.[3]

Because workers' compensation and most workers' job hazards are under provincial jurisdiction, city, regional and provincial union organizations have had the major involvement. At the federal level, national labour bodies—such as the CLC today—have generally devoted their attention to the related concerns of national pension, medical and hospital care and social support services, unemployment insurance, services for the disabled, vocational retraining and manpower policies.[4]

Many of these issues arise from the unhealthy workplace and deal with its problems. A full-time health and safety staff person at the CLC level—Dr. Victor Rabinovitch—was first appointed in 1978. While this was 22 years after the CLC's formation, there are emerging signs that a national health and safety labour service and strategy, including workers' compensation, is recognized and growing. In 1979, moves were begun to co-ordinate a national WCB analysis by the CLC. Perhaps this will lead to a model bill and to co-ordinated struggles. National research, education and action functions and goals are being developed and co-ordinated. The low-level radiation hazards of video display terminals is but one example. The Federal government's re-designed workers' health strategy—through the Canadian Centre for Occupational Health and Safety—calls for a national labour response.

Other renewed signs of vigour have appeared. The Ontario Federation of Labour's Occupational Health and Safety Training Centre and the work of the Metro Toronto Labour Council are solid achievements. The B.C. Federation of Labour and the Confederation of Canadian Unions (B.C.) have helped encourage a strong health and safety activism at rank-and-file and public political levels between 1975 and 1980. The Canadian Union of Public Employees has shown leadership on issues facing public employees.

These developments owe much to the history of trade union activism on health issues. In the early years (1886-1900) of the Trades and Labour Congress, emphasis was given to legislative reform lobbying over health and safety issues. Protective legislation was sought for railroad and factory workers and seamen. Legislation for basic sanitation in workshops, government inspectors, limitations upon child labour and compulsory examinations of engineers and firemen featured prominently.[5] Abolition of piecework, shorter hours of labour, and factories legislation demands arose from the first convention in 1886.

Hours of Labour

The workers' movement for shorter working hours in the nineteenth and twentieth centuries has been a workers' health issue in significant respects.

Paralleling earlier British and American developments, Hamilton, Montreal, Toronto, Halifax, and other trade unions and workers organized in 1871-72 and thereafter to achieve the nine-hour day. Nine Hour Leagues were formed. The movement was met with immediate and fierce business resistance. Lockouts, long strikes, mass public meetings, and arrests followed. It succeeded in part in the railways—Canada's largest employers—but was only won for other trades and workers piecemeal over the next few decades, and well into this century. It has still not been achieved entirely.

One historian has referred to the nine-hour pioneers as the "genesis of the Canadian labour movement."[6] The shorter hours issue was a key element in early union organization and worker publications in Canada. Internationally, it bound English, European and American workers in common struggles over decades.

In the formation of the first "Canadian Labour Union"—a forerunner of the current CLC—in September 1873, the following constitutional preamble sets out, in part:

> Whereas the workingmen of the Dominion of Canada, in common with the intelligent producers of the world, feel the necessity of co-operate and harmonious action to secure their mutual interests, just compensation for their toil, *and such limitation of the hours of labour as may tend to promote their physical and intellecttal well-being. . . .*"[7]

"Hours of Labour" and "Legislation" committees were formed to carry out this work.

The *Ontario Workman*, an early working-class newspaper in the 1870s, summed up the shorter hours movement in this way: "More of God's sunlight for the workers."[8]

Historical interpretations point out that the shorter working hours movement had its material side. This consisted chiefly of increasing available work for the unemployed and an increase in value on each hour's service. Even in the effect of wider work distribution, it can be seen that the risk of hazardous industry would be distributed as well.

But also, there was a direct reaction against "the demand of our time . . . for the rapid production of things" and the "physical and moral degradation of over-work."[9] General moral, social, and intellectual improvement was a major rallying point.[10]

Interestingly, shorter hours were also seen to provide for a healthy diversification in the type of physical and mental labour performed on the job and as a way to assist in lessening the domestic workload—"household drudgery"—by releasing the male spouse off-the-job. Obviously, the latter has not yet been achieved.

The point of a "healthy diversification" has been expressed in these terms, as early as 1887:

> Less hours of application to the production of a fractional part of a product will give more hours to the development of those muscles of the body in the self-employment at the home, and more time for the development of the moral and mental qualities through opportunities of civilization, observation and association.[11]

Today, it is worth noting for trade unions that business and government regulatory agencies do not really view the length or nature of the working day, week, year, or life as a workers' health issue. In collective bargaining, issues such as holidays, rest breaks, meal breaks, hours of work, and retirement should all be addressed in the context of the overall mental and physical health of the workers, with particular application to the job or industry involved.

Not only is the question of the amount of work a workers' health issue, but the pace and timing of that work is important. Here, shift work is a primary example. Even though there are numerous published studies showing the excess health risks associated with certain forms of shift work, government health and safety laws and enforcement agencies pay scant attention to the issue. For example too, if shift work increases automobile accident rates by exposing travelling workers to night driving, is that a workers' health issue needing to be addressed on the job? Or, if it increases the mental and physical ill-health of the worker and his family at leisure or in the home, through stress and fatigue, should it be addressed on the job?

The predominant view is that shift work is a question of the organization of labour which is management's prerogative or, sometimes, a "labour-management" issue which has nothing to do with workers' health or government enforcement.

Prevention laws have been concerned primarily with equipment, buildings, tools and the physical procedures of work, rather than the overall control and organization of work methods. This is a fatal flaw in the current regulation scheme. It illustrates further the craven role of government to business.

Similarly, even hours of work and "holiday" statutes are not now normally thought of as being related to workers' health. They are usually lumped in with "labour standards" laws, such as payment of wages.

Labour's shorter hours movement was a major factor contributing to the amount and severity of all Canadian strikes and work stoppages well into the Second World War.[12] For example, a Winnipeg plumbers' strike started in early July 1906 with shorter hours a key issue among the 180 plumbers. Before the strike ended in late September, it had spread to another 4,000 workers.[13]

Business often exploited the First World War to extend both the working week and daily hours up to ten- and 16-hour days.

> At a Toronto munitions plant in 1917, the management increased hours from 13 to 14 a day. At least 7 women refused to work the extra hour. Of these, 2 had husbands at the front, one had lost a brother overseas, one had a brother on active service, and one had been awarded the munitions workers good service medal. The 7 went to the office of the Toronto Daily Star. "Look at our hands!" cried one,

> and she thrust out hands blackened with oil from which the skin had peeled in big patches. A member of the delegation said: "One of the girls was too sick to come with us. Oil in her system is killing her. Two have died!" Another said: "They are killing us off as fast as they are killing the men in the trenches!" . . . The incident was not a lone one. At the Verdun Munitions Board plant, women worked 72 hours per week and upwards.[14]

This massive labour exploitation, added to the horrible casualties of business's European war, led to renewed labour mobilization after the war around hours of work. The Winnipeg Trades and Labour Council proposed a 30-hour week resolution to the 1919 Trades and Labour Congress Convention.[15]

The OBU (One Big Union) was formed in Calgary in 1919 and, among other matters, called for a six-hour workday in Canada.

An ILO convention of 1919 called for eight-hour days and 48-hour weeks in industrial work. Canada finally ratified this convention in 1935 but this was lost in the courts on a constitutional issue.

In 1959, Newfoundland loggers were striking to obtain a 54-hour week instead of the prevailing ten-hour day and six-day week.[16]

The 1961 Ontario (McAndrew) Royal Commission Report on Industrial Safety pointed out that since at least 1914, the Ontario Factory, Shop and Office Building Act had placed legal limits on hours (for youths and women) at an incredible maximum of 12½ hours daily and 72½ hours weekly.[17] Since most of the workers covered by that legislation were non-unionized and in smaller or owner-operated premises, it is easy to imagine the decades of exploitation they suffered at the expense of physical and mental health.

According to one source, trade union success around the turn of the century in achieving the eight-hour day, workers' compensation, and safety legislation was the result of labour mobilization at the political level and encouraged further political efforts.[18]

Even after the achievement of legislation limiting hours of work, such as the eight-hour day circa 1900 in British Columbia's underground coal mines, unions had to strike to enforce the law:

> In the case of the eight-hour day in the mines, the employers refused to obey the law or simply ignored it, and the unions had then to try and enforce the legislation. Even where unions struck to enforce the law, they were often opposed by the government.[19]

This history has parallels for today, when workers must use the legal right to refuse unhealthy work and their collective strength to enforce existing laws and ensure healthy conditions.

The Resource Economy: Work Camps, Relief Camps, Prisons

Work camps in railway, mining, forestry, pulp and paper, hydro-development, and road construction have been a permanent feature of the Canadian economy. The "bunkhouse men" totalled over 200,000 in some of the years between 1903-14, and were situated in 3,000 large camps. They made up almost 5 per cent of the Canadian male labour force.[20] Single and immigrant men, many unskilled and transient, were isolated in northern and rugged interior work camps. They often suffered from unsanitary living conditions, inadequate medical care and a brutal working regime. Much of this still continues today in smaller, more isolated camps, although modern planned company towns and the regular air ferrying of workers have evolved in larger, permanent work locations, relieving against some of the harsher conditions.

The early bunkhouses were often overcrowded, low-ceilinged, poorly lit, badly ventilated and irregularly inspected. Sanitation was haphazard.[21] Outbreaks of smallpox and other infectious diseases were common.

Periodic medical inspection by physicians and vaccinations were introduced in Ontario between 1901-10 but not regularly enforced. Isolation and a lack of unionization would help explain this failure.

> With some personal knowledge of medical supervision in such camps, . . . during the first fifteen years of this century, one will affirm that sanitary conditions in the bunkhouses, even then, were such that the work of the provincial authorities can only be described as having been superficial, if not positively neglectful of the real welfare of the workers in camps.[22]

In Ontario, workers originally paid directly, in the form of monthly assessments, for medical services, but rarely saw a physician or a nurse. Edmund Bradwin studied the medical system in the railway camps in Ontario and Quebec between 1900 and 1920 and found that doctors won medical service contracts from railway contractors, established main base hospitals and subsidiary hospitals of varying quality and engaged students as assistants. The students worked out of the subsidiary hospitals, visiting work groups as climate and geography allowed. The subsidiary hospitals were sometimes a tent, sometimes a mere "pretence," and sometimes under the care of an untrained orderly/cook. Bradwin cited the students as "the one redeeming feature" of the camp medical system. But their presence was irregular, as they too were exploited in wages and difficult to attract and hold. Bradwin also states that the "medical attitude toward the unsanitary conditions held that many camps . . . were either glaringly careless or purposely negligent."[23]

This again illustrates the major reason for traditional worker antagonism and cynicism towards company doctors. So long as the company is the doctor's client, there will not be general medical vigour to enforce conditions which require greater company expenditures. As Bradwin put it: "lastly and chiefly, . . . the medical system suffered from its very relation. . . ."[24] It is fundamentally undemocratic for health care to give no choice to the worker/patient in selecting medical care personnel and to provide no real means for exercising direct influence over health care approaches and services.

Physical injuries and diseases occurring in or attributable to work camps have been recognized as work-related. Injuries such as falls on bunkhouse steps have been so regarded. With the necessity and requirement of living in such camps as a condition of work, the worker would not be exposed to such risks but for the work. It is this principle that establishes the work connection.

But this recognition has not yet been carried through by the compensation system to emotional ill-health and alcoholism attributable to such conditions.

It is worthwhile to record Bradwin's early observations in the 1920s on this issue:

> What are the social out-croppings (of isolated work-camp life)? Time spent around any of the frontier towns reveals this in all its crudeness. The situation is simple. Men . . . are deprived during months at a stretch of the companionship of women, of home ties, and all that elevates life in a man; they are starved by isolation and monotony. When they reach the outskirts of civilization, the frontier town with its "aurer" lights, its music and noisy hilarity entices them from their deepest resolves. Vice too frequently pervades such places . . . the all-night orgies, the drunken sprees lasting for days . . . such is the vicious circle in which these men are held helpless . . .
> It is a characteristic of Canadian life which produces a shudder: the curse of hardness overspreads it, and the price of hardness is hideousness.

Despite these simple sociological observations, no Canadian workers' compensation board has ever recognized alcoholism itself as a work-related disease. This contrasts with medical science, which has recognized an increased rate of alcohol consumption and alcohol-related diseases among numerous specific industries and occupations. Writing in the British Journal of Addiction, Dr. Martin Plant of Royal Edinburgh Hospital's Alcohol Research Group reviewed the medical literature on work and alcohol and concluded the following eight factors are the most commonly suggested explanations of higher alcohol-related problems in some occupations:

—availability of alcohol at work;
—social pressure to drink at work;
—separation from normal social or sexual relationships;
—freedom from supervision;
—very high or very low income levels;
—collusion by colleagues;
—strains and stresses of dangerous work, responsibility, job security, boredom;
—recruitment of "unusual people" predisposed to drink heavily.[25]

Obviously, many of the above factors apply to workers in the mining, forestry, construction, railway and fishing industries. The effects of the isolated work camps and dangerous work were recognized by Bradwin over 50 years ago and the medical literature confirms it today.

Loggers from the Pacific to Atlantic have long fought for more sanitary camp living conditions. Union mobilization and militancy have often been based on the desperate working and living conditions.

Pacific coast sawmills in the late 1800s featured long hours—eleven and a half hours a day, six days a week, with Sundays off. There were three holidays a year—Christmas, New Year's, and Dominion Day. In 1886, the wage was $1.25 per day.[26]

Logging bunkhouses were unventilated, unlit, and unclean—breeding grounds for disease. "Living conditions in camps were so poor that the men would not work for long, and often left for town. . . ."[27]

The struggle for better camp conditions was one of the main organizing points in the B.C. lumber industry, especially among loggers.[28]

> Working conditions . . . did improve under union pressure and the united demands of the smaller groups, especially loggers in independently run logging companies.[29]

Better housing, with separated living rooms, cooking and dining rooms, recreation, washing and drying quarters, hot and cold running water, and better food started appearing towards the end of the 1910s. "Thus in the decade 1920 to 1930, more progress was made to improve working conditions than in the previous 50 years."[30]

The important point is that living conditions improved as the loggers and other forestry workers became more widely unionized in more militant unions.

Loggers worked in extremely harsh conditions, cutting spruce for airplanes, on the Queen Charlotte Islands during the First World War. The severe winter climate and the hazardous work were made worse by tent living, lack of recreation, production speed and food and equipment variability.[31]

At the end of the war, the International Workers of the World (IWW) appeared in the logging camps, a reflection of the loggers' unrest over working conditions.[32]

The introduction of new logging techniques did not always give proper attention to workers' health. For example, when railway logging first started on the British Columbia coast circa 1900, makeshift rails, road beds, engines, and techniques resulted in many physical accidents.

> This was the heyday of the railway logging road. In the beginning, there were no properly built logging cars and air brakes had not yet been introduced. Many a brakeman lost an arm or leg while scrambling over the logs to apply the hand brakes. So many accidents happened that the Provincial Department of Railways finally ruled that all logging trains had to be equipped with air brakes; the last hand-braked logging car was retired in 1925 . . .[33]
>
> When the little narrow-gauge Shay locomotive on the Eastern Lumber Co. line near Ladysmith turned over and killed the engineer, the Department of Railways stipulated that all logging roads should be standard gauge.[34]

As is generally the case, workers' mobilization eventually leads to legal reforms in health and safety.

For example, legislation was introduced in New Brunswick, Quebec, and Ontario in 1934 which provided new protections for isolated loggers and other forest workers.[35] The New Brunswick legislation provided for an industrial disputes commission which included jurisdiction over grievances related to camp living conditions. The Ontario law provided an inspectorate to supervise forest working conditions, including hours, food quality and sufficiency, medical and dental services, and camp sanitary and housing conditions, as well as on-the-job conditions. The Quebec law was an amalgam of both.

Traditional industrial or resource work camps are not the only source of worker unity. Wherever work and unhealthy conditions combine, worker struggle has resulted.

Relief camp conditions during the depression raised health concerns. Meagre wages—twenty cents a day—and military discipline aggravated the overcrowding, poor sleeping quarters, lack of sanitary conditions and long hours of the construction and general labour work.

The six demands of the Relief Camp Workers' Union (RCWU) presented to Prime Minister R. B. Bennett, on June 22, 1935, included the following:

—all workers and relief camps and government projects be covered by the Compensation Act
—adequate first aid supplies on all relief jobs

The demands were for democratic conditions and fair work and wages. Bennett's reaction was hostile. He and the Conservatives were defeated in the fall election and the relief camps were turned into work camps.[36]

An extension of the isolated work camps and the government relief camps is the history of prisoners' strikes and militancy, focused on working conditions in Federal and provincial prisons and reformatories. Many prisoners' sit-downs, slow-downs and strikes have evolved from work situations or revolved around working conditions or medical care in Canadian penal history.[37] Even before Confederation, prisons had farming operations connected with them; industrial workshops have usually existed in one form or another in all prisons; prisoners have been forcefully employed in heavy construction on public works, including prisons themselves; juveniles have been forced to work in heavy labour in reformatory settings; prisoners have worked on prison maintenance—cooking, laundry, cleaning, repair; prisoners ofter earn earlier release through work-release programs of one type or another.

Work camps in forestry have been a feature of minimum security institutions in British Columbia for many years.

Not remarkably, it wasn't until 1977 that the British Columbia Workers' Compensation Board even agreed to pay compensation benefits to prison workers injured while on work-release or pre-release programs where they were employed by private or public industry at the same wage levels and paying taxes like their fellow civilian workers. But for most work inside a prison or on prison premises, the prisoner is not considered to be an employee and eligible for workers' compensation.[38]

It is circumstances such as this which have fostered prisoner discontent and, often, rioting, strikes, and violent internal prison action. Their situations are a parallel to civilian workers' conditions.

Workers' Fatalities and Coroners' Inquests

An excellent set of documents has recently been published by David Jay Bercuson[39] which shows company-government inspection failure in the months leading up to the coal-mine explosion at Bellevue, Alberta in December 1910. Twenty-one miners died. There was no commission of inquiry. A coroner's inquest was denied access to company-government inspector correspondence on the grounds that it was "confidential and privileged." The inquest could find no cause and laid no blame. Subsequently revealed, the correspondence showed a long series of company health and safety hazards and failures. It also revealed an inspector's report two days before the explosion which gave the mine a clean bill of health.

One can imagine this type of scenario across the mining industry years ago. But is it very much different today?

Coroner's inquests into industrial fatalities in Canada appear to have a sorry history. In British Columbia, for example, even today, the Workers' Compensation Board inspectors are forbidden to take their past inspection reports to inquests and voluntarily produce them, including reports on the actual fatality involved. No overall annual summary and publishing of these inquest verdicts and findings is available—even to the government which requests them. We are unable to discover any actual criminal prosecution brought as a result of these inquests over the recent years. Inquests are often conducted in less than a searching manner and with a great disparity in quality, depending upon the region and coroner.

Past company safety and health records and government-company correspondence are not usually presented to the juries. Juries are not always composed of workers familiar with the work processes involved. Workers' families are often not represented or, if they are, not by a union. Insufficient care is often taken to ensure proper visual presentations of death circumstances or to visit the actual site. Policemen unskilled in industrial accident inquiry do most of the investigation. Poor forensic medical resources and lack of specially knowledgable lawyers and coroners is the rule, not the exception. Finally, most physicians have little, if any, training in occupational health and safety.

It is clear that no consistent, deliberate and forceful attempt is made to ensure implementation of coroner's jury recommendations in industrial fatalities. They are not self-enforcing and failure to implement them is not a civil or criminal offence.

The best estimate is that most of these conditions exist in the coroner's inquest system and industrial fatalities in every Canadian province today.

Additionally, of course, the coroner's inquest system is called into play only when some sudden, unexplained death occurs—invariably it is a collapse or explosion or some physical accident; not the slow, remorseless deaths caused by industrial pollutants resulting in heart or lung impairment or cancer.

This pattern is tragic because it undermines the democratic and social purposes meant to be served by providing a public forum of peer, citizen review of the circumstances of death. If any area of human endeavour requires such an approach, it is the workplace death.

The importance of unions and workers attending coroners' inquests and pushing for better quality inquests and enforcement of jury recommendations cannot be stressed sufficiently.

Industrial First Aid: A Workers' Health Issue

The industrial first aid movement in British Columbia provides a good case study of the struggle to obtain improved emergency care for injured workers. It is a story with historical and political interest and impact today. According to one source, up until the 1930s, industrial first aid training services were left almost entirely to St. John Ambulance across Canada. In 1931, the B.C WCB asked St. John to improve their program, making it more comprehensive and providing certification. St. John refused to co-operate. As a result, a group of industrial first aid attendants, with the assistance of the B.C. WCB, formed the Industrial First Aid Attendants' Association of British Columbia (IFAAA). This Association promoted a higher standard of first aid training than St. John Ambulance. St. John basic general training was 16 hours. The IFAAA successfully lobbied the British Columbia provincial government for certification of industrial first aid attendants based on an "industrial" standard and a course of 50 hours' duration.

The IFAAA and St. John Ambulance competed for teaching the "industrial" standard until 1962 when St. John Ambulance and the Association reached an odd agreement. The terms were that the Association withdraw from the training field in return for financial assistance from St. John. In 1973 the newly-elected NDP government broke the St. John Ambulance monopoly by giving approval to several community colleges to offer the "industrial" course. Better service to interior communities was the basic reason for this move. St. John mounted an intensive lobby against this development. It argued primarily that the industrial course was their main source of revenue, supporting their non-fee-generating public first aid volunteer services. Not long after the Social Credit party was returned in December of 1975, the Minister of Education, Pat McGeer, stopped the community college industrial first aid training. He named St. John Ambulance as the sole training agent in B.C. This issue had much more labour than educational relevance, but McGeer somehow prevailed.

In the spring of 1976, the B.C. Employers' Council launched an attack on WCB first aid services. They called for a reduction in the industrial first aid training standard, suggesting that the WCB withdraw from the industrial first aid field. This would have meant no government role in training first aid instructors and examining students, i.e., the government would lose its indirect control over course content. The newly-appointed chairman of the B.C. WCB, Dr. Adam Little, announced in 1977 that the Board's First Aid Department was to be disbanded and re-organized within the general Safety Inspection Department.

In 1978 the WCB gave notice of fundamental changes to the industrial first aid regulations. This included a reduction in the training standard and a reduction from 19 to 16 years old in the minimum age for practising industrial first aid. St. John actively supported the proposed reduction in the standard, as did the Alberta-based oil companies, drilling for natural gas in northern British Columbia. Organized labour in British Columbia strongly opposed the proposed changes. At the early 1979 public hearings, organized labour's public and unanimous opposition to the proposed changes was effective, forcing the WCB to back down and to retain the existing industrial standards.

First aid instruction must develop sensitivity to disease-producing hazards and to such situations as gas and toxic substance spills and emissions. It must also develop a pro-worker approach—rooted in the workers' perspective—and generate distinctive advanced courses for certain types of industries and hazards.

First aid quality and availability has been greatly assisted by trade union bargaining. Many industrial and public sector collective agreements provide for increased wage-levels depending upon the class of first aid ticket.

For example, the International Woodworkers of America central interior British Columbia local first achieved premium pay for first aid attendants in 1967 bargaining. Class C received 15¢; Class B, 20¢; Class A, 25¢; and Class AA 30¢.[40]

Health and Safety Strikes

As we point out in this book—and as has suddenly been "discovered" by business and government—strikes and lockouts are relatively minor problems compared to the economic and social harm caused by unhealthy working conditions. In fact, criminal anti-social conduct on the streets causes less physical and mental harm than the workplaces of Canada.

Neither provincial governments nor the Federal government have ever adequately kept track of work stoppages due in whole or in part to workers' health issues. Nor have they viewed contract demands or collective agreement provisions from a workers' health perspective. This failure also extends even to non-work-stoppage disputes which proceed through grievances to arbitration. For example, government and legal arbitration books and reports have traditionally not had a category for "health and safety." Such disputes are usually buried under headings such as "discipline" or "discharge."

When we examine the day-to-day issues facing workers on the job and look at collective agreements, a very large number of workplace health issues emerge. All of the following issues are examples of this point:

> Personal appearance or apparel standards where issues of safety or hygiene are raised (beards, hair length, personal sanitation, contact lenses); alcohol or other types of drug use; illness or physical incapacity; absenteeism; medical records, medical examinations and medical certificates (including information access, physician of choice, the content of pre- and post-employment tests or questions); age and mandatory retirement; sex and physical ability to work; hours of work, shift work, overtime, night work, holidays and rest breaks; food, sanitation and lodging services; danger pay, piece-work and other production incentive systems; insurance and benefit plans such as short-term (sick pay) and long-term disability, life insurance and pension schemes; first aid services, training and payment; joint safety and health committees; accident-free "prizes" and "bonuses," and the provision and payment for required personal protective equipment.

Workers' struggles over working conditions are as old as organized industry itself. Vancouver Island's coal fields were first opened up around 1849 when the Hudson's Bay Company imported Scots miners to work the original Fort Rupert seams. Conflict existed from the beginning between workers and the company, including grievances arising because of long hours and "almost useless working tools."[41]

When the Colonial Administration appointed a local magistrate in 1850 to keep the Fort Rupert miners in check, who should the appointee be but a physician, Dr. Helmcken, the Hudson's Bay Company doctor. Helmcken was the future son-in-law of James Douglas, Chief Factor of the Hudson's Bay Co. and the future governor of the Vancouver Island Colony. Apparently, Dr. Helmcken was forced before long to give up his magistracy in the face of such an obvious conflict. This appointment provides an interesting early background for the universal worker distrust of company doctors, lasting down to the present day.

A Colonial Office dispatch of October 19, 1850 indicates that other grievances of the workers "had been occasioned by the bad quality of food which had been served out to the English labourers, as well as by two miners being actually placed in irons illegally for some days for refusing to perform some work."[42]

As the Nanaimo fields were opened up after 1852 (by confiscation of vast quantities of native land without compensation), the imported English (Staffordshire) and Scots miners became politically active.

> Political protest did not arise here as early as in the older settlements and when it was given expression, its origins lay in the working conditions in the mines.
>
> . . .
>
> There was constant trouble in the mines, provoked by low wages, long hours, poor working conditions and inadequate housing.
>
> . . .
>
> The miners were in constant conflict against a system that condemned them to pouring out their life at a coal seam so that a privileged few might become wealthy.

> Literally, their blood was the price of riches piled up by the elect, for these were the most dangerous mines in the world. World statistics on mining published at the turn of the century, and commented on in the Labour Gazette, reported the following:
>
> The death rate per 1000 persons employed in coal mining is 1.29 for the British Empire, 2.38 for foreign countries, and for British Columbia and Nova Scotia, 4.15 and 3.32 respectively.
>
> For the thirty years from 1891 to 1919, there were a total of 3,038 accidents in British Columbia coal mines. 866 of these were fatal and 1,245 classed as serious. 55,124,969 tons of coal were mined during the 30 years. One miner paid with his life for each 143,000 tons mined.[43]

One of the contradictory elements of workers' health and labour history was revealed later in the century when unskilled Chinese labourers were contracted to work in the coal mines, as a source of cheap labour. The reaction of the European or white workers, including trade union and labour political parties, was to point to health and safety as a reason for supporting laws excluding Chinese from the province or excluding or limiting their right to work.

> Language difficulties rendered communications between Europeans and Chinese virtually impossible, and cultural differences widened the gap. The Europeans blamed the Chinese workers rather than the employers for depressed living standards, and especially for unsafe conditions and a terrible toll in fatal accidents in the mines. Thus began one of the most shameful chapters in British Columbia labour history, that split and weakened the ranks of labour until well into the twentieth century.[44]

The Vancouver Island coal-mining strikes of 1912-14 were among the most violent in Canadian history.[45] They were sparked by company refusal to recognize the workers' representative on the gas committee. This has been remembered in the traditional song "Are You From Bevan?"

During September and October 1918, there was a strike by 1,183 miners at Fernie and Michel, British Columbia in the eastern British Columbia Coalfields (District 18, UMWA) demanding single-shift operations.

> They contended that the existing method of working two shifts did not allow sufficient time for gas to escape and therefore created a serious safety hazard. The provincial Minister of Mines intervened . . .[46]

When productive days-lost totals are actually analysed in each industry, comparing ill-health to strikes and lock-outs, clear evidence is often obtained that work-related ill-health outstrips the standard labour disputes.

For example, in Richard Hyman's excellent analysis of strikes and British industrial relations,[47] he endorses the now accepted points that unemployment, sickness, and occupational injury and disease *each* account for more lost production time—work days—than do all strikes combined.

Estimating the figures in England in 1970, Hyman puts strikes as involving 10 million worker-days, industrial accidents (apparently not including diseases) at 20 million worker-days, unemployment at 200 million worker-days and certified sickness at 300 million worker-days.[48]

In an analysis of the British Columbia mining industry between 1967 and 1976, the Canadian Association of Industrial, Mechanical and Allied Workers (CAIMAW) found that at least 612,000 work days were lost in that ten-year period for *compensable* ill-health alone. That total was very conservative, since it used only official WCB data, which is notoriously faulty since it does not include reduced working life expectancy, physical productivity, casual absenteeism and non-reported or unrecognized diseases such as cancer and heart and lung disease.

But even using this conservative total, the number of days lost due to work-related ill-health either numerically exceeded or was a greater percentage of days lost than all strikes and lockouts combined for seven of the ten years studied. And, of course, some strikes and lockouts involved health and safety issues.[49]

On the other hand, there has been a consistent pattern in Canadian history of ignoring the fact that many strikes and lockouts—traditional "labour disputes"—are based upon workers' health concerns. An example of this is found in Stuart Jamieson's major analysis of Canadian industrial conflict (1900-66) which contains very few direct references to workers' health issues. That is certainly so in his concluding chapter's analysis of the broad factors underlying industrial conflict, even where he analyses broad socio-psychological factors.[50]

Mere statistical tabulations of strike frequency, size, and duration cannot be relied upon to help us understand workers' unrest, its causes, and its significance. There is a considerable difference between wildcats and legal strikes. If wildcat workers' health strikes were compared with all wildcats in frequency, size, and duration, we would gain better understanding of such strikes. But neither the federal nor any provincial government has ever provided such an ongoing, overall evaluation.[51]

Strikes and lockouts result from very few collective bargaining situations (generally less than 5 per cent), involve a small percentage of the unionized and total work force, and yearly account for less than one-half of 1 per cent of total man-days of employment.[52]

"Labour unrest" in Canada—as suggested by the number of strikes, their duration and frequency—has been prevalent in such industries as construction and railways (all provinces), coal-mining (Southwestern Alberta, Nova Scotia, British Columbia), lumber and fishing (British Columbia), steel, mining and smelting, and automobile manufacturing (Ontario), and textiles and shoe manufacturing (Quebec).[53] Since these industries are all notoriously hazardous—both physically and mentally—it is obvious that working conditions have been both underlying and direct factors in the organization of unions and in militant worker and union activity.

Jamieson at least recognized this possibility in the pre-First World War railway industry, citing remote living and working conditions and immigrant labour:

> Much of the work was carried on in remote districts hundreds of miles from any established settlements, where the workmen were wholly dependent upon contractors for providing food, shelter, health and comfort. This combination of factors led, at times, to widespread exploitation and intolerable living and working conditions, all of which were conducive to bitter unrest and conflict.[54]

Labour history provides numerous examples of workers' discontent over working conditions maturing into organized, deliberate strikes, whether "legal" or not.

In February 1907, over 400 female telephone operators walked out of Bell Telephone's office in Toronto. They were not unionized. The walkout led to a Royal Commission which gave official recognition that the basis of the dispute was in large part the demanding physical and emotional stresses and strains of the operators' work and the failure of Bell to recognize and improve the situation.

> The Royal Commission revealed that the operators' working conditions did not necessarily reflect their position as a "better class" of wage earner. In fact, the operator's shift work, close supervision, and ties to machinery made her job resemble blue collar, rather than white collar, work. The operator's task was extremely exhausting for great mental concentration, accuracy and speed were essential. Each woman looked after 80 to 100 lines, with 6,041 possible connections and placed about 300 calls an hour. Backless stools and a high switchboard, which some women could reach only by jumping up on the stool rungs, made the operators' work physically uncomfortable and tiring. If her own calls lagged, a worker was not allowed to relax, but had to help the operator next to her. In order to create a "business-like" atmosphere, the rules were strict: the women were instructed to line up five minutes before their shift entered the operating room, and when seated, had to "sit up straight, with no talking or smiling." Supervisors who paced behind the operators inspecting their work were told to "nag and hurry the girls."
>
> Other strains were added to the operator's rapidly paced work, such as the risk of physical injury and the knowledge that a monitor might be secretly listening in to check one's performance. Operators complained to the Commission that heavy headgear could produce painful sores and that women sometimes fainted and occasionally became hysterical from the pressure of rapid work. Maude Orton, a supervisor and leader in the strike, claimed that women sometimes were pushed to nervous breakdowns, and that she was compelled to take nerve medicine. "I never knew what nerves meant until I started to work at the Bell," she commented. The most dangerous work was on the long distance lines, where operators sometimes received severe electrical shocks, which could send them into convulsions and lay them off work for weeks.[55]

How appropriate this story is today, when the hazards of office workers—largely unorganized and largely female—are routinely, if not deliberately, overlooked.

Up to the late 1930s in Canada, less than 15 per cent of the non-agricultural work force was unionized and, today, across Canada, the figure is still less than 40 per cent. Therefore, the ability of most workers to effectively deal with on-the-job health hazards has been considerably hampered by the economic and legal powers of the employer.

The 1922 Cape Breton coal miners' strike was partially precipitated by long-standing worker grievances over living and working conditions about the mines. Grievances over housing and sanitary living conditions, better enforcement of safety regulations, and improvements in mine conditions "occupied a large part of union energies at the end of the war."[56] These conditions were brought into sharper focus in 1921-22 when the British Empire Steel Corporation (Besco) unilaterally instituted a 33.3 per cent decrease in wages to 12,000 workers in the industry.

> An important source of working class unity lay below ground too, in the unusual physical conditions which make up the everyday work of most miners: the wet, the dirt and the darkness, the coal dust and stale air, the ever-present danger and the back-breaking hard work.[57]

This daily ongoing struggle with the "natural" elements—working against the dangerous conditions of work—created militant and independent spirits, partly explaining the traditional radicalism of miners.

> The hardship and the peril connected with coal mining bred an endemic "radicalism" among the coal miners. "blood on the coal" helped shape the miners' attitudes to the coal operators and helped set the market price of their labour power. The miners' union aspired to win "compensation fully compatible with the dangers of our occupation." Between 1871 and 1939 more than 1,600 men were killed in the Nova Scotia coal mines, an average of about twenty-three deaths per year, but in the years 1914-1921, the average annual fatality rate was more than twice as high, mainly as a result of major mine disasters in 1917 and 1918, which killed 153 men. Pressing the case for nationalization of the mines in 1925, McLachlan (Secretary-Treasurer, U.M.W.A., District 26) opposed any form of compensation for the owners: "The workers have put too much into these mines . . . more than all the millions they (the operators) have put in. Over a period of years they have put the money in, the workers have put their blood in it."[58]

Apparently, the fatality rate per thousand workers in the Nova Scotia mines mirrored the U.S. rates but was almost three times greater than the British rate.[59] A review of some of this picture is found in the 1926 Nova Scotia Royal Commission Report on the Coal Mining Industry (the Duncan Report).

The organization of work contributed in its own way to issues and viewpoints. Piece rates, isolated working stations underground and lack of immediate standardized supervision and production rules encouraged worker-generated and controlled rules "of suitable underground behaviour to enforce safety, fairness and efficiency in mine operations."[60]

When the miners struck in August 1922, 1,200 Federal troops were dispatched to Cape Breton, with additional military and special police units held in reserve.[61] Because the Pictou County mines had high gas levels, the miners only withdrew maintenance service from the Cape Breton mines, a tactic which would increase both gas and water (flooding) levels, putting greater pressure on Besco to settle.[62] In return for lifting this ban on maintenance a week into the strike, the company agreed to negotiate.

Underground miners from the last century and office secretaries today have common health and safety concerns. Office secretaries are now developing struggles for the right to have and to open a window for sun and air. Methane gas explosions, cave-ins, and fires have killed thousands of miners. Toxic and carcinogenic substances; brain, nerve, and eye-altering radiation; lighting; and atmospheric conditions in offices are killing, shortening the life-spans of, or demoralizing office workers.

The Estevan wild cat strike of 1931—in the coal fields of southeastern Saskatchewan—which culminated in a bloody riot in Estevan on "Black Tuesday"—September 20, 1931—concerned working conditions equally as much as wages, a grievance system and union recognition.

The month-long strike featured a police-inspired riot which left 3 killed and 23 injured and was the subject of a Royal Commission Report (Wylie Commission—Royal Commission on the Estevan-Bienfait Mining Dispute, 1931). There are some important historical points here.

> (Commissioner Wylie) advocated better enforcement of health regulations, repair and maintenance of company houses, a sufficient supply of good drinking water, a more thorough inspection of the mines and a more detailed inspector's report, strict enforcement of the Mines Act and accompanying regulations, and a regular inspection of all tipple scales.[63]

The Judge also wanted twenty-five amendments to the Mines Act, including hours of work, ventilation, safety measures, mines inspections, first-aid facilities and wash facilities. These amendments were made within a year of Wylie's report, resulting in the Coal Mines Safety and Welfare Act which took effect on November 1, 1932.

There have been some recent official attempts to recognize the health and safety aspects of labour disputes.

The British Columbia Ministry of Labour has estimated that there were some 46 British Columbia labour disputes involving workers' health issues in the period April 1973 to December 1979 inclusive. These involved some of British Columbia's largest private and public employers and trade unions; involved units as high as 2,000 workers; typically lasted from one day to within one week, mostly for two or three days; and accounted altogether for over 75,000 lost worker-production days. Ten of the disputes lasted from seven days to 27 days. Dispute issues included the adequacy of first aid facilities, train manning levels, safety inspection, the use of personal protective equipment and toxic and other environmental pollutant levels.[64] Virtually all of these work stoppages have taken place during the term of a collective agreement.

These totals do not include numerous workplace production stoppages which last less than one day or in which less than ten total worker-days are lost. They also do not account for labour disputes which on the surface concern only economic issues. Many such strikes involve a long-standing or significant workers' health concern, even general working conditions, which explain a tough workers' stand on that economic issue or in otherwise extending the duration of the strike, lock-out or walk-out.

These totals also do not account for such concerted workers' health job actions as work-to-rule which often is used as an alternative to strike or walkout.

Table 11-1 illustrates the situation in British Columbia up to August 1980. It gives a picture of the unions, issues, and types of strike patterns involved.

The plain fact is that workers have always recognized the need to protect themselves and to promote their long-term health by rank-and-file mobilization and job action. And like it or not, the reality is that job action—legal or illegal—is the only real way to achieve those ends when all the talking and cooperative efforts fail to deliver, as they so often do.

We are at a point in Canada today when government, business, and labour leaders must recognize that working conditions will not really change until as much importance is attached "at the top" to health issues as to economic issues. Until health and safety issues occupy as large a part of the traditional business hierarchy and the bargaining relationship as do wage issues, workers' health will suffer. Canadian society and working Canadians' health will be the better for intelligent, necessary job action over workers' health and safety. Unfortunately, more official effort seems devoted to creating tripartite meetings, organizations, and committees, and to continuing what Bob Sass has called the "conventional wisdom." In this case, the conventional wisdom is that co-operation for co-operation's sake is more important than helping workers to get mobilized and active.

Table 11-1

Labour Disputes Relating to Health and Safety Issues, British Columbia, 1980

Location	Employer or Employer Association	Union and Local	Date Commenced	Date Terminated	No. of Workers Involved	Duration of Man-Days
Province-Wide	B.C. Railway *Issue:* Breakdown in Negotiations and Safety Conditions	Council of Trade Unions	Dec. 11/79	Jan. 24/80	2,000***	31,000 for '80
Vancouver Nanaimo	Canadian Pacific Ferries** (2 disputes) *Issue:* Breakdown in Negotiations and Possible Reduction in Crew Size	Merchant Service	Jan. 7/80	Apr. 28/80	90***	2,958
Kitsault	Commonwealth Constr. *Issue:* Working Conditions, Skin Mites in Camp	B.C. & Yukon Building Trades	Feb. 5/80	Feb. 7/80	350	700
Kimberley	Cominco** *Issue:* Working Conditions, Seniority, Discipline and Safety Provisions	Steelworkers, 651	Mar. 10/80	Mar. 11/80	800***	400
Kamloops	Afton Mines** *Issue:* Employee suspension and Fear of Mercury Emissions Exceeding Safety Levels	Steelworkers, 8637	Mar. 20/80	Mar. 27/80	270***	952

Elkford	Fording Coal** *Issue:* Working Conditions, Unsafe Equipment	Steelworkers, 7884	Apr. 19/80	Apr. 21/80	925***	1,775
Terrace and Nass River	Canadian Cellulose* *Issue:* Working Conditions, Training, Posting of Jobs, Safety	I.W.A., 1-71	Apr. 21/80	Apr. 22/80	300	300
Chetwynd, Cranbrook Dawson Creek Ft. St. John Hudson Hope	B.C. Hydro Peace Canyon Dam Constr. Site *Issue:* Employee Suspension, Assistance in a Generating Station	I.B.E.W., 258	Apr. 22/80 Apr. 28/80	Apr. 23/80 Apr. 30/80	100***	227
Pt. Coquitlam	CPR** *Issue:* Safety Conditions — Vancouver Worker Lost Leg While Switching Rail Cars	UTU, 422	June 17/80	June 18/80	91	91
Pt. Hardy	B.C. Ferry Corp.** *Issue:* Safety — Faulty Fire Alarm System	B.C. Ferry & Marine Workers	Aug. 12/80	Aug. 12/80	55	55

* Courtesy of B.C. Ministry of Labour, Research and Policy Planning Branch (Colin Aykroyd).
** Federal Stoppage.
*** Maximum Number of Workers.

NOTES

1. James Connell, "The Red Flag" (1889), *I.W.W. Song Book*, 34th ed. (1973).
2. E. Blanche Norcross, *Nanaimo Retrospective: The First Century* (Nanaimo Historical Society, 1979), Appendix E.
3. Charles Lipton, *The Trade Union Movement of Canada: 1827-1959*, 2nd ed. (Montreal: Canadian Social Publications Ltd., 1968), p. 28.
4. See, for example, David Kwavnick, *Organized Labour and Pressure Politics: C.L.C. 1956-68* (Montreal: McGill-Queen's University Press, 1972).
5. H. A. Logan, *Trade Unions In Canada* (Toronto: Macmillan, 1948), p. 63.
6. John Battye, "The Nine Hour Pioneers: The Genesis of the Canadian Labour Movement," *Labour/Le Travailleur*, Vol. 4, 1979.
7. D. J. O'Donoghue, "The Labour Movement in Canada," in G. E. McNeill (ed.), *The Labour Movement: The Problem of Today* (Boston: A. M. Bridgman & Co., 1887), p. 592 (emphasis added).
8. Cited in Lipton, *Trade Union Movement of Canada*, p. 54.
9. McNeill, *Labour Movement*, pp. 474, 476.
10. Battye, *Nine Hour Pioneers*, pp. 27-31.
11. McNeill, *Labour Movement*, p. 477.
12. Stuart Jamieson, *Times of Trouble: Labour Unrest and Industrial Conflict in Canada, 1900-66* (Ottawa: Privy Council Office, 1968), p. 17.
13. Ibid., p. 75, citing *Labour Gazette*, Vol. III, 1906-7, p. 770.
14. Lipton, *Trade Union Movement in Canada*, pp. 167-68, citing House of Commons *Debates*, August 2, 1917.
15. Ibid., p. 230.
16. Ibid., p. 313.
17. *Report* (Toronto: October 1961), p. 45.
18. Paul Phillips, *No Power Greater: A Century of Labour in B.C.* (Vancouver: Boag Foundation and B.C. Federation of Labour, 1967), pp. 163-64.
19. Ibid., p. 163.
20. Edmund Bradwin, *The Bunkhouse Man* (Toronto: University of Toronto Press, 1928, 1972), p. 7.
21. Ibid., p. 140.
22. Ibid., p. 141.
23. Ibid., p. 148.
24. Ibid., p. 154.
25. Martin A. Plant, "Occupations, Drinking Patterns and Alcohol-Related Problems: Conclusions From a Follow-Up Study," *British Journal of Addiction* 74 (1979): 268.
26. G. W. Taylor, *Timber: History of the Forest Industry in B.C.* (Vancouver: J. J. Douglas, 1975), p. 111.
27. Ibid.
28. Ibid., p. 114-15.
29. Ibid., p. 115.
30. Ibid.
31. Ibid., p. 107.
32. Ibid., p. 109, who describes "serious unrest . . . created by agitators," rather than recognizing the workers' basis for grievances.
33. Ibid., p. 74.

34. Ibid., p. 75.
35. Eugene Forsey, "Legislative Protection of Forest Workers," *C.J.E.P.S.* Vol. 1 (1935): 290-91.
36. For a full account, see Ronald Liversedge and Victor Hoar (eds.), *Recollections of the On To Ottawa Trek* (Toronto: McClelland and Stewart Ltd., 1973).
37. See, for example, *Canada Royal Commission to Investigate the Penal System* (Archamboult Report) (Ottawa, 1938), esp. chapters 5, 6 and 9.
38. See *B.C. WCB Reporter Series Decision* #241, Vol. III, April 26, 1977.
39. Bercuson, "Tragedy at Bellevue: Anatomy of a Mine Disaster," *Labour/Le Travailleur* 1978, pp. 221-31.
40. Ken Bernsohn, *Slabs, Scabs & Skidders: A History of the I.W.A. in the Central Interior* (Prince George, B.C.: I.W.A. Local 1-424).
41. Jack Scott, *Sweat and Struggle: Working Class Struggles in Canada, 1789-1899*, Vol. I (Vancouver: New Star Books, 1974), p. 151.
42. Ibid., p. 153.
43. Scott, *Sweat and Struggle*, pp. 157-160.
44. Ibid., p. 175.
45. Jamieson, *Times of Trouble*, p. 45.
46. Ibid., p. 163.
47. Richard Hyman, *Strikes* (Glasgow: Fontana/Collins, 1972).
48. Ibid., p. 34.
49. Submission of CAIMAW to B.C. Ministry of Mines and Petroleum Resources re: Mines Regulation Act (Vancouver: June 1977), pp. 17-21 and Tables IX, X and XI.
50. Jamieson, *Times of Trouble*.
51. For a discussion of wildcat strikes see Terence G. Ison, *Occupational Health and Wildcat Strikes*(Kingston: Queen's University, Industrial Relations Centre, 1979).
52. Jamieson, *Times of Trouble*, p. 22.
53. Ibid., p. 25.
54. Ibid.
55. Joan Sangster, *The 1907 Bell Telephone Strike: Organizing Women Workers*, pp. 109-30, in *Labour/Le Travailleur* 3 (1978): 111 (Kitchener: Dumont Press Graphix).
56. David Frank, "Class Conflict in the Coal Industry," in Gregory S. Kealey and Peter Warrian (eds.), *Essays in Canadian Working Class History* (Toronto: McClelland & Stewart, 1976), p. 164.
57. Ibid., p. 166.
58. Idid., p. 167.
59. Ibid., n. 11, citing various sources.
60. Ibid., p. 168.
61. Ibid., p. 170.
62. Ibid., p. 177.
63. S. D. Hanson, "Estevan 1931," in Irving M. Abella (ed.), *On Strike: Six Key Labour Struggles in Canada, 1919-1949* (Toronto: James, Lewis & Samuel, 1974), pp. 68-69.
64. Colin Aykroyd, *B.C. Labour Research Bulletin* 1978, Vol. 6, No. 6, p. 16 (Table I) and 1980, Vol. 8, No. 1, p. 34 (Table 4).

Chapter 12

Community Struggles

As we indicated in the article, the Windsor Occupational Safety and Health Council (W.O.S.H.) is modelled after the C.O.S.H.-concept developed in the U.S. during the seventies.

Our application of this idea, however, is not exactly traditional. Where the more established C.O.S.H.'s in the States (Philadelphia, Chicago, etc.) demand a membership based on union locals, we view our membership in terms of individual health and safety activists, environmentalists, women's movement activists, spouses of workers, high school teachers, etc. At first glance this may seem rather unimportant, but in fact, this type of perspective has quite different political consequences in terms of our relations with the trade unions, health professionals, and the general community.

We believe that there is a strong, organic link between the workplace and its problems with the general environment. To this end we have tried to interest members of the general community in joining W.O.S.H., as well as, W.O.S.H. supporting such environmental causes as the anti-nuclear movement and the fight locally against toxic waste dumping. We believe that this type of coalition is necessary to stem corporate threats and manoeuvres such as plant closures, etc. . . .[1]

W.O.S.H.

The Windsor Occupational Safety and Health Council (W.O.S.H.) was formed in the fall of 1979 in Windsor, Ontario.[2] Beginning in the early 1970s, Committees for Occupational Safety and Health (C.O.S.H.) were formed in several United States cities, however, it was not until W.O.S.H. that such a committee was formed on a city-wide basis by rank-and-file unionists in Canada.

Prior to the emergence of W.O.S.H., some factories concerned themselves with workers' health. Some of the most active union representatives were the United Automobile Workers representatives at the Canadian Rock Salt Mine and at Bendix Corporation, and the Oil, Chemical Workers' representative at Wyeta Ltd. There were two significant factors leading to the formation of W.O.S.H. First, during the spring of 1979, a course for health and safety representatives in Windsor was given by the Ontario Federation of Labour. This heightened both their awareness of hazards and potential remedies, including legal pressure. Also, in July of the same year, a public forum was held in Windsor concerning the health hazards of asbestos at the two Bendix plants. Organized by the United Auto Workers and the Ontario Public Interest Research Group, it drew a large audience, including many interested citizens who were not Bendix workers. A news conference and the subsequent publicity provided a sense of solidarity and a feeling of momentum to workers' struggles in Windsor. In the fall, Oil, Chemical and Atomic Workers' chairperson Larry Gauthier wrote an article for the Windsor branch of the Ontario Secondary School Teachers' Federation Newspaper, appealing for teachers and workers to cooperate on workers' health issues and suggesting a city-wide committee be formed. The first meetings of W.O.S.H. were held in November 1979.

Once established, W.O.S.H. began an investigation of the plastics industry in Windsor. Workers had complained of headaches and nausea, hair and skin discoloration, respiratory difficulties, severe nosebleeds, and loss of feelings in the hands—strong signs of chemical assault in the workplace. Representatives from all the plastics plants in Windsor were brought together for an intensive session constructing a medical questionnaire with the aid of Dr. Marshall. The meeting was unique since it was an industry-wide approach, not a plant-by-plant one. The representatives became more aware of the relationship between their ill health and working conditions. Then the questionnaire was translated into three languages other than English for immigrant workers.

In early 1980, W.O.S.H. approved a constitution and elected officers. Gerry Becigneul, a long-time activist in the UAW local at Canadian Rock Salt, was chosen as chairperson. Because of the role played by experienced trade unionists, W.O.S.H. received public support from unions. To increase visibility and gain more support, W.O.S.H., O.P.I.R.G. and the Downwind Alliance for a Safe Energy Future (a local anti-nuclear group) co-sponsored a meeting which featured Dr. Barry Commoner, well known environmentalist, as a speaker. Right after the meeting, W.O.S.H. held a news conference which disclosed Ontario Ministry of Labour documents showing that Bendix failed to comply with 1966 directives, and that the Labour Ministry had failed to enforce its own directives. Combined with the revelation that one 34-year-old Bendix worker was diagnosed as having two inoperable lung tumors and that another Bendix worker, Mike Coverhill, had exercised his right to refuse work in dangerous asbestos areas, the Chief Physician for the Ministry suggested public hearings be held.

The call for public hearings concerning standards for toxic substances was an excellent opportunity to further raise the issues of workers' health and try to get city-wide support for a healthier environment. Ralph Nader, U.S. consumer advocate, visited Windsor on February 11, 1980, meeting with 125 trade unionists concerning occupational health. This further heightened the sense of solidarity and united action among concerned people.

Two days after Nader left, the U.S. Bendix Corporation announced it was selling one of the Bendix plants in Windsor to General Motors for a parking lot. Already saddled with a huge unemployment rate, Windsor was to have 65 fewer jobs due to this ultimate corporate weapon. The Workmen's Compensation Board of Ontario announced the next day that ten of the 17 claims submitted by the UAW on behalf of Bendix workers had been rejected. The announced closure and rejection of claims dealt a harsh blow to the workers' health movement in Windsor.

Who Runs W.O.S.H.?

What often happens in newly-formed organizations which deal with workers' health and/or legal issues is that they are dominated by professionals such as doctors, lawyers, health and safety specialists, or union leaders. However, this has not been the case with W.O.S.H. Most members of W.O.S.H. are not professionals in occupational health and safety or members of the union hierarchy. Because most of them are rank-and-file workers, W.O.S.H. members have been forced to educate themselves and others concerning workers' health. Rather than running to a professional every time a technical issue arises, they are learning how to interpret scientific data and conduct scientific investigations. This is not to say that professional help is not at times useful, but it must contribute to the self-education and self-reliance of workers rather than just sustaining a dependency.

> Workers ought not to rely on professionals for improvements in health and safety but rather see the whole issue of occupational health as part of their historical struggle, similar to their fight to reduce the work day from 12 hours.[3]

Although many W.O.S.H. members belong to unions, they are concerned rank-and-file workers and health and safety representatives rather than union officials. The political stance and non-hierarchial structure of W.O.S.H. makes it an uneasy ally with traditional unions. However, with solid rank-and-file support unions must address the issues.

In discussing corporate blackmail in the form of a choice of jobs or health, the committee concludes:

> Being pushed into making this choice, graphically exposes the callous disregard of the economic system for the life of the workers. *These workers will come to realize that, if they are to have a safe workplace, the workers must control the whole process of work.*[4]

The Union of Injured Workers

The following is abstracted from *What Is The Union of Injured Workers?*[5]

CANADA, AN UNSAFE PLACE TO WORK!

> Every year the number of workers injured on-the-job increases. This year more than 450,000 workers will be injured. And the number of workers who were assessed for permanent disabilities in 1973 was 128 per cent greater than for the five

previous years (4,429 in 1968, 10,233 in 1973, according to Workmen's Compensation Board statistics).

Some of these injured workers are members of trade unions. Many more are unorganized. The Union of Injured Workers (UIW) was formed in 1974 to organize these workers and fight for their rights.

The four-point program of the UIW calls for:

1. JOB SECURITY or FULL COMPENSATION
2. COST-OF-LIVING INCREASES COMPOUNDED EVERY THREE MONTHS
3. ABOLITION OF THE BOARD DOCTORS
4. ENFORCEMENT OF EXISTING SAFETY LAWS

JOB SECURITY OR FULL COMPENSATION

The key demand is job security or full compensation. Why is this demand central? The answer to this question lies in the reality of the situation. The Toronto Star (April 10, 1976) reported the comments of a federal Liberal Party spokesman, "Industrial safety in Canada is sadly inadequate and there are more men days lost through accidents than strikes." Both United Nations and ILO statistics point to Canada as one of the most dangerous places to work of 10 western industrialized nations. The Department of National Health and Welfare estimates that 15 per cent of Canada's population are disabled in one way or another. And even the Financial Post (May 29, 1976) was forced to admit that ". . . the handicapped have emerged as the single most disadvantaged group among all job seekers."

As trade unionists you at least have your jobs. The situation for the permanently disabled worker is quite different. For this reason the UIW says jobs must be guaranteed by legislation to all injured workers who are able to return to work. (This type of legislation was passed by the governments of England in 1944 and Italy in 1947).

The new labour legislation should cover the following:

1. That companies with more than 50 workers reserves 5 per cent of the jobs for injured workers.
2. An injured worker will have the right to choose a job.
3. Injured workers will not be subject to layoff.
4. If an injured worker returns to work and finds that the injury is aggravated, then he/she will be given the option of taking a pension (100 per cent compensation).

Labour Minister Dr. Bette Stephenson acts as though this legislation already exists in Ontario. On November 4, 1976 Dr. Stephenson said, "Indeed, I think it has been a traditional policy within the provincial government to hire handicapped people. Whether they are injured workmen or not is yet another qualification. There has been in the Workmen's Compensation programmes a promotion of an activity to persuade the private sector to rehire or to hire injured workmen for specific jobs which they are physically capable of carrying out." Injured workers know better. We cannot depend on the "good intentions" of the government or employers. Laws must be passed which compel employers to hire injured workers.

JOIN THE UIW

The UIW has locals in Toronto, Hamilton, London, Windsor, Kitchener-Waterloo and Ottawa. Although the main focus of the UIW is to change the out-dated Workmen's Compensation Act we also believe it is important to help injured workers with their cases. To assist workers, case workers and law students are available in Toronto, Hamilton and Windsor. The Toronto office is open from 10 a.m. to 7 p.m. Monday to Friday. The Hamilton office is open from 10 a.m. to 12 noon daily and 7 p.m. to 9 p.m. Tuesday. The Windsor office is open from 1 p.m. to 4 p.m. Monday to Friday.

While the above gives us some idea of the Union, many questions remain about its history, struggles and goals. In order to pursue these issues, we interviewed Phil Biggin, one of the founders and current President of the Union of Injured Workers, in February 1980.

Biggin and the UIW

Phil Biggin was relatively soft-spoken, although firm and sure of his statements. As we sat in his comfortable but modest townhouse in a co-operative project near downtown Toronto, he spoke of the struggles encountered by the Union of Injured Workers in its nearly six-year history. His alert eyes, graying hair, and quick mind impressed upon me the fact that he had innumerable experiences in both formal academic and "real life" education. Born in Banff, Alberta and raised in Vancouver, Phil obtained a degree in biology from the University of British Columbia and went on to do graduate studies at Temple University in Philadelphia. Hardly a career pattern of the person who would become a founder and leader of the Union of Injured Workers and castigated by both government and union officials as a "Marxist-Leninist."

However, he was entering the United States during the 1960s, when being on a university campus meant addressing the draft, the Vietnam War, racism, poverty, and other social ills. Having a basic sense of justice and seeing the effects first hand of racism and militarism, Phil Biggin became increasingly politicized. He became involved in the emergence of the Philadelphia Free Press and in community issues of racism and poverty, and increasingly disillusioned with formal academia. Like many other students of the time, he dropped out of what seemed to be the largely irrelevant and self-aggrandizing pursuit of degrees and devoted himself to attacking the ills of society. Due largely to his political activity, his visa was not extended and he had to leave the United States in 1973.

After moving to Toronto he got a job in a can company, where he injured his knee. Subsequently he went through the hassles of therapy, compensation struggles, and job problems. Discovering the enormous problems which arise when you are injured, and finding many others with the same problems and hassles, Phil helped found the Union of Injured Workers in 1974, made up of persons injured on the job who wanted to promote the cause of injured workers. Now, six years later, the Union has greatly expanded and solidified in its efforts, while, as Phil notes, many other self-help community action organizations have come and gone. Why has the Union of Injured Workers survived and grown while other organizations have gone by the wayside?

According to Phil, the UIW exists and survives because trade unions were not doing an adequate job helping workers with their compensation cases and because there is a need to organize unorganized workers. Does this mean they are anti-organized labour? Of course not, says Biggin. "We want to work hand and hand with labour and we recognize the Ontario Federation of Labour (OFL) as the legitimate representative of workers. However, organized labour, like various government officials, has been quick to label the UIW as subversive communists of the "Marxist-Leninist variety." Phil states that while the Metro Labour Council endorsed them the OFL did not, because of the UIW's alleged Marxist leadership. According to Biggin, the OFL has taken that position since 1979 without even giving him a chance to rebut the "charges." Phil states that "before they do red-baiting in the future they should at least give the people they are red-baiting the opportunity to defend themselves." He relates his experience of visiting Vancouver and calling the British Columbia Federation of Labour and their saying they had heard nothing but bad reports about the UIW.

Nonetheless, Phil is quick to point out that, by and large, they have gotten along with the unions. In fact, when he and seven other members were charged in 1978 for demonstration activity, one third of the defense funds were from unions. He concludes that "our organization is fairly respected in a lot of circles."

How about the UIW's relationship with government? Well, according to Phil, the Ontario government has reacted to the UIW in such a way as to increase its support. Through harassment and intimidation, the provincial government has actually helped solidify the union and gain new support. Phil gives the example of the picketing of the legislature in 1975 by the UIW. The overreaction by the government in calling in the police to get them off the steps just increased the resolve of workers and gained more sympathy and support. As Biggin points out, "It was foolish of government because they wouldn't have stayed—most had bad back injuries and couldn't stay!" According to Phil, shortly after the demonstration the government enacted legislation against demonstrations in front of the legislature.

Another example of government harassment was the charging of Biggin with "wilfully obstructing persons in the lawful use or enjoyment of private property by encouraging persons to block the entrance of the building," after a May 29, 1978 demonstration. Improved payments for persons on compensation was the goal of the demonstration. As often happens in politically motivated cases, delays and other attempts to drain the energy and funds of the UIW were practiced. The first trial date was postponed due to lack of a courtroom. Subsequently, on November 24, 1978, Phil and his witnesses showed up again, but the Crown was not prepared to continue on its original charge and attempted to present a new charge to the court, which was rejected. Withdrawing its initial charge, the Crown laid a new charge immediately after the court session—the

May 28, 1978 UIW demonstration outside the Ministry of Labour, Toronto, protesting the fact that there had been no increases in injured workers' pensions in over three years. Six injured workers and one caseworker were arrested. Nine days later, UIW president Phil Biggin (megaphone in hand) was charged. Some three weeks after the demonstration, the Labour Minister raised pensions 25 per cent.

charge which was unsuccessfully promoted in court! After a trial on June 11 and 13, the Crown's case was dismissed with the Judge finding no evidence that any actions of Mr. Biggin interfered with persons who had a property interest in the building or with employees. On a Crown appeal to the Supreme Court of Ontario, Mr. Justice Hollingsworth dismissed the appeal with costs and recommended to Crown counsel Mr. Hugh Campbell that the matter not be further pursued. Nonetheless, the Attorney General, Roy McMurtry, applied to the Court of Appeal for leave to appeal Justice Hollingsworth's decision.

The use of the law and judicial proceedings for political purposes, particularly to harass and intimidate, is evident in these instances. However, what of the use of the law to help workers, such as fighting for the right of workers to sue? Phil says, "basically our approach is we don't want to make lawyers wealthy." (The legal fees for the eight workers charged in 1978 amounted to $15,000, with Phil's case of mischief costing $5,000.) He is not opposed to class action but really doesn't want to see things diverted into the courts because of their narrow and technical way of frustrating people. In Phil's case, he asked a lawyer to speak to the people in the audience, not the judge, but the judge saw that as grandstanding. Workers often don't understand the language of the court and it is confusing and frustrating. As Biggin points out, "You're taking it into the courts and you're taking it away from the people." He doesn't believe workers should have to give up their right to sue in accepting compensation. Maybe the right to sue should be tested. But it is an abstraction and takes years in the process. "What we are interested in is organizing injured workers, not some kind of intellectual exercise in the courts to prove some point that never makes much of an impact." The UIW would much rather see many workers get a just and decent compensation, rather than a few receiving large sums.

The WCB Sees "Red"

According to Phil Biggin, the WCB of Ontario is paranoid about the Union of Injured Workers. He has been told that the WCB has set aside money for surveillance of the UIW.

In February 1980 Michael Starr, chairman of the WCB, refused to see a woman in his office because she was accompanied by Biggin. Starr said that he did not recognize the Union of Injured Workers because it is headed by a Marxist-Leninist who believes in violence. On the front page of the *Globe and Mail*, February 12, 1980 was an article entitled "Leader's Politics is the Reason Group Barred, Starr Says." According to Starr, the incident did not contradict his avowed "open-door policy" because "It's an open-door policy, but not for everybody. I reserve the right to refuse to see certain people." Biggin responded that he was a member of the NDP and an outspoken critic of Communist or Marxist groups who try to use injured workers for their political goals. However, he adds, even if he was a Communist, that would not have anything to do with the legitimacy of his representing injured workers as the elected President of the Union.

The February 13, 1980 editorial of the *Toronto Star*, entitled "Keep Politics Out of Compensation," began:

> In Canada, an individual's political beliefs are a personal, private matter. It's not illegal to be a Communist, a Socialist or a Marxist-Leninist.

The remainder of the article takes Starr to task for violating basic democratic principles. "Starr is Ordered to Allow Injured Woman a Hearing," read the article headline in the February 14, 1980 *Toronto Star*. Labour Minister Robert Elgie instructed Starr to meet the woman, accompanied by Phil Biggin. Shortly thereafter, Elgie announced the appointment of Paul Weiler, former chairman of the British Columbia Labour Relations Board, to act as a one-man commission studying the compensation system. His report is expected in the summer of 1981. Starr was subsequently replaced as Chairman of the Board.

What Do They Want?

In spite of the above-noted problems, the Union of Injured Workers continues to push forward in pressing for its four-point program demands:

1. Job security or full compensation
2. Cost-of-living increases every three months
3. Abolition of the board doctors
4. Enforcement of the existing safety laws and enactment of better safety laws

Of much importance is job security for injured workers. The following proposal outlines the Union of Injured Workers position.

The UIW proposes that the new labour legislation should cover the following:

1. That companies with more than 20 workers reserve 5% of jobs for injured or handicapped workers
2. That an injured worker have the right to a job he/she can do without suffering
3. That injured workers not be subjected to first layoffs
4. That injured workers have the option of full (100%) compensation if they return to work and find that the injury is aggravated.

A great majority of injured workers are capable of ordinary employment provided that there is guaranteed job security. Given equal opportunities disabled or handicapped workers will show every indication of being as productive as workers who have not been injured. According to the Canadian Chamber of Commerce report in 1975, "those who had hired the handicapped had benefited from employees who were as good as, or better than, regular employees."

Job Security or Full Compensation

Injured workers, who have given their lives and limbs to build Canada must be treated with dignity and understanding after their health and means of livelihood have been taken from them. The UIW wants all injured workers and the handicapped to be guaranteed the right to a job after they have been injured or full compensation equal to the wage they would receive if they are able to work; the right to be free from discrimination in searching for employment; and the right to control over one's own body rather than being forced to be examined by medical doctors whose allegiance is to the WCB rather than to the worker.

Justice for the injured worker and the handicapped is long overdue. Society has a responsibility which it must keep.[6]

Why eliminate WCB doctors? Phil points out that the doctors are paid employees of the WCB and will take the perspective of the Board. "If you're working for a corporation you have to like it." The WCB policy is to keep pensions as low as possible, and their doctors will help enforce that policy.

What has been the greatest accomplishment of the Union of Injured Workers? Biggin views the greatest success as the organization's perseverance and growth in spite of its militancy. In the six years of its existence, the more it has involved itself in court struggles and community issues, the more credibility it has gained—even the *Toronto Star* has supported it! While originally operating just in Toronto, they now also operate in Hamilton, London, Kitchener-Waterloo, Windsor, Ottawa, Sudbury, and Thunder Bay. In fact, it has grown not only throughout Ontario, but in other provinces as well. It has over 3,000 members who, although injured workers, support the organization through their dues.

When an organization not only survives but also grows with a shoestring budget, an all-volunteer staff, and continual official harassment, it must be meeting a need. The Union of Injured Workers obviously is.

United Injured and Disabled Workers' Association

The following letter describes the emergence and aims of the United Injured and Disabled Workers' Association, a British Columbia organization which was registered in Victoria on July 30, 1979.

UNITED
INJURED AND DISABLED WORKERS'
ASSOCIATION OF B.C.
P.O. Box 65718, Stn. F.
Vancouver, B.C.
V5N 5K7

The above Association is being formed by a group of injured and disabled workers who have been frustrated and disilllusioned on an individual basis in having their problems with the Workers' Compensation Board settled.

On December 7th, 1978, a meeting of a few people with a common problem was held and a decision to form the Association to work with all the injured and disabled workers was formulated.

We have had eleven meetings since then and are now a group of approximately 300 in the Vancouver and surrounding area. At the present time we are applying for registration under the Societies Act of B.C. Many people are coming forward to offer assistance as advisors and in the very near future we will be printing a newsletter which will be sent to all interested in becoming part of the Association at all levels.

Your names are being recorded in our files and we would appreciate hearing from you regarding your ideas and suggestions to help make this a strong, successful Association which will remain active for many years in protecting workers' health and rights within the WCB of this province.

The response from all over the province has been tremendous and we would ask any of you from the different areas to please let us know if you would care to assist us by becoming Area Representatives. If so, we would be pleased to send you a copy of our Constitution and membership forms as soon as they are printed. Possibly your local news media would be interested in helping to contact people with an interest in the Association.

Our main concern is for the injured and disabled workers, victims of industrial accidents, who have not received adequate compensation. It is time that the injured and disabled worker was dealt with in a more humane manner.

Our aims as an Association are to work together and to inform as well as to assist members regarding avenues of appeal available to them within the structure of the Workers' Compensation Act.

This Association will also be presenting briefs to the Cabinet, the Ministry of Labour, and to the Workers' Compensation Board regarding changes in the Act and Board Policy. Briefs will also be forthcoming covering industrial disease, pollution, and chemicals as they affect the worker in the labour market.

We will be in contact with the Injured Workers' Association of Manitoba and the Union of Injured Workers of Ontario and offer to work with them in order to obtain fair and just legislation for the injured and disabled worker. We are a non-profit Association and Executives are volunteers. The members are all injured and disabled workers and only they can vote and hold office. We feel that in this way they can better understand and help others while at the same time helping themselves.

Thank you for your interest in the Association.

Founders: Len Reid 325-6524
Walter Bury 874-0146

"Injured Workers Vow to Continue Picketing Compensation Board," read the *Vancouver Sun* headline on November 27, 1979. Thus, shortly after incorporating, the United Injured and Disabled Workers began its action-oriented program by picketing the WCB offices the day the B.C. Federation of Labour called for the resignation of WCB Chairman, Dr. Adam Little. The association, with B.C. Federation of Labour backing, has called for a stop to unfair medical judgments by WCB doctors and for fairer treatment of disabled workers.

After several years of hassles with the British Columbia Workers' Compensation Board over his back injury and subsequent complications, Walter Bury helped found the United Injured and Disabled Workers Association. Bury explains its efforts this way:

> The battle now is to expose them [the WCB], what they are and what they are doing to people. That's why the association was formed.
>
> It's going to take until the time that we will have to parade out there like the Union of Injured Workers in Ontario that were taken away in paddy wagons. If it takes that it will take that . . . and I'll face any one of those bureaucrats. I've faced them on TV, I've faced them in Victoria, I've faced them over here at the WCB, and I'll keep on facing them. That is the only thing I have left in life.

East Montreal Group

East Montreal and adjacent Pointe-Aux-Trembles are heavily industrialized sectors of Montreal Island. The industries there are largely composed of petroleum refineries, foundries, smelters, and petrochemical industries. Around these heavy industries have grown a number of service companies. All told, more than 25,000 workers live and work in the area. And one unique occupational health and safety organization has grown up around the workers to provide service for needs related to on-the-job safety.

Le Comité Travailleurs Industries Lourdes de l'Est (Committee for Heavy Industrial Workers in East Montreal) and its subgroup, Le Comité Aide aux Travailleurs de l'Est (East Montreal Workers' Self-Help Group), together cover all aspects of workers' health and safety.

Initially the committee, formed in 1978, was spurred by doctors and professionals working in the J. Octave Roussin community clinic, which services East Montreal. These professionals came in daily contact with workers who were exposed to hazards on the job but felt powerless in terms of preventing the mounting casualties. Their alternative was a committee and in January 1978 the Committee for Workers in Heavy Industry was born. In the fall of the same year a sub-group, linked but not dependent on the community clinic, and with workers in control, was formed. Together the two committees form one of the most extensive occupational health and safety organizations outside the sphere of government.

The "self-help group" (as they will be referred to in the rest of this section) has no affiliation with a political party or with a union. Instead it functions separately and fills the gap of unions who for whatever reasons have failed to emphasize or press health and safety issues on the job. However, the group tries to work in liaison with unions and government to effect change. The group has taken on the tasks of lobbying for legislative changes, providing both workers and employers with information about hazards on the worksite and, if necessary, applying pressure on employers to ensure a safer work environment. In addition, the group handles workers' compensation claims and appeals, as well as group insurance and pension problems. The committee's priority is aiding workers to force health and safety issues on the job, and dealing with compensation claims. But the Montreal self-help group also finds itself involved in financially supporting workers if need be, while the often lengthy process of gaining the right to compensation runs its course.

The self-help group aids both unionized and non-unionized workers. Ninety-nine per cent of the population in East Montreal and Pointe-Aux-Trembles either work for huge multinationals or in industries with fewer than 100 workers.

Because the self-help group is loosely affiliated with the community clinic, independent doctors are on hand to provide workers with health assessments. In addition, if a worker is not able to find out what chemical or synthetic fibre he/she is working with, the clinic provides a technician to do an analysis.

The self-help group's office is nestled in a corner of the community clinic and staffed by three full-time workers, all of whom are injured workers. As a consequence staff members do not receive salaries, but use compensation awards for support. The self-help group for that reason is able to keep costs down to a minimum and function as a viable organization where others have failed.

In 1978 and 1979 the group handled 100 compensation claims for injured workers. That figure mounted to 350 in 1980, with an anticipated 1500 cases to be handled by the end of 1981. A large portion of the claims, given the nature of the industries in the area, are for difficult-to-prove, chemically-induced diseases.

In 1978, when the provincial government was drafting new legislation to replace existing archaic occupational health and safety standards and regulations, the self-help group jumped in to undertake lobbying. The white paper on occupational health and safety, the government's answer to on-the-job problems, was severely criticized in numerous meetings with ministers and in a detailed brief presented to a legislative commission.

The group has been noted in numerous press reports and elsewhere as being instrumental in the reshaping of the white paper and the ensuing passage of a reworked Bill 17. Quebec's occupational health and safety act is touted as the most progressive in Canada. The legislation was passed in December of 1979. The act includes, for instance, the right to refuse dangerous work, reassignment of pregnant workers in cases of fetal risk, the establishment of health and safety committees, etc.

While the self-help group is proud of the role it played in the formation of the legislation and views Bill 17 as a great improvement, the group's tasks are far from complete. Structures must be in place to make sure provisions in the act are enforced and that the document is not shelved. Now the committee is monitoring the act's implementation. In addition, the committee is beginning to work in the environment field, to aid in protecting today's and tomorrow's workers from pollutants emitted by refineries in East Montreal.

The 3 Rs of Workers' Health

Increasingly workers are organizing and demanding to be protected from assault in the workplace. An important aspect of the current struggle is the attempt to establish three basic rights for workers as outlined by Robert Sass, Director, Occupational Health and Safety Branch, Saskatchewan:

1. Workers must have the *right to know* about dangers in the work environment.
2. Workers must have the *right to participate* in the day-to-day detection, evaluation, and reduction of workplace hazards.
3. Workers must have the *right to refuse* to work in conditions known or believed to be unusually dangerous without fear of repercussion.[7]

The following excerpt from the policy statement of the Canadian Union of Public Employees (CUPE) shows that the 3 Rs of Workers' Health are important goals for their workers.

HEALTH AND SAFETY: PROTECTION FOR CUPE MEMBERS

A POLICY STATEMENT

submitted by the CUPE National Executive Board to the National Convention of the Canadian Union of Public Employees, Vancouver, B.C., October 24-28, 1977.

WHEREAS
the incidence of illness and injury resulting from work-related health and safety problems has reached epidemic proportions in Canada; and

WHEREAS
CUPE members risk a myriad of occupational diseases and disabling accidents resulting from the attempt by employers to increase productivity by keeping the costs of production down; and

WHEREAS
our union requires a policy and program to enable workers to protect themselves against health and safety hazards.

THEREFORE BE IT RESOLVED
that the following policy statement of the National Executive Board on Occupational Health and Safety be adopted by this Convention:

Occupational health and safety hazards are a direct result of an economy which places primary emphasis on increasing production and profits through keeping the costs of production down. The quality of the work environment is generally a secondary consideration—if it is given attention by employers at all. A dramatic change in priorities is long overdue. And CUPE must play a forceful and dynamic part in this process of change. . . .

We uphold the principle that every worker must have the right to refuse work considered harmful to oneself, a workmate, or the public without the threat of being penalized. In affirming this principle, it should be viewed as an immediate objective and form the basis around which we develop a program to monitor and eradicate health and safety hazards. We reject the view that workers are incapable of responsibly discharging this right. . . .

In order that the Union Health and Safety Committee can successfully fulfill its responsibilities, each CUPE Local, with the support of the other constitutional bodies within the services of the National Union, should demand that:

- Each collective agreement contain a clause on health and safety;
- Management recognizes and meets regularly with Union elected representatives who will sit on a Joint Labour-Management Health and Safety Committee. This committee shall be distinct from the Union Health and Safety Committee. It shall be the job of the Joint Labour-Management Health and Safety Committee to try and amicably work to ensure that a healthy and safe work environment is created and maintained;
- All Union elected individuals engaged in health and safety responsibilities be compensated at their regular rates of pay while involved in safety and health inspections, analysis, meetings, or related activities;
- Union members have the right to accompany government health and safety inspectors during the worksite investigations;
- Union members have the right to inspect health and safety conditions without restraints and to call upon independent outside sources or CUPE staff members to participate in any inspection activity analysis of safety and health hazards;
- The Union has the right to review employer accounts and records considered relevant to health and safety concerns;
- The Union has the right to take strike action if an employer refuses to rectify a

health and safety problem which threatens the health and safety of an employee or the public;

- Management create a Health and Safety Expenditure Fund to be used for properly monitoring and creating a healthy and safe work environment;
- Every employee shall have the right to refuse to perform work considered unsafe or unhealthy to oneself, workmate, or the public.

As noted at the end of Chapter 10, worksite safety committees have been instituted in five provinces with varying degrees of success. Their effectiveness is largely dependent upon the amount of power they give workers.

The right to refuse varies from province to province, as noted in Table 12-1. Unfortunately, in some provinces the right to refuse is of limited value because of the wording of the statute and/or the lack of protection for the worker exercising the right.

Osgoode Hall law professor and expert on occupational health and safety Terence Ison states that "access to risk information by working people is critically relevant to the democratic quality of life."[8]

While we might think that the right to know is present throughout our democratic society, most workplaces are anti-democratic. That is, secrecy and keeping information away from the worker is often the "way of business" for employers. It has been pointed out time and again how workers have been subjected to health hazards without proper training and warning concerning their dangerousness. For example, two workers were killed at the Syncrude oil plant in northern Alberta when they entered a reactor containing deadly nitrogen gas. A subsequent inquiry by the occupational health and safety department revealed that the workers were not told that they were working near poisonous gas.[9] If they had been informed of its dangers, they would not have entered the container. The following case is only one of many where a worker discovered the hazards of work only after being violently assaulted.

PROFILE: "The Sentence"

"When they told me, I didn't believe them." Jean Coté is a pragmatist, yet on that day and the ones which ensued he felt compelled by hope to doubt this ugly discovery. Still, the stunning reality of his diagnosis eventually sank in. He was forced to set aside unfounded skepticism and accept the verdict. There was no going back.

Jean is thirty-one. At that age most people are not thinking about retirement, let alone preparing for it. Jean, however, must. He harbours a disease which has usually been associated with an aged body. The events leading up to the diagnosis of silicosis and his condemnation to a shorter life span are vividly recollected by Jean.

In 1978 he was packing his bags to leave for a job on the James Bay Hydro project in northern Ontario. There was just one final detail to take care of. Prior to working on the hydro dam all workers were required to take a complete physical examination. Jean didn't anticipate any problems and saw the need for

Table 12-1

Status of Employees' Right to Refuse Work Due to Danger at the Worksite*

Jurisdiction	Right given?	How	Has "danger" been defined?
P.E.I.	No		No
Nfld.	Yes	Industry Health & Safety Regulations Section 8.24	Yes, as "danger to his health and safety"
Nova Scotia	Not fully	*Industrial Safety Act* Section 15(1)(2)	No
New Brunswick	Indirectly yes	*Occupational Safety Act 1976* Section 8(3)	No
Quebec	Yes	For Construction Yes "White Book" Gives Policy Statement of "Yes" Bill 17 gives right.	Yes
Ontario	Yes	Bill 70 1976 *Industrial Safety Act*	No
Yukon	Not yet	Will be given in Health & Safety Ordinance awaiting approval.	No
Manitoba	Yes	Section 43 of the *Workplace Safety & Health Act* — June 1976.	Yes, as "unusually dangerous"
N.W.T.	Not yet	Will be given in Act under preparation.	No
Saskatchewan	Yes	Saskatchewan *Occupational Health & Safety Act 1977*	Yes, as "unusually dangerous" to his health
Alberta	Yes	*Occupational Safety & Health Act 1976*, Chapter 40, Section 27.	Yes, as defined in Section 27.
British Columbia	Yes	Industrial Health and Safety Regulation.	Yes
Federal	Yes	Part IV of Canada Labour Code	Yes, as "imminent danger" which is explained.

* *Canadian Occupational Health and Safety News*, January 21, 1980, p. 4.

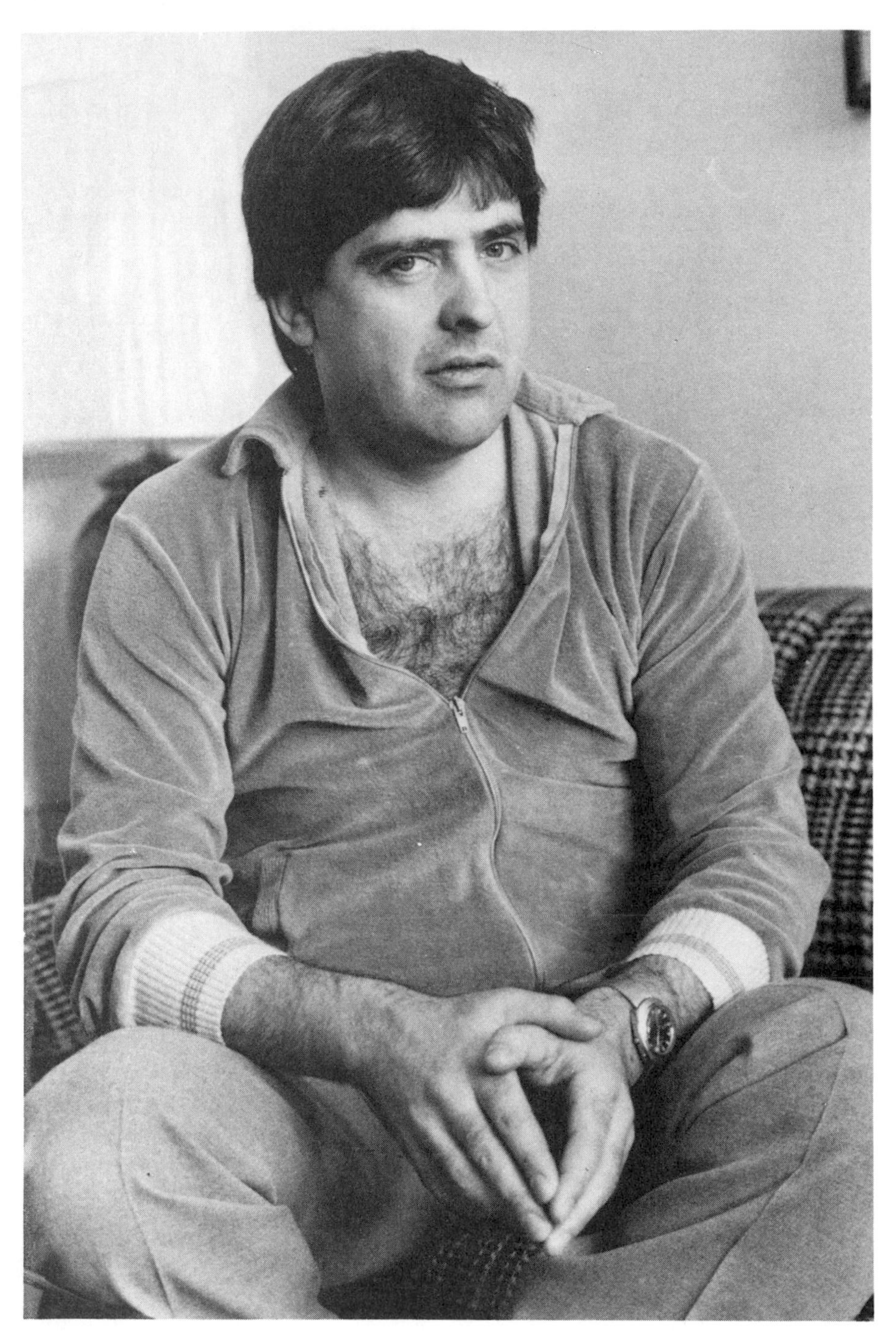

Jean Coté

a medical report as strictly a formality. Sure, he had been feeling much more tired these days, but attributed his continuous fatigue to being overworked. After all, no one can work sixty hours a week without feeling the physical and emotional impact. But the doctor who performed the examination attributed his tiredness to something else. Jean was told he couldn't work on the project and was directed to a specialist for further tests. One month later, in May of 1978, he was advised that he had developed silicosis. "At first I didn't realize the ramifications. I didn't really believe them. We [Jean and his wife] were overwhelmed by the situation and wondered how bad it would get. . . ."

Jean had begun work as a sandblaster at the age of 17, working for a small Montreal firm. Like others his age, he was primarily interested in a job that would pay well. And it did. But of the potential side effects of his work—the occupational hazards—Jean knew little. All work, he agrees, is dangerous to some degree, but like numerous other people Jean thought dangers consisted of such things as accidents or miners' lung. No one on his job site, whether boss, supervisor or knowledgeable fellow workers, ever advised him differently. Jean insists that he was never told that sandblasting work had the potential to destroy a worker's lung capacity. "I didn't know. I had no idea sandblasting could cause silicosis. At first I was angry. You know I didn't even like that job. I did it for the money."

In terms of protection, Jean followed instructions. Masks with carbon filters were provided and Jean wore them to avoid the fine powder produced by gypsum. He didn't smoke. He was athletic, spending spare time playing his two favorite sports, hockey and baseball. During almost 15 years as a sandblaster he never sought an examination for lung problems, nor were any tests taken through work. And for the most part, Jean felt healthy, until a year before what he calls "his sentence" was handed down.

He began developing a cough and noticed that he would spit black. "I became much more tired. But I thought it was because I was working twelve-hour days." The fatigue has since increased.

After his diagnosis in 1978, Jean applied for workers' compensation. He lowered his work hours substantially, and finally left his job in November of that year. In February of 1979, the CAT (Committee d'accidents de travail—Quebec's WCB) awarded him 35 per cent disability for silicosis. In May of 1979, after further tests, the award was revised to 50 per cent, allowing him $639 per month.

Jean, because of his age, sought rehabilitation and began taking courses to educate himself in retail sales. In Quebec, if a disabled worker returns to work he is guaranteed, through provincial compensation, the income he earned when his condition was first diagnosed. Jean, for instance, once back to work, could earn no less than $1500 per month, the monthly wage he was paid in 1978 for being a sandblaster.

In the summer of 1980, Jean did try work again. However, he quit after one month because his condition had progressed to the point where a full-time occupation created extreme exhaustion. In July of 1980 his compensation claim was once again revised to read 100 per cent disability. In reality, Jean has lost 60 per cent of his lung capacity, but in Quebec that level of disability is compensated totally and amounts to 90 per cent of his 1978 wage. Consequently he now receives $1350 per month.

Jean is one worker who has had little difficulty in getting compensation. His family physician referred him to the occupational health and safety self-help committee for East Montreal Workers, a group of workers, many of whom suffer from job injuries, who help others through the bureaucratic hoops of compensation. Since Jean did not smoke, was young, and had held down one job for his entire working life, there were few factors in question other than determining the degree to which his lung capacity had deteriorated. That one detail, however, did involve months of assessments prior to his award.

"X-rays of my lungs look like spider webs," notes Jean, describing the fibrosis that has invaded both of his lungs. Jean was not the only one surprised at his condition. Doctors who examined him agreed that silicosis is rarely found in someone so young. Most people tend to develop it after working for twenty years or more with silica dust, and consequently most are forty or older.

Both Jean and the doctors are puzzled by the exact reason for his susceptibility. "I don't know how it happened. It's nature I guess . . . it has to do with my constitution. My sensitivity to the material." Jean's condition is worsening rapidly. Between February 1979 when silicosis was compensated and April 1980, his lung incapacity rose from 35 per cent to 60 per cent.

Jean is not able to provide an elixir for avoiding silicosis. In retrospect, however, he believes that the right to know should be entrenched in law. Workers and their bosses should be educated in methods of protection, and safe levels of exposure to the dust should be established and carefully monitored.

Beyond those suggestions, however, Jean's ideas falter. He is still reeling from the shock of the discovery. "I was forced to realize they [the doctors] were right, because I have to stop midway up a flight of stairs to take a rest and I've never done that in my life."

In just three years, Jean's condition has deteriorated rapidly. The time of disputing the evidence has passed, although he still describes the experience as "dream-like." He now knows he cannot work full-time. What he doesn't know, however, is how the disease will affect the length of his life. He tries not to think about it, but cannot avoid analysing what went wrong. He wishes he'd tried other jobs. . . .

The only way to avoid silicosis with any certainty, emphasizes Jean, is to avoid the jobs that cause it, although he realizes that is easier said than done.

Nonetheless, until the worker is able to control health and safety on the job site, Jean sees no one else accepting the responsibility for protecting the worker. It's wrong, but it's reality. "Don't do it, not even for the money. I did it for the money, but I didn't know."

Given the choice, Jean would have chosen the right to know and voted with his feet.

How can we change this need for informing workers of health hazards? Knowledge is power, and ultimately money, to employers, so the "solution" is to be found in changes in power.

> Governments appear to be receptive to the idea that workers have a right to know what hazards they face at work. However, habits of secrecy are still deeply engrained. Moreover, the workers' right to know will no doubt continue to be balanced against the political and economic desirability of keeping the companies "on side." Further, a whole network of regulatory and enforcement arrangements have been built around a direct relationship between departmental staff and management which excludes unions and workers. *To bring about change requires a serious commitment at the political level.*[10]

A recent example of the political fight for workers' health is represented by Quebec Bill 17, "An Act Respecting Occupational Health and Safety," which became law December 21, 1979. After a long and arduous struggle, workers were able to establish the 3 Rs of workers' health. The legislation provides the worker with the right:

> to training, information and counselling services in matters of occupational health and safety, especially in relation to his work and his work environment, and to receive appropriate instruction, training and supervision.[11]

Furthermore,

> a worker has a right to refuse to perform particular work if he has reasonable grounds to believe that the performance of that work would expose him to danger to his health, safety or physical well-being, or would expose another person to a similar danger.[12]

Concerning worker participation, besides the establishment of health and safety committees in certain workplaces, the bill provides for worker participation at the board level. More specifically, a new agency entitled *La Commission de la Santé et de la Sécurité du Travail* has been established to implement the legislation. It has an executive committee with an equal number of workers and employers who are invested with the power to carry out the commission's duties. Such participation of workers at this level is unique in Canada. While it is too early to measure its impact, it undoubtedly has helped increase the interest and concern of Quebec workers with health issues.

Conclusions

Ultimately, we believe that the reduction of health hazards in the workplace will come largely from the initiative of workers and their allies. In a recent overview of the issues surrounding workers' health problems, a technical report for the Economic Council of Canada notes the following as one type of strategy:

> Changing the Power Relationships in the Workplace
>
> In general it is the employer who is held legally responsible for safety in the workplace. This principle is often thought of by management as conferring to them

the sole, if not principal, right and prerogative in matters reflecting their workers' health. However, throughout the western world occupational safety and health is becoming a matter of joint responsibility for employers and employees. In many countries the legislation provides for a more or less structured system of participation by workers in health and safety matters. This is achieved in basically two ways: (1) by the establishment of joint labour-management health and safety committees, which may or may not be mandated by legislation (in Canada, it is now mandated in six provinces (Ackroyd, 1978)); and (2) by legislating meaningful right-to-refuse hazardous work. The advantages of joint union-management health and safety committees were cited earlier and will not be repeated at this point. A notable shortcoming of this instrument, as the government response to occupational health and safety problems, is that for many workplaces there are no unions to implement such committees. It is this problem that can partially be overcome by the right to refuse hazardous work legislation, since the power to influence safety and health policies in the workplace is conferred to the individual worker and not to the union per se.[13]

While the above-noted policy option is only one of several mentioned by the authors, we believe it is the most important for improving workers' health.

In June 1981 the Economic Council of Canada issued its final report on *Reforming Regulation*, including the area of occupational health and safety. While the general thrust is one of economic deregulation following the policies of President Reagan in the United States, they do not suggest deregulation in the areas of health and safety. Their specific conclusions and recommendations are reproduced below:

Conclusions and Recommendations

Occupational health and safety regulations are embodied in a host of federal and provincial statutes. We made no attempt to sieve through them to identify where specific standards may conflict, overlap, or no longer apply. We have no doubt that many of them could be identified and that many firms and businessmen are frustrated by what they may perceive as unwarranted intrusions on managerial rights or on working procedures that have been negotiated through collective bargaining. Nonetheless, as we have seen in the case of environmental regulation, the fact that specific regulations impose additional costs and are vexatious to individual employers is not reason enough for their elimination. Indeed, for sound economic reasons, that may precisely be their purpose. Hence, in the systems for preventing workplace accidents or industrial disease and compensating the injured parties, we see room for modest changes only. Moreover, in making specific recommendations, we recognize that substantial variations exist in the approaches and commitments to better occupational health and safety within separate jurisdictions. Our recommendations will thus have different significance and applicability, depending on the government and regulating agency concerned.

The Council endorses the current emphasis on the prevention of industrial health and safety hazards. To the extent that the federal and provincial regulations now in play encourage safe conditions and practices in the workplace, they reduce the real costs that accidents and illness impose on all Canadians. Employers and workers know this and widely support the achievement of better standards of health and safety.

Some jobs will always entail considerable risk, as oil riggers, miners, loggers, and chemical workers well know. But what Canadians have affirmed collectively through their legislators is that individual workers must not be expected to bear all the financial, as well as physical and mental, risk and that the principal financial risks should be shared more broadly with the shareholders of the employing firms and the purchasers of their products.

There are, of course, limits to which workplaces can be rendered safe and beyond which the costs of compliance for both employers and employees far outweigh the potential benefits. There is a vast, though none too satisfactory, literature that purports to put values on human life and limb, and judges in rendering legal settlements must make such decisions often. The Council has not entered this debate, but we recognize that in the course of daily work activity decisions are constantly being made that implicitly encompass such calculations.

Clearly, governments cannot through regulation anticipate every exigency. The Council thus endorses increased labour participation in the identification of hazards, the improvement of working conditions, and in the process of enforcing occupational health and safety measures. Therefore,

> *We recommend that the federal and provincial goverments adopt and support the concept of workplace health and safety regulation through joint committees with functional authority, as well as the right of workers to refuse, without penalty, work they believe to be prejudicial to their safety or health and the right of workers to be informed fully about the generic names of ingredients of all substances used in the workplace.*

The Council is heartened by the intention of Labour Canada to amend the Canada Labour Code in support of these objectives. To encourage labour and management to use joint health and safety committees, it is our view that the federal government, and those provincial governments that have not already done so, should take steps to ensure that enforcement and standards are applied evenly across all provinces.

The concept of greater increased labour participation does not rule out a continuing role for government regulation, inspection, or enforcement. Indeed, it is our perception that both the corporate sector generally and organized labour would be unhappy if the present system of government intervention were eliminated and replaced by one of legal liability alone. There will always be room for more than one policy instrument to prevent occupational injury and disease.

In small businesses or where the labour force is unorganized, the application of health and safety standards may require special effort, even though the number of establishments may mean that governments' preventive efforts must be concentrated on perceivably high-risk activities and employers. Much will depend upon the sense of understanding and respect established between provincial inspectors and employers and their workers, and the Council endorses the practice of health and safety inspections taking place with an employee present.

We have observed the difficulties of undertaking adequate inspections of potentially hazardous situations in all jurisdictions. We recognize, of course, that for all governments there are competing claims for resources and that occupational health and safety concerns represent only one such claim. Nonetheless, investment in prevention has led to significant resource savings and reduced human suffering. Consequently,

We recommend that the federal and provincial governments review their staffing and pay qualifications for occupational health and safety administrations, with a view to increasing the number of inspectors and inspections and strengthening the enforcement procedures.

At both the federal and some provincial jurisdictional levels, a consolidation of health and safety regulations so that they could be administered by a single department under the direction of a single minister would help eliminate duplicate regulations and facilitate more comprehensive enforcement. Accordingly,

We recommend that governments, as appropriate, review the legislation and regulations within their jurisdictions that are concerned with occupational health and safety, with a view to consolidating them under one administering department.

As part of their information and monitoring responsibilities, governments must investigate and apply specific standards, in such areas as ventilation or toxic exposures, or performance standards of a more general nature. Recent and future developments in genetic engineering, microbiology, and related fields offer dramatic opportunities for increasing the well-being of Canadians, but they also increase the hazards they face. Therefore,

We recommend that the federal and provincial governments provide adequate resources for the Canadian Centre for Occupational Health and Safety to enable it to carry out the research and liaison that will put Canada at the forefront of nations in dealing with such issues as those involving hazardous chemicals and radiation, which will be of concern in the years ahead. We also believe that provincial governments should consider the merits of establishing advisory bodies to collect information and report annually on occupational health and safety issues.

In this connection we have noted the absence of national health standards applicable to Canadian workplaces. Evidently, as in the case of the environmental air and water quality standards, federal standards may be less exacting than those adopted by some provinces. Nonetheless, they could provide a common reference point for all Canadian jurisdictions. Hence,

We recommend that the federal and provincial governments consider developing a set of national health and safety standards, with the assistance of the Canadian Centre for Occupational Health and Safety.

By and large, occupational health and safety agencies and regulations in Canada have not been singled out for the very serious criticisms that have been levelled by the business community at their counterparts in the United States. This reflects favourably, in our view, on the predominantly provincial nature of the regulatory system and on the extensive use of performance standards that allow firms to make cost-efficient choices in complying. Moreover, in introducing extensive legislation and regulatory changes during the 1970s, the provincial governments took pains to consult with a wide spectrum of the interested public, including trades and safety associations.

We do not share the view advanced in some quarters that the whole gamut of health and safety regulations could be replaced by economic incentive schemes or injury taxes. This is because our concern has been with prevention, and there is little evidence that economic mechanisms alone, even if they could be applied efficiently and equitably, offer suitable preventive alternatives to other established methods. We have, however, noted with approval the use of experience rating and penalties in the Workmen's Compensation Board schedules of payroll taxes on employers, a practice that is consistent with traditional insurance principles. In addition, we are of the view that there is merit in having legislation as a measure of last resort and provision for heavy fines or equivalent penalties in order to curb deliberate noncompliance.

In our brief look at the workers' compensation system, we were impressed by the high level of expertise the various boards have achieved in dealing with the multitude of claims and appeals that come forward daily. We were also struck by the complexity of the issues associated with the boards' activities and by the arguments that the workers' compensation system should be expanded in order to have universal application. This would broaden the financial base of the program; it would also require expansion and improvement of the boards' administrative organization. The Council also recognizes the need for the boards not only to be, but to be seen to be, impartial, and we accept the suggestion of the Ontario Federation of Labour that labour should be more adequately represented on Workmen's Compensation Boards. Therefore,

> *We recommend that provincial governments review the structure of their Workmen's Compensation Boards to ensure that labour is adequately represented and that resources are available to ensure efficient administrative and appeals processes.*

Occupational health and safety regulations generally give broad and discretionary interpretive powers to administrators and inspectors and, in some cases, to employers and joint committees. This situation can lead to lax interpretation and enforcement or it can lend itself to sound decisions by persons who deal with a multitude of situations in the various individual work sites throughout Canada. There will, of course, be human error and some negligence in any workplace, and there are bound to be recriminations and self-serving rationalizations. In general, it is our opinion that, while the relatively calmer occupational health and safety debate in Canada compared with that in the United States may be reassuring, it also warrants at least some critical examination. It may result from the effective decentralization of decisions among joint working committees and among eleven levels of government; the avoidance of detailed site-specific instruction in the regulations that may be highly inappropriate to some situations; the ability of Canadian administrators, employers, and labour to learn from, and go along with, U.S. research and standards, particularly in matters of occupational health, or with their willingness to work together towards the common elimination of hazards. Or, alternatively, it may reflect different enforcement of regulations in an area affecting the genuine well-being of Canadians.

In the final analysis, much of the effort to improve occupational health and safety will depend upon the political will. Canadians generally eschew the sense of human indifference in the workplace that not infrequently accompanies business competition elsewhere. They have shown that they are prepared to pay a price for their concern for occupational hazards. The relative levels of workers' compensation benefits in Canada, for instance, are far higher than those available in the

> United States, and the standards of workplace safety are far higher than those that prevail in many countries with which we trade. They entail costs, and in terms of our international competitiveness, this means that we must demonstrate enterprise and ingenuity to offset them. For where the health and safety of Canadians are concerned, the potential benefits in reduced human suffering and lower medical and rehabilitation expenses make such costs well worth bearing.[14]

We generally concur with these points, particularly the need for the three Rs of workers' health. It is now up to workers and their allies to press for these rights and make them meaningful.

NOTES

1. Letter from Jim Brophy, W.O.S.H., to Charles Reasons, October 28, 1980.
2. This discussion of W.O.S.H. is from the following article, unless otherwise noted: Jim Brophy and John Jackson with the assistance of the Windsor Occupational Safety and Health Council, "The Story of W.O.S.H.," *Canadian Dimension*, June 1980, pp. 39-45.
3. Robert Sass, "Why Experts Can't Solve the Occupational Health Crises," *The Miners' Voice*, May 1977, p. 8.
4. "The Story of W.O.S.H.," p. 45.
5. Published by the Union of Injured Workers, Toronto, n.d.
6. *Job Security for Injured Workers—A Proposal for New Labour Legislation* (Toronto: Union of Injured Workers, n.d.).
7. Robert Sass, "Occupational Health & Safety Rights," mimeographed, June 20, 1980.
8. *Canadian Occupational Health and Safety News*, Vol. 3, No. 23 (November 10, 1980):2.
9. "Victims Not Told About Gas," *The Calgary Herald*, February 18, 1981.
10. Joan C. Brown, "Occupational Health and Safety—The Right to Know," *Labour Gazette*, Vol. 213 (February/March, 1978):75.
11. Fourth Session, Thirty-First Legislative Assemblée Nationale du Quebec, *Bill 17: An Act Respecting Occupational Health and Safety* (L'Editeur Official du Quebec, 1979), p. 9.
12. Ibid.
13. Pran Manga, Robert Broyles, and Gil Reschenthaler, Technical Report No. 6, *Occupational Health and Safety: Issues and Alternatives* (Ottawa: Economic Council of Canada, March 1981), pp. 283-84.
14. Economic Council of Canada, *Reforming Regulation* (Ottawa: Supply and Services Canada, 1981), pp. 106-8.

Appendix A

A Worker-Oriented Guide to Government, Union, and Community Assistance

Workers' and Public Sources

Committee for Workers' Health
1937 West 2nd Avenue
Vancouver, B.C.
Attention: Dr. Harold Kasinsky

Industrial Accidents Victims Group of Ontario (I.A.V.G.O.)
944A St. Clair Avenue West
Toronto, Ontario
416-651-5756

Injured Workers Consultants (I.W.C.)
717 Pape Avenue, Suite 300
Toronto, Ontario
416-416-2411

Injured Workers Group,
Centre for Spanish-Speaking People
582A College Street
Toronto, Ontario, M6G 1B3

Medical Reform Group
P.O. Box 366, Station J
Toronto, Ontario, M4J 4Y8
Attention: Brian Gibson, Donald Cole, Jamie Meuser

Occupational Health and Safety Project,
Centre for Labour Studies
Humber College

205 Humber College Blvd.
Rexdale, Ontario, M9W 5L7
Attention: Mr. Gary Cwitco

Occupational Health and Safety Project,
Labour Studies Programme
Capilano College
2055 Purcell Way
North Vancouver, B.C., V7J 3H5
604-986-1911 (L. 334)

Occupational Health Committee,
Canadian Advisory Council on the Status of Women
Box 1541
Station B
Ottawa, Ontario, K1P 5R5

Occupational Health and Safety Comittee,
Law Union of British Columbia
c/o 1400-207 West Hastings Street
Vancouver, B.C., V6B 1K5
Attention: Craig Paterson

Occupational Health and Safety Committee,
Law Union of Ontario

Committee on the Weiler Study
c/o 354 Bathurst Street
Toronto, Ontario
416-976-5900
Attention: Mr. Andrew King

Ad Hoc Committee on Workers' Compensation
-same address as above
Attention: Mr. Richard Fink

Ontario Public Interest Research Group
421 Avenue Road
Toronto, Ontario
Attention: Doug Saunders, Ontario Director

Ontario Public Interest Research Group
Cody Hall
University of Windsor
Windsor, Ontario, N9B 3P4

Research Action and Education Centre
c/o Keith Brown
P.O. Box 988
Gravelbourg, Saskatchewan, S0H 1X0

Student Legal Aid Assistance Society
Faculty of Law
Unversity of Windsor
Windsor, Ontario, N9B 3P4
Attention: Peter Cassidy

Sudbury Community Legal Services Society
60 Ayre Street South
Sudbury, Ontario, P3C 4A7
Attention: David Leitch

Toronto Occupational Health Resources Committee
c/o 3-203 Beverley Street
Toronto, Ontario

United Injured and Disabled Workers' Association of British Columbia
P.O. Box 65718, Station F
Vancouver, B.C., V5N 5K7
Attention: Mr. Merril Turpin, President
Mr. Walter Bury, Vice-President

Union of Injured Workers (U.I.W.)
765 St. Clair Avenue West
Toronto, Ontario
416-657-1215
Attention: Mr. Phil Biggin, President

L'Union des Travailleurs Accidentes De Montréal (U.T.A.M.)
71232 rue St. Denis
Montréal, Québec, H2S 2S5
514-279-7224

Windsor Occupational Health and Safety Council (W.O.S.H.)
824 Tecumseh Road East
Windsor, Ontario, N8X 2S3
519-254-4192

Women's Action on Occupational Health
Women's Health Collective Society
1501 West Broadway
Vancouver, B.C.
604-736-6696

Trade Union Sources

Alberta Federation of Labour
306-11010-142nd Street
Edmonton, Alberta
Attention: Mr. Ray Sentes, Health and Safety Director

British Columbia Federation of Labour
3110 Boundary Road
Burnaby, B.C.
604-430-1241

Canadian Labour Congress
2841 Riverside Drive
Ottawa, Ontario, K1A 8X7
613-731-3052
Attention: Dr. Victor Rabinovitch
Program Director
Occupational Health and Safety
Labour Education and Studies Centre
Ms. Marie-Claire Fortin, Project Officer

Canadian Union of Public Employees
21 Florence Street
Ottawa, Ontario, K2P 0W6
613-237-1590
Attention: Mr. Colin Lambert, Special Projects
Office (Health and Safety)

(CUPE has played a leading role in occupational health and safety and has numerous publications and briefs of interest, including the CUPE Hazard Inventory of particular interest to public workers, service and office workers and women.)

Confederation of Canadian Unions (B.C. Division)
c/o 5648 Imperial Street
Burnaby, B.C., V5J 1E9
604-438-6211
Attention: Occupational and Environmental Health
Committee, Ms. Cathy Walker, Chairperson

Fédération des Travailleurs du Québec
5e étage-1290 rue St. Denis
Montréal, Québec, H2X 3J7
514-288-7431

Hamilton Occupational Health and Safety Committee
c/o Hamilton and District Labour Council
Room 116-1031 Barton Street East
Hamilton, Ontario, L8L 3E3
Attention: Ed Hunt

Labour Council of Metropolitan Toronto
Suite 407-15 Gervais Drive
Don Mills, Ontario
416-429-3663

Publishes "Health Alert," an excellent health and safety newsletter. Commenced Vol. I, No. 1 in September 1976, Jennifer Penney (ed.).

Manitoba Federation of Labour
104 Union Centre
570 Portage Avenue
Winnipeg, Manitoba, R3C 0G4
204-775-4575
Attention: Mr. Richard Martin, President
Health and Safety Committee

New Brunswick Federation of Labour
P.O. Box 524
96 Norwood Avenue
Moncton, New Brunswick, E1C 8L9
Attention: Mr. Phil Booker, President
Health and Safety Committee

Newfoundland and Labrador Federation of Labour
P.O. Box 6104
St. John's, Newfoundland, A1C 5X8
Attention: Health and Safety Committee

Northwest Territories Federation of Labour
Box 969
Yellowknife, N.W.T., X0E 1H0
Attention: Mr. Phil Molly, President
Health and Safety Committee

Nova Scotia Federation of Labour
275 Mapleview Drive
North Sydney, Nova Scotia, B2A 3K3
902-539-4933
Attention: Mr. Gerald Yetman, President
Health and Safety Committee

Ontario Federation of Labour
703-15 Gervais Drive
Don Mills, Ontario, M3C 1Y8
Occupational Health and Training Centre
Health and Safety Director: Ed Waddell
Centre Staff: Linda Jolley, Mike Krueber, Clarence MacPherson, Wendy Baird, Margaret Abela, Judy Robins.
Publications: "At the Source," "Manual on Occupational Health and Safety."

Saskatchewan Federation of Labour
103-2079 12th Avenue
Regina, Saskatchewan, S4T 1J3

Attention: Ms. Nadine Hunt, President
Health and Safety Committee

Yukon Federation of Labour
106 Strickland
Whitehorse, Yukon, Y1A 2J5
Attention: Mr. Casey McCabe, President

Government or Private Sources

Advisory Council on Occupational Health and Occupational Safety
400 University Avenue, 15th Floor
Toronto, Ontario, M7A 1T7
Chairman: Dr. J. F. Mustard
Labour Members and Officers:
C. G. Pilkey, O.F.L.
L. Sheffe, U.A.W.
F. A. Waddell, O.F.L.
J. M. More, O.C.A.W.
L. Heard, U.S.W.A.
H. Kobryn, Construction Trades
Publications include:
—*Interim Statement* (1977 to 31 March 1978)
—*First Annual Report* (1978-79)
—*Second Annual Report* (1979-80)

Canadian Centre for Occupational Health and Safety
Health Sciences Centre
1200 Main Street West
Suite 3N25
P.O. Box 2000, Station A
Hamilton, Ontario, L8N 3Z5
416-527-6590

Dr. Gordon Atherley, President
Dr. Jim Purdham, Project Director
Wendy E. King, Research Officer

(The Centre was created by Federation legislation in 1978 and has a governing council and executive board composed of labour, corporate and government representatives. It is self-governing and reports to Parliament through a Minister.

Its purpose is primarily informational and its major function is to collect, evaluate and disseminate information on occupational health and safety.

Workers, Unions and others may write to the Centre and request information or research assistance on workplace health problems.)

Canadian Occupational Health and Safety News
—published 25 times a year
—first issue commenced 20 March 1978
Corpus Information Services
1450 Don Mills Road
Don Mills, Ontario

Canadian Public Health Association
Suite 210-1335 Carling Avenue
Ottawa, Ontario, K1Z 8N8
Attention: Environmental Health and Accident Prevention Division.

Labour Canada
Occupational Safety and Health
Ottawa, Ontario, K1A 0J2
819-997-3520
Attention: Jim W. McLellan

Library, Workers' Compensation Board of British Columbia
5255 Heather Street
Vancouver, British Columbia, V5Z 3L8
604-266-0211

New Brunswick Occupational Health and Safety Commission
P.O. Box 6000
Fredericton, N.B., E3B 5H1
506-453-2467, -2307, or -3706.
Attention: Mr. Bryan J. Walker, Chairman

Selected services are available regionally at the following locations and numbers: Bathurst (546-6625 or -6691); Charlo (684-5274); Chatham-Newcastle (622-1576); Edmunston (735-8824 or 445-2761); Lawrence Station (466-2134); Minto (327-3357); Moncton (858-2510); Saint John (658-2510); Sheila (395 2204); and St. Quentin (235-2552).

Occupational Health and Safety Project
Kinesiology Department
Simon Fraser University
Burnaby Mountain
Burnaby, British Columbia
604-291-4584
Attention: Mr. Tom Smith, Director

Occupational Health and Safety Section Library,
Ontario Ministry of Labour
10th Floor-400 University Avenue
Toronto, Ontario, M7A 1T7

—has a collection exceeding 50,000 library items; library commenced approximately 1920.
Publications: *Occupaitonal Health and Safety Topics, Workplace*

The *Topics* publication is an excellent source of references and has provided special listings such as:

—Safety and Health Committees (Vol. I, No. 1)
—Occupational Medical Records (Vol. I, No. 2)
—Physical Fitness (Vol. I, No. 3)
—Acceptance of Risk (Vol. I, No. 4)

—Backache (Vol. I, No. 5)
—Occupational Stress, Parts I and II (Vol. I, Nos. 6/7)
—Shiftwork: Physiological and Physchological Aspects (Vol. I, No. 8)
—Occupational Health and Small Business, Parts I and II (Nos. 9/10)
—Pre-Employment and Periodic Medical Examinations (Vol. I, No. 11)
—Right to Refuse Unsafe Work (Vol. I, No. 12)
—Toxicology and Carcinogenic Testing (Vol. II, No. 1)
—Confidentiality of Occupational Medical Records (Vol. II, No. 2)
—Smoking and Occupational Health (Vol. II, No. 3)
—Alcohol and Drug Abuse in the Workplace (Vol. II, Nos. 4/5)
—Non-Ionizing Radiation, Parts I and II (Vol. II, Nos. 6/7)
—Women and Occupational Health (Vol. II, Nos. 8/9/10)

Occupational Health Resource Centre
Institute of Human Performance
Simon Fraser University
Burnaby, B.C., V5A 1S6
604-291-4589, 291-3319 or 879-8587
Attention: Larry Stoffman or Susan Kennedy

Saskatchewan Health and Safety Newsletter
Occupational Health and Safety Branch
Saskatchewan Labour
1150 Rose Street
Regina, Saskatchewan, S4P 3V7
Attention: Mr. Bob Sass, Associate Deputy Minister and Director of Occupational Health and Safety Branch (Mr. Sass maintains a mailing list and circulates materials of interest from time to time).
The Branch has available assorted publications such as:
—*Industrial Chemical Labelling*
—*Workplace Monitoring*
—*Stressors and Work Populations*

Western Occupational Health Resources
509 East 12th Street
North Vancouver, British Columbia, V7L 2K5
604-985-3798
Attention: Ms. Susan Kennedy

Appendix B

Canadian Workers' Compensation Boards*

Alberta

Workers' Compensation Board
9912-107 Street, P.O. Box 2415,
Edmonton, T5J 2S5
Information 427-1100
Chairman, R. H. Jamha 427-1266
Member, P. Kolba 427-1264
Member, Dr. A. E. Hohol 427-1265
Administration
Executive Director, T. P. Griffin 427-1269
Claims Services
Executive Director, G. E. Hickson 427-1268
Finance
Executive Director, J. R. Thomson 427-0885
Assessment Review Committee
Chairman, A. W. Runck 427-1334
Claims Review Committee
Chairman, Vacant 427-1289
Accounting Services
Director, E. T. Hunt 427-1273
Administrative Services
Director, R. Burkin 427-1256
Assessments
Director, D. V. Holmes 427-1224
Claims Director, D. L. Palmer 427-1019
Medical Services
Director, Dr. W. F. Hall 427-1181
Personnel Director, H. A. Morris 427-1284
Systems and Data Processing
Director, I. E. Bering 427-1106
Vocational Rehabilitation

* Source: *The Corpus Administrative Index*, Corpus Information Services Ltd., 1450 Don Mills Road, Don Mills, Ontario (June 1980, serial).

Director, E. M. Jones 427-1294
Legal:
Sr. Solicitor, J. D. Carr 427-0402
BRANCH OFFICES:
132-16th Ave. N.E., Calgary, T2E 1J5
10022-102 Ave., Grande Prairie, T8V 0Z7
1277-3 Ave. South, Lethbridge, T1J 0K3
#204, 623-4 St. S.E., Medicine Hat, T1A 0L1
#401, 4808 Ross St., Red Deer, T4N 1X5
REHABILITATION CENTRE
7123-119 St., Edmonton, T6G 1V7
Administrative Director,
W. L. Jarman 434-3441

British Columbia

Workers' Compensation Board
5255 Heather St., Vancouver, V5Z 3L8
Chairman, Dr. Adam S. Little 266-0211
Commissioner, Sam Brown 266-0211
Commissioner, Mike Parr 266-0211
Commissioner, Joe Miyazawa 266-0211
Board Secretary, N. Attewell 266-0211
Administration and Finance
Executive Director, J. A. Taylor 266-0211
Finance Director, Vacant 266-0211
Assessment Director, R. D. Gunn 266-0211
Data Processing
Director, R. A. Mules 266-0211
Information Services
Director, G. McMillan 266-0211
Employee Relations
Director, G. Balfour 266-0211
General Administrative Services
Director, R. Holloway 266-0211
Physical Plant Facilities
Director, A. Allman 266-0211
Compensation Services
Executive Director, A. H. Mullan 266-0211
Claims Director, A. Quinn 266-0211
Vocational Rehabilitation
Director, R. Patillo 266-0211
Prevention Services
Executive Director, J. D. Paton 266-0211
Inspection
Director, P. E. Knowlan 266-0211
Research and Education
Director, A. L. Riegert 266-0211

Legal Services
Executive Director, I. E. Tufts 266-0211
Medical Services
Executive Director, Dr. J. S. Gibbings 266-0211
Physical Rehabilitation
Director, Dr. L. H. Bartlett 273-7711

Manitoba

Workers' Compensation Board
333 Maryland St., Winnipeg, R3G 1M2
Chairman, W. J. Johnston, Q.C. 786-5471
Commissioners:
D. Proctor, W. F. Kennedy
Executive Secretary, Russell G. Jones 786-5471
Asst. Executive Secretary, R. A. Boyes 786-5471
Chief Financial Officer, F. A. Ball, C.A. 786-5471
Director of Medical Services, K. O. Wylie, M.D. 786-5471

New Brunswick

New Brunswick Workmen's Compensation Board
Corner of Portland and Hilyard Streets,
P.O. Box 160, Saint John, E2L 3X9
Chairman, Robert Jones 652-2250
Vice-Chairman, J. Adolphus Picot 652-2250
Commissioner, Maurice P. Fisher 652-2250
Secretary, Donald Ayer 652-2250
Executive Director, H. M. Heckbert 652-2250

Newfoundland

Workers' Compensation Board
146-148 Forest Rd.,
St. John's, A1A 3B8
Chairman, Ed Maynard 754-2940
Commissioner, A. Rose 754-2940
Commissioner, Vacant 754-2940
Consultant, W. J. May 754-2940
Part-time Advisor, George Fewer 754-2940
Part-time Advisor, John Murphy 754-2940
Executive Director, R. H. Baggs 754-2940
Accounting and Assessment Director, G. T. Brown 754-2940
Claims Director, M. J. Bursey 754-2940
Rehabilitation Director, Donald Myron
Chief Medical Officer, Dr. L. E. Lawton 754-2940

Northwest Territories

Workers' Compensation Board
Yellowknife, X1A 2L9
Chairman, J. D. C. MacLean 873-7555
Secretary to the Board, Bryan C. Roberts 873-7557

Nova Scotia

Workmen's Compensation Board
5668 South Street,
Box 1150, Halifax, B3J 2Y2
Chairman, John Lynk 424-8663
Vice-Chairman, C. B. Coutts 424-8663
Commissioner, R. K. Murrant 424-8663
Commissioner, J. D. Aucoin 424-8663
Commissioner, J. H. Vaughn 424-8663
Chief Medical Officer, Dr. T. E. Dobson 424-4496
Executive Director, James Cottenden 424-5758
Claims Department
Director of Claims, J. P. Floyd 424-5955
Accident Prevention Department
Chief, J. F. Herbin 424-3987
Assessment Department
Chief Assessment Officer, C. M. MacAuley 424-5787
Account & Audit Department
Data Center Mgr., W. E. Ross 424-5900
Comptroller, H. R. Gill 424-5882

Ontario

Workmen's Compensation Board
2 Bloor St. E., Toronto, M4W 3C3
Telex: 02-29306
Chairman, Lincoln M. Alexander, Q.C. 965-8880
Executive Asst., J. M. Davies 965-8882
Vice-Chairman, Administration, A. G. MacDonald 965-8905
Vice-Chairman, Appeals, Thomas D. Warrington, Q.C. 965-8920
Commissioners of Appeals:
D. F. Hamilton 965-8930
Dr. W. F. Jacobs 965-8922
J. K. Godin 965-8956
Thomas A. McEwan 965-8924
Registrar of Appeals, D. Farquharson 965-8926
Secretary of the Board, J. F. McDonald 965-8884
Asst. Secretary, A. Joma 965-8883
Board Solicitor and General Counsel, W. R. Riddell 965-8757
Actuary, J. C. Neal 965-1661

Medical Services
Executive Director, Dr. W. J. McCracken 965-8827
Claims Services
Executive Director, W. R. Kerr 965-8773
Financial Services
Executive Director, Robert Brewerton 965-8660
Communications
A/Executive Director, L. R. Cameron 965-8948
Safety Education
Executive Director, W. A. White 965-8726
Human Resources
Executive Director, J. G. Betts 965-8720
Administrative Resources
Executive Director, V. G. Sweeney 965-8752
Vocational Rehabilitation
Executive Director, J. Wisocky 963-0154
Hospital & Rehabilitation Centre
115 Torbarrie Road, Downsview, M3L 1G8
Director, Dr. R. Johnson 244-1761
Administrator, J. C. Eagan 244-1751

Prince Edward Island

Workers' Compensation Board
60 Belvedere Avenue, Box 757
Charlottetown, C1A 7L7
Minister Responsible, Hon. Leo F. Rossiter 892-3498
Chairman, M. E. Campbell 894-8555
Secretary, C. E. Ready 894-8555
Members:
R. Livingston 894-8555
Arthur Brown 894-8555
Claims Division
Chief Claims Officer, Vacant 894-8555
Safety Division
Supervisor, J. H. Muise 894-8555
Finance Division
Accountant, L. J. Maclellan 894-8555
Assessment Division
Assessment Officer, Vacant 894-8555

Quebec

Commission de la santé et de la securité du travail
(Workmen's Compensation Commission)
524, Bourdages Street, Québec, G1K 7E2 .... (418) 643-5850

1199, avenue de Bleury, Montréal . . . . (514)873-3990
Chairman and Director general,
Judge Robert Sauvé 643-5850
Administration
Vice-chairman, J.-Gilles Massé 643-5850
Inspection
Vice-chairman, Gilles Néron 643-5850
Prevention
Vice-chairman, Jean-Louis Bertrand 643-5850
Compensation, Medical assistance, Rehabilitation
Vice-chairman, Lionel Bernier 643-5850
Assistant to the chairman, Madame Nicole Kerjean 643-5850
Secretary; Pierre Lafrance 643-5850
Legal Services
Director, vacant 643-5850
Crime Victims Compensation
Director, Jean-Marc Bertrand 643-5850
Research
Director, Emilien Landry 643-5850
Human Resources
Director, Roger Tremblay 643-5850
Communications
Director, Pierre Lafrance 643-5850
Medical Services
Director, Dr Jean-R. Lemieux 643-5850
Finance
Director, Paul-E. Boucher 643-5850
Budgeting
Director, Justin Pilote 643-5850
Data Processing Services
Director, André Bélanger 643-5850
Internal Auditing
Director, Robert Talbot 643-5850
Administrative Services
Director, Roger Tremblay 643-5850
Regional Directors:
Saguenay-Lac-Saint-Jean, Pierre Ringuet
Ouataouais, Gaston Bergeron
Laval-Laurentides, Simon Bonin
Longueuil, Jean-Robert Ouellet
Mauricie-Bois-Francs, André Forest
Ile-de-Montréal, Claude Mérineau
Québec, Jacques Fournier
Bas-Saint-Laurent-Gaspésie, Dominique Landry
Nord-Ouest, Jean-Guy Dugré
Côte-Nord, Clément Gagnon
Cantons-de l'Est, Michel Roy

Review Board Directors:
Ile-de-Montréal, Claude Mauger
Laval-Laurentides, Paul-A. Egan
Rive-Sud, Jean-Marc Jodin
Québec, Jean-Paul Laferrière

Saskatchewan

Workers' Compensation Board
1840 Lorne Street, Regina, S4P 2L8
Chairman, Brian King 565-4379
Board Member, H. Elkin 565-4381
Board Member, M. Bourne 565-4382
Executive Director, J. A. McLean 565-4383

Yukon

Workers' Compensation Board
Minister, The Hon. Meg McCall 667-5603
Executive Secretary, B. Booth 667-5224
Assessment Administrator,
John Waycott **667-5613**
Claims Administrator,
Ms. Dorothy Wasylynchuk 667-5319
Assessment Auditor, Dale Schmekel 667-5491

Appendix C

Selected Sources and Documents on Workers' Compensation

MAJOR REFERENCES

"Accidents at Work." Pamphlet of the Society of Labour Lawyers. London: Fabian Society, 1974. 15 pp.

The Adjustment of Pensions for Employment Accidents and Occupational Diseases to Variations in Economic Conditions. Report V. Geneva: International Social Security Association, 1971. 43 pp.

"Benefits in the Case of Industrial Accidents and Occupational Diseases, Report V(1)." Geneva: International Labour Office, 1964 (48th Session). 58 pp.

"Benefits in the Case of Industrial Accidents and Occupational Diseases, Report V(2)." Geneva: International Labour Office, 1964 (48th Session). 135 pp.

Chaplan, Margaret and John. F. Burton Jr. *Workmen's Compensation: A Bibliography.* A. G. Bush Library, Industrial Relations Centre, University of Chicago, 1225 East 60th Street, Chicago, Illinois 60637 (BIB-108, 9-2-200), September 1971. Contains approximately 400 entries of U.S. material up to September 1971 under the headings General Discussions and Theory, History, Accidents and Safety, Coverage, Income Maintenance Benefits, Laws and Legal Issues, Rehabilitation and Medical Care, Administration and Operation of Program, Insurance, Foreign and General Statistics, Services and Periodicals.

Cheit, Earland Margaret Gordon. *Occupational Disability and Public Policy.* New York: Wiley & Sons, 1963. 446 pp.

Claims Adjudication Manual. Vancouver: B.C. Workers' Compensation Board. Describes claims policies of the B.C. Board.

"Considerations on Workers' Compensation and Universal Sickness and Accident Insurance: Identical or Fraternal Twins." Research Department, Canadian Union of Public Employees, Ottawa, October 1980. 16 pp.

Current Concerns in Workmen's Compensation (The Grey Paper). Toronto: Ontario Workers' Compensation Board, December 1979. 21 pp.

Eastman, Crystal. "Work Accidents and the Law." In *The Pittsburgh Survey: Findings in Six Volumes.* New York: New York Charities Publication Committee, 1910.

Examination of the Financial Structure of the Workmen's Compensation Board and An Assessment of the Actuarial Deficits. Toronto: Wyatt Company, June 1978. 500 pp.

Gilbey, Bill. "Trade Unionist Upset by Changes in Workers' Compensation Act [Saskatchewan]." *Briarpatch*, Vol. 10, No. 2 (March 1981): 13-14.

Glasbeek, H. J. and R. A. Hasson. "Fault—The Great Hoax." In Lewis Klar (ed.), *Studies in Canadian Tort Law*. Toronto: Butterworths, 1977. See section entitled "Workmen's Compensation," pp. 417-19.

Guest, Dennis. "Workers' Compensation in The Emergence of Social Security in Canada." Vancouver: University of British Columbia Press, 1980.

Hanes, David G. *The First British Workmen's Compensation Act, 1897*. New Haven: Yale University Press, 1968.

Hasson, Reuben. *The Wyatt Report on Workmen's Compensation: A Nightmare*. Toronto: Ontario Law Union Health and Safety Collective, 1978. 10 pp. Also published in *La Revue de Droit Social/Low Income Law*, Vol. I, No. 3 (1980), 18-20.

How to Solve Your Case with the W.C.B. Toronto: Union of Injured Workers, 1978. 15 pp., English and Italian.

Ison, Terence G. "Human Disability and Personal Income." In Lewis Klar (ed.), *Studies in Canadian Tort Law*. Toronto: Butterworths, 1977, pp. 425-53.

Ison, Terence G. *Information Access and the Workmen's Compensation Board*. Research Publication #4. Toronto: Ontario Commission on Freedom of Information and Individual Privacy, January 1979.

Ison, Terence G. *Sickness and Injury Compensation—A Proposal for Reform in British Columbia*. Vancouver: 1968.

King, Andrew and Nick McCombie. "Workers' Comp.: Legal Right or Social Welfare?" *This Magazine*, Vol. 15, No. 1 (February-March 1981): 34-38.

Larson, Arthur. *Workmen's Compensation for Occupational Injuries and Death*. New York: Matthew Bender, 1980. There is a two-volume desk edition and a ten-volume treatise. This is the major single U.S. legal source of information on workers' compensation. There is no corresponding Canadian source book.

Legge, B. J. *The Canadian System of Workmen's Compensation*. n. p., 1972. 150 pp.

Lloyd, David (ed.) *Workmen's Compensation Law Review*. Vol. I (1974) to Vol. IV (1977/78). Buffalo, N.Y.: William S. Hein & Co. A compendium of major U.S. law review articles on the subject.

Lubove, R. "Workmen's Compensation and the Prerogatives of Voluntarism." *Labour History*, Vol. 8, No. 3 (1967): 254-79.

Meredith, Sir William. "Laws in Relation to the Liability of Employers." Interim Report. Toronto: Ontario Sessional Papers, Vol. XLIV, Part XIV.

"Occupational Accidents and the Law." Report of the Society of Labour Lawyers. London: Fabian Society, 1970. 17 pp.

"Occupational Diseases." Workmen's Compensation Board of Ontario, 2 Bloor Street East, Toronto, Ontario, M4W 3C3, 1980. 21 pp.

Ontario Workmen's Compensation Board Adjudication Branch Manuals, Parts I and II. Toronto, n. d. Describes claims policies of the Ontario Board.

Page, S. John, "Case Comment: Re: Gianoukakis and the Workmen's Compensation Board." *La Revue de Droit Social/Low Income Law*, Vol. I, No. 3 (Jan. 1980): 12-17.

Paterson, Craig. "Practice Under the Workers' Compensation Act of British Columbia." In *Practice Before Administrative Tribunals*, The Continuing Legal Education

Society of British Columbia, Vancouver, B.C., November 1980. 70 pp., tables, forms.

Paterson, Craig. "W.C.B. Investment Decisions: Health Issues Take a Back Seat." *Left-words* Vol. 3, No. 3 (June 1981).

Paterson, Craig and Judith Neamton. *Workers' Health, Safety and Compensation: A Preliminary Bibliography of Canadian Commissions and Inquiries.* Vancouver: Capilano College Labour Studies Program, August 1978. 53 pp., index. Contains references to all Canadian inquiries into Workers' Compensation up to 1978, the reports of which are invaluable guides to the history and policy of compensation.

Piva, Michael J. *The Workingmen's Compensation Movement in Ontario. Ontario History*, 67 (1) (March 1975): 39-56.

Pope, Louise. *The Impact of Social Change on the Organization of Welfare Services, 1891-1921: Social Policy Considerations in the Movement Towards Workmen's Compensation.* M.S.W. Thesis, University of Toronto, 1966.

Reed, G. W. T., Q.C. "Workmen's Compensation in Ontario." In Law Society of Upper Canada, Special Lectures, "Employment Law." Toronto: Richard De Boo Ltd., 1976, pp. 95-148.

Report of the Select Committee of the Legislative Assembly on Workers' Compensation. Government of Alberta, April 1980.

Report of the Workers' Compensation Study Committee. Government of New Brunswick, February 1980.

Sanderson, Barbara L. *Selected Bibliography on the Legal Aspects of Workmen's Compensation.* Vancouver: B.C. WCB, 1977.

Somers, Herman and Anne. *Workmen's Compensation.* New York: John Wiley, 1954.

Statistics Canada. "Workers' Compensation." Cat. #86-501 (April 1980). An excellent statistical overview of Canadian WCBs, the first comprehensive statistical report of this type prepared in Canada. It covers all twelve schemes, using the reporting years 1975-77, providing data on pensions, claims, benefit levels, assessments, costs, assets and liabilities. 63 pp., 26 tables and charts, English and French. Prepared by the Social Security Section of the Health Division of Statistics Canada.

Submission of the Ontario Federation of Labour to the Paul C. Weiler Task Force on Workmen's Compensation in Ontario. Toronto: June 1980. 47 pp.

Weiler, Paul C. "Reshaping Workers' Compensation for Ontario." Report submitted to Robert G. Elgie, M.D., Ontario Minister of Labour. Toronto: November 1980. 146 pp., tables.

"The Weiler Report: A Step Forward for Injured Workers?" Toronto: Committee on the Weiler Study, 1981. 4 pp.

Weinstein, J. "Big Business and the Origins of Workmen's Compensation." *Labour History*, Vol. 8, No. 2, (1967): 156-74.

Will Injured Workers Get a Fair Hearing? Committee on the Weiler Study, Toronto, June 1980. 53 pp.

Willis's Workmen's Compensation Acts, 1925-1943, 37th ed. London: Butterworths, 1945.

Workers' Compensation Legislation in Canada. Labour Canada, Ottawa: September 1, 1980. 38 pp., tables. An excellent summary and overview of the major provisions across Canada.

Workers' Compensation Reporter Series, Vol. I (1973) to Vol. V (1980). Vancouver: B.C. Workers' Compensation Board. The only ongoing published series of policy decisions by any Canadian WCB. Includes criminal injuries, compensation and occupational health and safety decisions.

"Workmen's Compensation." Section 50,000 in *Canadian Employment Safety and Health Guide* (2 vols.) Don Mills, Ontario: CCH Canadian Limited Topical Law Reports, 1980.

Association of Workers' Compensation Boards of Canada
16 Lincombe Drive
Thornhill, Ontario
(#416-881-1093)

Executive Director: Mr. Ken Harding

The Association has been in existence sporadically since 1917-18. Minutes of Annual Conventions are in existence, but not published as a body. Its stated purpose has been to sponsor informal information exchange among the provinces. Mr. Harding was formerly a senior executive with the Ontario WCB and has been retained on a per-diem basis as an Executive Director only since June 1980 (part-time since 1978). The Association does not provide any direct services to workers or trade unions, although Mr. Harding can supply a wealth of historical information about WCB administration, personnel, and legislative schemes. With Mr. Harding's appointment, the Association may take on more active roles of inter-governmental liaison. For example, simple and available comprehensive WCB data is required by trade unions, industry and government personnel.

MINOR REFERENCES*

"Accidents are Costly." *Labour Gazette* 1976: 293.

"B.C. Reforms." *Labour Gazette* 1974: 458.

"C.N.T.U. Protest." *Labour Gazette* 1976: 10.

Gauvin, M. "Labour Legislation in Canada, 1974, Part 4: Workmen's Compensation." *Labour Gazette* 1975: 542-52.

Gauvin, M. "Labour Legislation in Canada, 1975, Part 5: Workers' Compensation." *Labour Gazette* 1976: 495-97.

Gauvin, M. "Labour Legislation in Canada, 1976, Part 5: Workers' Compensation." *Labour Gazette* 1977: 374-77.

Gauvin, M. "Labour Legislation in Canada, 1977, Part 5: Workers' Compensation." *Labour Gazette* 1978: 560-63.

Genest, J. "La Commission des Accidents du Travail (Quebec)." *L'Action Nationale* 67 (1978): 710-26.

Harrington, M. "Newfoundland Fishermen Want Act Changed." *Financial Post*, April 12, 1980.

"High Employer Premiums." *Labour Gazette* 1976: 66-67.

House, M. F. "Labour Legislation in 1973, Part 2: Workmen's Compensation." *Labour Gazette* 1974: 207-13.

Jones, D. F. "Compensation For Injuries Needs Overhaul." *Financial Post*, November 24, 1979.

* As extracted from *Canadian Periodical Index* for years 1974-79.

"Ontario Benefits Raised." *Labour Gazette* 1974: 610.
"Ontario W.C.B. Undergoing Major Changes." *Labour Gazette* 1973: 715-16.
"Quebec (Asbestos) Miners Compensated." *Labour Gazette* 1975: 676.
Starr, M. "How Employers Can Save by Improving Safety Record." Digest of Address. *Financial Post*, March 29, 1975.
"W.C.B. Allowances." *Labour Gazette* 1974: 607.
Weinstein, L. Treating the Victims of Industrial Accidents. *Labour Gazette* 1974: 191-93.
Wigle, W. S. "Compensation Laws Deny Workers Basic Right of a Day in Court." *Financial Post*, August 24, 1974.
Wirfs, R. M. "B.C. Workers' Compensation: A Model for Other Jurisdictions." *Labour Gazette* 1977: 404-7.
"Workmen's Compensation." *Labour Gazette* 1974: 397.
"Workmen's Compensation Benefits Increased." *Labour Gazette* 1975: 676.

Appendix D

Selected Legal Source Materials on Canadian Occupational Health and Safety Laws

Canadian Employment Safety and Health Guide. Two volumes. Don Mills, Ontario: CCH Canadian Limited Topical Law Reports, 1980. Contains all provincial and federal occupational health statutes together with sections entitled "Employers' and Workers' Duties and Rights," "Occupational Safety," "Occupational Health," "Toxic Substances," "Administration, Inspection and Enforcement," "Workmen's Compensation," and "New Developments."

Canadian Occupational Health and Safety Law. 10 volumes. Covers statutes and regulations of federal government and all provinces, with annual amendments. Available from Corpus Information Services, 1450 Don Mills Road, Don Mills, Ontario.

Critical Notes on (Ontario's) "Bill 70: An Act Respecting the Occupational Health and Occupational Safety of Workers." Research Department, Canadian Union of Public Employees, Suite 800, 233 Gilmour Street, Ottawa, Canada K2P 0P5, December 1977. 72 pp.

Directory: Occupational Safety and Health Legislation in Canada, 1980. Ottawa: Labour Canada, 1980. 86 pp.

Directory: Occupational Safety and Health Legislation in Canada, 1974. Toronto: Labour Safety Council of Ontario, Ministry of Labour. 162 pp.

Doern, G. Bruce. *Regulatory Processes and Jurisdictional Issues in the Regulation of Hazardous Products in Canada*. Background Study No. 41. Ottawa: Science Council of Canada, 1977.

Franson, Robert T. et al. *Canadian Law and the Control of Exposure to Hazards*. Background Study No. 39. Ottawa: Science Council of Canada, 1977.

Gibbs, G. W. and P. Pintus. "Occupational Safety and Health Legislation in Canada Applicable to Mining." Appendix II in *Health and Safety in the Canadian Mining Industry*. Kingston: Queen's University, Centre for Resource Studies, 1978.

Hazards at Work: Law and the Workplace. Proceedings of a Conference (November 1977). Corpus Information Services, 1450 Don Mills Road, Don Mills, Ontario.

Ince, John G. *Environmental Law: A Study of Legislation Affecting The Environment of British Columbia*. West Coast Environmental Law Association, #1012, 207 West Hastings Street, Vancouver, B.C. V6B 1H7. 1976. 209 pp.

Kuhner, Thomas S. *New Directions in Ontario Health and Safety Legislation*. Paper presented at McGill University Conference on Industrial Health and Safety, March 29, 1978, Montreal, Quebec. Toronto: Ontario Ministry of Labour, 1978. 18 pp.

Laframboise, H. L. *The Federal Scene*. Paper presented at McGill University Conference on Industrial Health and Safety, March 29, 1978, Montreal, Quebec. Ottawa: Labour Canada, 1978.

Mitchell, Heather. *Federal Control of Toxic Substances in Canada*. Paper presented to the International Institute for Environment and Society, Berlin, March 14, 1978. Available through Canadian Environmental Law Association, 5th Floor South, 8 York Street, Toronto, Ontario, M5J 1R2.

Nash, Michael Izumi. *The Best and the Worst: Reviewing Canadian Occupational Health and Safety Law*. Published paper prepared for USWA Conference on Occupational Health, Washington, D.C. Sept. 1979. 51 pp. Mr. Nash is available at Canadian Environmental Law Association, 8 York Street, 5th Floor South, Toronto, Ontario, M5J 1R2.

Occupational Health in Canada—Current Status, Ottawa: Health and Welfare Canada, June 1977. Contains useful government organization charts and brief explanations for each jurisdiction together with references to non-government organizations in each jurisdiction, such as trade unions, industry, safety, and professional groups. 119 pp.

Appendix E

Selected Canadian Books and Articles on Workers' Health, 1974-80

MAJOR REFERENCES

Books

Backhouse, Constance and Leah Cohen. *The Secret Oppression: Sexual Harassment of Working Women*. Toronto: Macmillan, 1978.

Gibbs, G. W. and P. Pintus. *Health and Safety in the Canadian Mining Industry*. Kingston: Queen's University, Centre for Resource Studies, 1978.

Grand'Maison, J. *Milieux de Travail à Réinventer*. Montréal: Presses de l'Université de Montréal, 1975.

Howard, Ross. "Jobs Versus the Environment: Mercury Pollution by Reed Paper Limited and Dow Chemicals." In Ross Howard, *Poisons in Public*. Toronto: James Lorimer & Co., 1980.

Howard, Ross. "Lead Poisoning and the Laws." In Ross Howard, *Poisons in Public*. Toronto: James Lorimer & Co., 1980.

Hushion, Ogilvy Associates Ltd. *An Assessment of the Effectiveness of Government Decision-Making Processes in the Field of Occupational Health and Safety*. Technical Report No. 5. Ottawa: Economic Council of Canada, March 1981.

Leyton, Elliot. *Dying Hard: The Ravages of Industrial Carnage*. Toronto: McClelland and Stewart, 1975. Treats the radiation hazard from fluorspar mining industry at St. Lawrence, Newfoundland.

Manga, Pran, Robert Broyles, and Gil Reschenthaler. *Occupational Health and Safety: Issues and Alternatives*. Technical Report No. 6. Ottawa: Economic Council of Canada, March 1981.

Pethick, Derek. "The Nanaimo Mine Disaster: 1887." In *British Columbia Disasters*. Langley, B.C.: Stagecoach Publishing Co., 1978.

Policies and Poisons: The Containment of Long-term Hazards to Human Health in the Environment and in the Workplace. Science Council of Canada, Report #28. Ottawa: October 1977.

Powell, Clair. "Asbestos Study Opens Pandora's Box." *Briarpatch*, Vol. 9, No. 6 (July/August 1980).

Scott, Jack. "The Most Dangerous Mines in the World." In *Sweat and Struggle: Working Class Struggles in Canada, 1789-1899*. Vancouver: New Star Books, 1974.

Scott, Jack. "The Nine-Hour Movement and Child Labour." In *Sweat and Struggle: Working Class Struggles in Canada, 1789-1899*. Vancouver: New Star Books, 1974.

Stephens, David E. *It Happened at Moose River*. Windsor, N.S.: Lancelot Press, 1974. A popular account of the Moose River mine disaster of 1936.

Tataryn, Lloyd. *Dying for a Living: The Politics of Industrial Death*. Ottawa: Deneau and Greenberg, 1979.

Articles

"Accident-Injury Experience and Cost in Canadian Industry . . . 1965-74." Ottawa: Labour Canada Economics and Research Branch, July 1975.

Aykroyd, Colin. "An Examination of the Right to Refuse Unsafe Work." *B.C. Labour Research Bulletin*, Vol. 6, No. 6 (June 1978).

Aykroyd, Colin, "O.S.H.A. Symposium for Labour Educators on Occupational Safety and Health." *B.C. Labour Research Bulletin*, Vol. 8, No. 1 (January 1980).

Aykroyd, Colin, "Occupational Health and Safety Update." *B.C. Labour Research Bulletin*, Vol. 8, No. 1 (January 1980): 27-42.

Basuk, J. and A. Nichols. "An Overview of the Hazards Due to Ionizing Radiation in the Canadian Context." Ottawa: Science Council of Canada, 1977.

Bercuson, David Jay. "Tragedy at Bellevue: Anatomy of a Mine Disaster." *Labour/Le Travailleur* 1978: 221-23.

Bergeron, P. et al. "Report of the Asbestosis Working Group." Ottawa: Health and Welfare Canada, 1976.

"A Bibliography on the 'Right to Know.'" *Canadian Occupational Health and Safety News*, Vol. 2, No. 20, p. 3. Contains some 27 references to articles and studies in U.S., England, and Canada since 1975.

Blackburn, Karen. "You're Totally Disabled When You're Dead." *North Country: Ontario's News Magazine*, Vol. 1, No. 3 (July-August 1974): 10-14. Describes pension disability rating system of Ontario WCB and the Union of Injured Workers.

Brophy, Jim and John Jackson. "The Story of the Windsor Occupational Safety and Health Council." *Canadian Dimension*, Vol. 14, No. 7 (June 1980).

Brown, Joan C. "Occupational Health and Safety—the Right to Know." *Labour Gazette*, Vol. 78, No. 2/3 (February-March 1978).

Clark, R. S. "Work Injury Experience and Cost in Canadian Industry, 1969-78." Ottawa: Labour Canada, October 1979.

Daniels, Doug. "The Class Basis of Stress." *Briarpatch*, Vol. 9, No. 5 (June 1980).

Deverell, John and the Latin American Working Group. *Falconbridge: Portrait of a Canadian Mining Multinational*. Toronto: James Lorimer & Co., 1975. See pp. 90-100, 104-197.

Doern, Bruce. "The Political Economy of Regulating Occupational Health: The Ham and Beaudry Reports." *Canadian Public Administration*, Vol. 20 (1977): 1-35.

"Dying for a Living." *Canadian Dimension*, Vol. 14, No. 7 (June 1980).

"Fatalities in Canadian Industry, 1965-74." Ottawa: Labour Canada Economics and Research Branch, May 1975.

"Fatalities in Canadian Industry, 1967-76," *Labour Gazette*, Vol. 12 (1977): 556-61.

Gallagher, Pat and Don Kossick. "Grain Dust: Union Proves Health Hazard." *Next Year Country: Saskatchewan News Magazine*, Vol. 3, No. 3 (August-September 1975): 10-13.

George, Anne. "Occupational Health Hazards to Women: A Synoptic View." Ottawa: Advisory Council on the Status of Women. See also summary in *B.C. Labour Research Bulletin*, Vol. 6, No. 5 (May 1978).

Gibbs, Dr. G. W. "Health Hazards—Confrontation on the Job." A paper presented to the Conference on Occupational Health and Safety, McGill University, Montreal, Quebec, March 1978).

Glasbeek, H. J. "The Worker as Victim." *Canadian Forum*, March 1980, pp. 17-19.

Ison, Terence G. "The Dimensions of Industrial Disease." *Canadian Medical Association Journal* 200 (1978): 118. Also in *Hazards at Work*. Toronto: Corpus Information Services, 1977, pp. 63-74. Also in Queen's University Industrial Relations Centre Reprint Series No. 35. Kingston: Queen's University, 1978.

Ison, Terence G. "Occupational Health and Wildcat Strikes." Queen's University Industrial Relations Centre Reprint Series No. 45. Kingston: Queen's University, 1979.

Ison, Terence G. "Work Now — Grieve Later" (18 pp.), A paper presented to the Conference on Occupational Health and Safety, McGill University, Montreal, Quebec, March 1978. Toronto: Osgoode Hall Law School, York University, 1978.

Lax, Clifford C. "The Toronto Lead-Smelter Controversy." In William Leiss (ed.), *Ecology Versus Politics in Canada*. Toronto: University of Toronto Press, 1979.

Leonard, Lynda. "Occupational Health and Safety: A Critical View." *Labour Gazette*, April 1978.

McArthur, Mary. "Exposure to Asbestos. A Certain Death!" *Canadian Dimension*, Vol. 14, No. 7 (June 1980).

McQuaig, Linda. "Occupational Death," *Maclean's*, May 19, 1980.

Manga, Pran and Robert Broyles. "The Occupational Health and Safety Act (Bill 70) and Health Care Institutions in Ontario." *Canadian Journal of Public Health*, Vol. 72, No. 1: 17-19.

Neamton, Judith and Craig Paterson. "Workers' Health, Safety and Compensation: A Preliminary Bibliography of Canadian Federal and Provincial Government Commissions and Inquiries." Capilano College Labour Studies Publication Series #1, Capilano College, North Vancouver, British Columbia (1978).

Paehlke, Robert. "Occupational Health Policy in Canada." In William Leiss (ed.), *Ecology Versus Politics in Canada*. Toronto: University of Toronto Press, pp. 97-129.

"The Person Papers: Health Hazards at Work." Ottawa: Canadian Advisory Council on the Status of Women, 1976.

Price-Munn, Nancy. "Hazard Inventory for Garment and Textile Workers." Occupational Health and Safety Project, Humber College, Rexdale, Ontario.

Rabinovitch, Arthur. "Workers' Compensation as a Source of Occupational Health Statistics." Ottawa: Health and Welfare Canada, November 1976.

Rabinovitch, Victor. "Crisis in the Workplace." *Perception*, Vol. 2 (March/April 1979): 21-23.

"Reproductive Health Hazards in the Workplace: Position Paper." Ottawa: Canadian Advisory Council on the Status of Women, June 1980.

Reschenthaler, G. B. "Occupational Health and Safety in Canada: The Economics and Three Case Studies." Montreal: Institute for Research on Public Policy, 1979.

"The Role of the Occupational Environment Branch (B.C.)." *B.C. Labour Research Bulletin*, Vol. 6, No. 6 (June 1978).

"Safety Enforcement Policies and Practices in Canada, 1975," Ottawa: Economics and Research Branch, Canada Department of Labour, 1975.

Sass, Robert. "Occupational Health and Safety: Contradictions and the Conventional Wisdom." *Labour Gazette* 1977: 157-61.

Sass, Robert. "Stress: The Tolerated Bedfellow." *Canadian Dimension*, Vol. 14, No. 7 (June 1980).

Sass, Robert. "The Underdevelopment of Occupational Health and Safety in Canada." In William Leiss (ed.), *Ecology Versus Politics in Canada*. Toronto: University of Toronto Press, 1979, pp. 72-96.

Sauvé, R. "Changements en matière de santé de securité au Québec." A paper presented to the Conference on Occupational Health and Safety, McGill University, Montréal, Québec, March 1978.

Sentes, Ray. "Labour Arbitration and the Refusal to Perform Hazardous Work." *Relations Industrielles*, Vol. 32, No. 1 (1977).

"Sexual Harassment of Working Women in British Columbia: A Discussion Paper." British Columbia Federation of Labour's Women's Rights Committee, and the Vancouver Women's Research Centre, February, 1980. 42 pp.; bibliography.

Smith, Doug. "Lead Poisoning in Manitoba." *Canadian Dimension*, Vol. 14, No. 7 (June 1980).

Surry, Jean. "An Annotated Bibliography For Industrial Accident Research and Related Fields." Toronto: Occupational Health and Safety Division, Ontario Ministry of Labour, 1978. This useful source, although somewhat out of date, contains hundreds of article references from around the world under the topics: General Accident Research; Industrial Accident Research; Agricultural Accident Research; Hospital and Laboratory Accident Research; Transportation Accident Research; Home, Recreation and Public Place Accident Research; Human Engineering; and General. 158 pp.

"A Survey of Developments in Occupational Health and Safety." *B.C. Labour Research Bulletin*, Vol. 6, No. 6 (June 1978).

Swartz, Donald. "New Forms of Worker Participation: A Critique of Quality of Working Life." *Studies in Political Economy*, No. 5 (Spring 1981): 55-68.

Swift, Jamie and The Development Education Centre. "The Big Nickel: Inco at Home and Abroad." Kitchener: Between the Lines Publishers, 1977. See chapter "Broken Bodies," pp. 123-41, which describes Inco's mine and smelter operation at Sudbury.

Task Force on Arsenic. *Final Report*. Ottawa: Canadian Public Health Association, 1977.

Tudiver, Neil. "Vinyl Chloride in Manitoba." *Canadian Dimension*, Vol. 14, No. 7 (June 1980).

Walker, Cathy. "Uranium Mining Banned in B.C." *Canadian Dimension*, Vol. 14, No. 7 (June 1980).

"Will Injured Workers Get a Fair Hearing?" "Committee On the Weiler Study, Toronto, June 1980.

"Working-Injury Experience and Cost in Canadian Industry, 1967-76. *Labour Gazette*, December 1977.

Wortman, Susan. "The Unhealthy Business of Making Clothes," *Canadian Dimension*, Vol. 14, No. 7 (June 1980).

MINOR REFERENCES*

"Accident Prevention." *Canadian Labour* 23 (March 1978): 24, 29; French text: 23, 38.
"Accidents are Costly." *Labour Gazette* 1976: 293.
"Accident Rates Related to Management Safety Policy." *Labour Gazette* 1977: 149.
"B.C. Grain Elevators Still a Hazard." *Canadian Labour* 24 (August 24, 1979): 6; French text: 6.
Bagnall, J. "There's Safety in Numbers." *Financial Post*, July 8, 1978.
Bannon, S. "Canada Safety Council: Focus on Industrial Safety and Health." *Labour Gazette* 1976: 525-30.
Booth, A. "Safety First." (Quebec) *Financial Post*, October 28, 1978.
Bourgeois, P. "McGill University 26th Annual Conference: Are Health and Safety Negotiable?" *Labour Gazette* 78 (July 1978): 307-10.
Brown, I. "Budding Safety Act May Sprout Thorns [Ontario Bill 139]." *Financial Post*, January 22, 1977.
Brown, J. C. "Inspectorate." *Labour Gazette* 78 (October 1978): 461-66; November-December 1978: 554-59.
Brown, J. C. "Occupational Health and Safety: The Importance of Worker Participation." *Labour Gazette* 78 (April 1978): 123-28.
"Call for New Mechanisms (Ontario)." *Labour Gazette* 78 (August 1978): 335.
"Canadian Centre for Occupational Health and Safety Addressed by J. C. Munro." *Labour Gazette* 77 (December 1977): 550-52.
"Centre for Occupational Health and Safety." *Canadian Personnel* 26 (May 1979): 43.
Chafe, F. "Current Safety Issues: Editorial." *Canadian Labour* 23 (March 1978): 1; French text: 1.
"Commitment Cuts Accidents." Digest of Address by M. Starr. *Financial Post*, November 26, 1977.
"Construction Safety (Ontario)." *Labour Gazette* 1974: 688-89.
Davidson, J. "We Didn't Trust Them and They Didn't Trust Us [Polysar]." *Canadian Personnel* 25 (October 1978): 28-29.
"Death and Injuries, 1977. *Labour Gazette* 1978: 491.
Dekar, A. D. "Psychologie de la prudence et management de la securité." *Commerce*, Dec. 1976: 26-28, 30; Jan. 1977: 22-25, Feb. 1977: 4-6; Mar. 1977: 8-10, 12; Apr. 1977: 10-12, 14.
"Explosion! The Great Halifax Disaster of 1917." *Reader's Digest* 111 (December 1977): 233-36, 238-42.
Gauvin, M. "Labour Legislation in Canada, 1976: Part 4: Occupational Safety and Health." *Labour Gazette* (July 1977): 321-24.
Gauvin, M. "Labour Legislation in Canada, 1977: Part 3: Occupational Safety and Health." *Labour Gazette* (September 1978): 416-19.
Glazner, J. "Health and Safety: The Bill Will Be Huge." *Executive* 17 (1975): 27, 29-31.
Godin, P. "Les damnés de l'amiante." *Le Maclean* 16 (January 1976): 15-20.
Goldstein, K. N. "How to Reduce the Cost of Accidents at Work." *Financial Post*, March 4, 1978.
"Health and Safety (Quebec)." *Labour Gazette* 1977: 22.

* As extracted from *Canadian Periodical Index* for years 1974-1980.

"Health and Safety (United States)." *Labour Gazette* 1974: 551.
Hebert, G. "Management et prévention des assicents du travail." With English summary. *Relations Industrielles* Vol. 31, No. 1 (1976): 3-31.
House, M. F. "Labour Legislation in 1973: Part I: Industrial Safety and Health." *Labour Gazette* 1974: 140-44.
"I.A.P.A. Annual Conference." *Labour Gazette* 1975: 414.
"In Saskatchewan, They Let You Know What's Poisoning You." *Saturday Night* 93 (November 1978): 4-5.
"Inadequate Warning of Industrial Hazards: Address by J. Major." *Canadian Labour* 23 (March 1978): 2-4, 14; French text: 2-4, 35.
"Industrial Accidents (France)." *Labour Gazette* 1974: 839.
"Industry Report on Grain Hazards 'Useful Guide.' " *Canadian Labour* 24 (March 30, 1979): 7; French text: 7.
Julien, B. C. "Les accidents: un iceberg." *Commerce* 79 (1977): 70-72, 74.
Kehoe, M. "Legislation Safety — Union Proposals." *Canadian Labour* 23 (March 24, 1978): 21-23; French text: 20-22.
Law, C. E. "Safety Work Research Must be Made Public." *Financial Post*, March 10, 1979.
"Legislative Controls." *Labour Gazette* October 1976: 527-29.
Louther, W. "Roads of Death, Rivers of Gall [Texas]." *Maclean's* 92 (May 28, 1979): 30-31.
McDermott, D. "Health and Safety — A Priority for Unions." *Canadian Labour* 24 (October 26, 1979): 9-10; French text: 9-10.
Major, J. "Strong Workplace Safety Law in Quebec." *Canadian Labour* 25 (February 29, 1980): 9-11; French text: 9-11.
"Major Diseases Linked to Industrial Processes." *Labour Gazette* 1976: 575.
Manga, P. and R. W. Broyles. "O.H.A. Fights New Bill [70] on Health and Safety." *Perception* 2 (May-June 1979): 43-44.
"Manitoba Changes Laws on Safety [Workplace Safety and Health Act]." *Financial Post*, September 10, 1977.
Martland, S. "Resisting Multinational Asbestos: The Struggle for Workplace Safety in Newfoundland." *Alternatives* (1978): 52-54.
Meechan, V. "Things That Go Bump in the Night [Glace Bay, N.S.]." *Maclean's* 92 (March 12, 1979): 23.
Miller, D. G. "Emergency: Nurses and Glace Bay Mining Disaster — 1978." *Canadian Nurse* 75 (May 1979): 46-50.
Morgan, R. "Tracing Causes of Industrial Illness." *Canadian Labour* 23 (March 1978): 19-20; French version: 23-24.
"Most Workers At Risk (United States)." *Labour Gazette* 78 (September 1978): 390.
"N.B.F.L. Withdraws from I.S.C. Conferences." *Canadian Labour* 24 (June 8, 1979): 8; French text: 8.
"Newfoundland Unionists Gear up for Health and Safety." *Canadian Labour* 24 (October 12, 1978): 6; French text: 6.
"Occupational Health and Safety Laws." *Canadian Labour* 24 (October 26, 1979): 6; French text: 6.
"Praise, Rather Than Blame, Improves Safety Record." *Canadian Personnel* 20 (1973): 38-39.
Puttee, A. "Persistence and a Good Cause." Editorial from *The Voice* March 18, 1910. Reprinted in *Canadian Ethnic Studies* Vol. 10, No. 2 (1978): 98-99.

Rabinovitch, V. "Federal Inaction on Health and Safety." *Canadian Labour* 24 (May 11, 1979): 11-12; French text: 11-12.
"Reproductive Process Endangered." *Labour Gazette* October 1975: 516-17.
"Review Asbestos Claims—Ontario W.C.B." *Labour Gazette* 1975: 235.
"Right to Refuse an Unsafe Job (Quebec)." *Labour Gazette* 78 (November-December 1978): 491.
"Safety Action at the Workplace." *Canadian Labour* 24 (October 26, 1979): 5; French text: 5.
Vinet, A. "Santé et Securité au Travail." *Relations Industrielles* Vol. 34, No. 2 (1979): 383-85.
Sass, R. "Social in the Technical: Effects on Workplace Health and Safety." *Alternatives* 9 (Winter 1979): 45-48.
Starr, M. "Two Exceptional Companies." *Canadian Personnel* (September 1978): 17-19.
Sormany, P. "Perdre sa vie à la gagner." *L'Actualité* (March 1979): 20.
"Stop the Slaughter in Industry—Steelworkers." *Labour Gazette* 1975: 415-17.
"Sweden Takes Another Step." *Labour Gazette* 78 (August 1978): 335-36.
Tataryn, L. "Tortured Future of Elliot Lake." *Saturday Night* 91 (June 1976): 13-20.
"U.S. Government Sued." *Labour Gazette* 78 (May 1978): 170.
"Unger, H. "Do Workers Have a Right to Know about On-the-Job Dangers that Might Kill Them?" *Canadian Business Magazine* 50 (October 1977): 44.
Vandal, J. "Gagner sa vie sans la perdre." With English summary. *Perception* 2 (March-April 1979): 17-18.
Vitek, J. "Occupational Diseases Still Increasing, I.L.O." *Labour Gazette* 1975: 243-44.
"Vocational Disease Increasing [West Germany]." *Labour Gazette* 1977: 528.
Watkins, L. "Stench of Death [Point Tupper, Nova Scotia]." *Maclean's* 88 (November 3, 1975): 20.

Appendix F

Selected Workers' Health Films

CANADA

Acceptable Risks. Slide-tape show, 15 minutes. Available from Windsor Occupational Safety and Health Council, 824 Tecumseh Road East, Windsor, Ontario, N8X 2S3 (519-254-4192). Purchase $75 (institutional $100), rental $10.

This show, produced by W.O.S.H., provides insight into the whole issue of occupational health and safety. It examines the problems in several of Windsor's industries. The actions taken by workers to alleviate these dangers are outlined.

L'Amiante Ça Tue (1977). Directed by Richard Boutet. Colour, 16 mm., 30 minutes. In French. Available from Development Education Centre, 121 Avenue Road, Toronto, Ontario, M5R 263.

Asbestos: A Program for Protection. A slide-tape show, 25 minutes. Available from Windsor Occupational Safety and Health Council, 824 Tecumseh Road East, Windsor, Ontario, N8X 2S3 (519-254-4192). Loan: transportation costs.

This show, produced by the National Institute for Occupational Safety and Health in the United States, describes in considerable detail the steps to be taken in the safe removal of asbestos from buildings.

Coke Ovens: A High Risk Job (NFB, 106C 0178 527). Colour, 12 minutes 8 seconds. Available from National Film Board of Canada (for addresses see p. 305).

Union and company representatives at Stelco Ltd., Hamilton, Ontario, describe the hazards for topside workers of working on the ovens, and the efforts being made to improve conditions.

Georges Dionne: Un Mineur de l'amiante (NFB, 106 0278 524). Colour; 11 minutes 15 seconds. In French. Available from National Film Board of Canada (for addresses see p. 305).

Georges Dionne started working at 10 cents an hour sweeping up asbestos dust. Drinking water came out of a bucket covered with this dust. Retired because of asbestosis after 43 years in the asbestos mines of Thetford Mines, Québec, he talks about his experience as miner, union militant, and concerned citizen.

Dr. Epstein Talks About Chemicals in the Workplace (NFB, 106C 0178 530). Colour; 7 minutes 23 seconds. Available from National Film Board of Canada (for addresses see p. 305).

Dr. Samuel Epstein, professor of occupational and environmental health at the School of Medicine, University of Illinois, feels strongly that the worker should have the right to know what chemicals he is exposed to. A recent American government report estimated that 80% of the chemicals in the workplace are as yet unidentified. Dr. Epstein advises workers what to do if they want to avoid being unwittingly exposed to dangerous chemicals.

Dr. Epstein Talks About the Chemical Explosion (NFB, 106C 0178 531). Colour; 8 minutes 37 seconds. Available from National Film Board of Canada (for addresses see p. 305).

Since the 1930s, the world has accommodated a huge growth in the use of chemicals, bringing widespread hazards as well as benefits. According to Dr. Epstein, the occupational carcinogens of today can become the environmental carcinogens of tomorrow.

Dr. Epstein Talks About Distortion of Information (NFB, 106C 0178 532). Colour; 13 minutes 2 seconds. Available from National Film Board of Canada (for addresses see p. 305).

Dr. Epstein believes that distortion of the data base on which decisions are made has become so serious as to endanger the proper functioning of a democratic system. He names incidents to prove his argument.

La Maladie, C'est les Compagnies (1977). Directed by Richard Boutet. Colour, 16 mm., 30 minutes. In French. Available from Development Education Centre, 121 Avenue Road, Toronto, Ontario, M5R 2G3.

Anthony Mazzocchi Talks About Chemicals and the Workers (NFB, 106C 0178 528). Colour; 9 minutes 10 seconds. Available from National Film Board of Canada (for addresses see p. 305).

"Every human being should have the right to make a product without having to put a piece of his life into that product." Anthony Mazzocchi, vice-president of the Oil, Chemical and Atomic Workers' Union in the United States, discusses the political and social reasons for occupational diseases.

Le Mépris N'Aura Q'Un Temps (1969, C.N.T.U.) Black and white, 16 mm., 95 minutes. In French with English subtitles. Available from Development Education Centre, 121 Avenue Road, Toronto, Ontario, M5R 2G3.

Our Health is Not for Sale (1978, NFB, 106C 0178 165). Directed by Boyce Richardson and David Newman. Produced by Andy Thomson and Peter Katadotis. Colour, 16 mm., 25 minutes 57 seconds. Available from National Film Board of Canada (for addresses see p. 305).

In the 1970s workers all over Canada began to realize that instead of leasing their labour they were selling their health. By recalling some of the more infamous strikes of the decade, this film examines the plight of the worker who frequently has no right to know what dangers he is exposed to.

The film can be a useful tool at union meetings, particularly if used in relation to discussing collective bargaining. Because of the vivid footage of such workplaces as the Inco copper smelter, it should be of interest to a general audience. But it would be most valuable to show after the more basic films have introduced health and safety issues.

The Right to Live (1977, Union of Injured Workers). Colour, 16 mm., 60 minutes. Available from Development Education Centre, 121 Avenue Road, Toronto, Ontario, M5R 2G3.

Robert Sass: Workers in Saskatchewan (NFB, 106C 0178 529). Colour; 9 minutes 12 seconds. Available from National Film Board of Canada (for addresses see p. 305).

The province of Saskatchewan is a leader in legislation for a cleaner workplace. Robert Sass, director of the Provincial Occupational Health and Safety Division, describes how workers must depend on their own efforts, and not on those of "experts," to clean up the workplace. He feels that unions have been too concerned about "time away from work, not time at work."

Homer Séguin Talks About Radiation at Elliot Lake (NFB, 106C 0178 526). Colour; 8 minutes 10 seconds. Available from National Film Board of Canada (for addresses see p. 305).

Homer Séguin, staff representative of the United Steelworkers of America in Elliot Lake, Ontario, describes the radiation tragedy among uranium miners in that small town. Lung cancer caused by radiation is a death sentence. According to Séguin, it must be prevented because it can't yet be cured.

Dr. Selikoff Talks About the Latency Period (NFB, 106C 0178 533). Colour; 6 minutes 40 seconds. Available from National Film Board of Canada (for addresses see p. 305).

Dr. Irving Selikoff, a leader in the identification of the health hazards posed by asbestos, describes how workers can suffer many years after the fact from overexposure to metal dusts, chemicals, and other dangerous substances. It can take 20, 30, or 40 years for the effects to show. There is a major decision that has not yet been made, namely, that people's health will no longer be deliberately endangered.

12,000 Men (NFB, 106C 0178 569). Colour, 16 mm., 34 minutes 27 seconds. Available from National Film Board of Canada (for addresses see p. 305).

The history of coal mining is a story of backbreaking labour, dangerous working conditions, meager salaries, and occasionally violent labour strife. The film documents the situation on Nova Scotia's Cape Breton Island in the 1920s explaining how the extraction and exploitation of one of the largest coal deposits in Canada led the miners there into an epic struggle for survival.

Two Union Leaders Talk About Workers and Health (NFB, 106C 0178 525). Colour, 16 mm., 9 minutes 17 seconds. Available from National Film Board of Canada (for addresses see below).

Jim Gill, director of legislation and community affairs of the United Auto Workers in Canada, and Dave Patterson, President of Local 6500 of the United Steelworkers of America in Sudbury, Ontario, describe briefly how workers are trying to get more control over conditions in their places of work—and progress is slowly being made. Since these films were produced, seven of the ten provinces plus the federal government have passed legislation giving the worker the legal right to refuse a job which he considers hazardous. P.E.I., Nova Scotia and New Brunswick have not passed a specific law to this effect.

Who Will I Sentence Now? (NFB, 106C 0178 043). Directed by Boyce Richardson and David Newman. Produced by Peter Katadotis. Colour, 16 mm., 28 minutes 50 seconds. Available from National Film Board of Canada (for addresses see below).

A grim document about diseases contracted in the workplace, the film takes us to Sudbury and Elliot Lake, Ont., Thetford Mines, Qué. and St. Lawrence, Nfld. It shows workers, widows, doctors, and a union leader in a fact gathering campaign designed to throw light on a social problem that is only now beginning to be recognized at the modern industrial workplace.

NATIONAL FILM BOARD OF CANADA

The NFB films listed above were directed by Boyce Richardson and produced by Andy Thomson and Peter Katadotis (unless otherwise indicated).

These films are distributed by the National Film Board of Canada and may be borrowed free of charge or purchased at your nearest NFB office, with the exception of offices in Rimouski, Trois-Rivières, Sherbrooke and Chicoutimi in the province of Québec. They are also available for sale on videocassette.

As well, the films are available through Labour Canada's National Industrial Relations Film Library on a no-charge basis and are distributed for the Library by NFB.

The following NFB Offices can supply the NFB films listed above.

National Film Board of Canada,
1161 West Georgie Street,
VANCOUVER, B.C.
V6E 3G4
Telephone: (604) 666-1716

National Film Board of Canada,
P.O. Box 2950, Station "M",
CALGARY, Alberta
T2P 3C3
Telephone: (403) 231-5338

National Film Board of Canada,
550 Sherbrooke Street West,
MONTREAL, Quebec
H3A 1B9
Telephone: (514) 283-4685

National Film Board of Canada,
647 St. James Street,
WINNIPEG, Manitoba
R3G 3J5
Telephone: (204) 985-4131

National Film Board of Canada,
Mackenzie Building,
1 Lombard Street,
TORONTO, Ontario
M5C 1J6
Telephone: (416) 369-4093

National Film Board of Canada,
150 Kent Street,
OTTAWA, Ontario
K1A 0M9
Telephone: (613) 996-4861/2

National Film Board of Canada,
1572 Barrington Street,
HALIFAX, N.S.
B3J 1Z6
Telephone: (902) 426-6001

Films can also be booked through the following NFB Offices:

BRITISH COLUMBIA

National Film Board of Canada,
545 Quebec Street,
PRINCE GEORGE, B.C.
V2L 1W6
Telephone: (604) 564-5657

National Film Board of Canada,
811 Wharf Street,
VICTORIA, B.C.
V8W 1T2
Telephone: (604) 388-3868

PRAIRIE REGION

National Film Board of Canada,
Centennial Building,
10031-103 Avenue,
EDMONTON, Alberta
T5J 0G9
Telephone: (403) 420-3010

National Film Board of Canada,
424-21st Street East,
SASKATOON, Saskatchewan
S7K 0C2
Telephone: (306) 665-4245

National Film Board of Canada,
1917 Broad Street,
REGINA, Saskatchewan
S4P 1Y1
Telephone: (306) 359-5012

ONTARIO

National Film Board of Canada,
10 West Avenue South,
HAMILTON, Ontario
L8N 3Y8
Telephone: (416) 523-2347

National Film Board of Canada,
Suite 205,
659 King Street East,
KITCHENER, Ontario
N2G 2M4
Telephone: (519) 743-4661

National Film Board of Canada,
195 First Avenue West,
NORTH BAY, Ontario
P1B 3B8
Telephone: (705) 472-4740

National Film Board of Canada,
New Federal Building,
Clarence Street,
KINGSTON, Ontario
K7L 1X0
Telephone: (613) 546-6748

National Film Board of Canada,
366 Oxford Street East,
LONDON, Ontario
N6A 1U7
Telephone: (519) 679-4120

National Film Board of Canada,
910 Victoria Avenue,
THUNDER BAY, Ontario
P7C 1B4
Telephone: (807) 623-5224

QUEBEC

National Film Board of Canada,
72 Cartier Street West,
CHICOUTIMI, Quebec
G7J 1G2
Telephone: (418) 543-0711

National Film Board of Canada,
124 Vimy Street,
RIMOUSKI, Quebec
G5L 3J6
Telephone: (418) 723-2613

National Film Board of Canada,
Suite 502, Pollack Building,
140 St-Antoine Street,
TROIS-RIVIÈRES, Quebec
G9A 5N6
Telephone: (819) 375-5811

National Film Board of Canada,
2 Place Quebec,
St-Cyrille Blvd. East,
QUEBEC, Quebec
G1R 2B5
Telephone: (418) 694-3852

National Film Board of Canada,
315 King Street West,
Suite 03,
SHERBROOKE, Quebec
J1H 1R2
Telephone: (819) 565-4915

ATLANTIC REGION

National Film Board of Canada,
Prince Street,
Sydney Shopping Mall,
SYDNEY, Nova Scotia
B1P 5K8
Telephone: (902) 562-1171

National Film Board of Canada,
Terminal Plaza Building,
1222 Main Street,
MONCTON, New Brunswick
E1C 1H6
Telephone: (506) 858-2463/4

National Film Board of Canada,
Canada Permanent Building,
1 Market Square,
SAINT JOHN, New Brunswick
E2L 1E7
Telephone: (506) 658-4996

National Film Board of Canada,
Building No. 255,
Pleasantville,
ST. JOHN'S, Newfoundland
A1A 1N3
Telephone: (709) 737-5005

National Film Board of Canada,
St. Duncan's Basilica Rec. Centre,
202 Richmond Street,
CHARLOTTETOWN, P.E.I.
C1A 1J2
Telephone: (902) 892-6612

National Film Board of Canada,
4 Herald Avenue,
CORNER BROOK, Newfoundland
A2H 6C3
Telephone: (709) 634-4295

UNITED STATES*

Another Day's Living (1980). Directed by Ken Light and Charles West. A Labor Occupational Health Program Film in co-operation with the International Woodworkers of America. Colour, 16 mm., 30 minutes. Rental $50 one showing, from LOHP Films, P.O. Box 315, Franklin Lakes, New Jersey 07417. Purchase $350, from LOHP Films, 2521 Channing Way, Berkeley, California 94720.

Primarily a health and safety film, it covers the forest industry from logging to timber and plywood mills. The lives of loggers and woodworkers are documented through the workers' eyes. Chemical dust, noise and other disease issues are canvassed, as well as traumatic injuries.

Asbestos: Fighting a Killer. Produced by Bonnie Bellow and Nick Egleson. Slide show and tape. Available from Oil, Chemical, and Atomic Workers, International Union, 1126-17 St. N.W., Washington, D.C. 20036.

* From Labour Occupational Health Program *MONITOR*, Vol. 8, No. 3 (May-June 1980): 7-9.

Asbestos: Fighting a Killer is a must for anyone interested in occupational disease. Its vivid photographs and powerful commentary are interwoven with the voices of workers who use asbestos, talking of their experiences. Interviews and songs make the show move along at a fast and interesting pace.

It discusses causes and effects of exposure to asbestos and shows ways workers can protect their health.

Bonnie Bellow and Nick Egleson have produced several other high-quality slide-tape shows, including one on textile hazards for the Amalgamated Clothing and Textile Workers Union, and one on organizing for OCAW.

Health Hazard in the Shop. Colour, 16 mm., 25 minutes. Available from University of Wisconsin, School for Workers, 1327 University Avenue, Madison, Wisconsin 53701.

The School for Workers at the University of Wisconsin has been offering films that differ from current trends in occupational health audio-visual materials, in that they are dramatizations. They have been effectively used in educational programs specifically discussing issues such as OSHA inspections or employee rights and responsibilities under the OSH Act.

These are good how-to-do-it films, easy to incorporate into training sessions or conferences. Generally, they are too specific to be shown to audiences unfamiliar with occupational health. The information and points made in the films are important, and one should overlook their sometimes stilted acting and context.

Occupational Hazards of Construction. Four slide-tape modules: Health and Safety Hazards of Construction, Chemical Hazards, Walking/Working Surfaces, and Hazards of Noise. Available from Labor Occupational Health Program, 2521 Channing Way, Berkeley, Ca. 94720.

These educational materials developed by California-based LOHP discuss both potential hazards of a construction site and the differences between safety and health hazards. The major show, Introduction to Health and Safety Hazards of Construction, is the most versatile of the four. The others are more specific and are probably most valuable to a building trades audience, but the vivid photography and taped narration have been effectively used by other groups. The Walking/Working Surfaces show discusses hazards of using ladders and scaffolds, and is probably appropriate only for use by an audience of building trades workers.

More Than a Paycheck. Directed by Frank Cavanaugh. narrated by John Wayne. Colour, 16 mm. Produced by George Washington University. Available from U.S. Department of Labor (OSHA).

More Than a Paycheck is a thoughtfully-made film that looks at workplaces where cancer-causing materials are used. But, unfortunately, it lacks the impact, emotion, and urgency of many of the other occupational health films. Visually, the footage is quite beautiful and in many cases shows work scenes seldom seen.

More Than a Paycheck shows a wide variety of workplace scenes, and contains strong narration by Dr. Irving Selikoff talking about the "seeds of cancer in the workplace." It also offers some solutions that industry is attempting to implement in the workplace. Comments by industry spokespeople from Johns-Manville and Exxon tend to make one feel that the overall problem is being dealt with by most industries. But statistics and descriptions by workers of the hazards they face show otherwise.

Generally, this film should be looked at as an introduction to carcinogens and the workplace. But it is bland in its approach to a gripping issue, and is not likely to excite an audience or direct viewers to action.

Responsibilities of Union Health and Safety Committees. Colour, 16 mm. Available from University of Wisconsin, School for Workers, 1327 University Avenue, Madison, Wisconsin 53701.

Responsibilities of Union Health and Safety Committees is a dramatization, filmed in an industrial shop in the Midwest.

See description under *Health Hazard in the Shop*.

The Shop Accident. Colour, 16 mm., 26 minutes. Available from University of Wisconsin, School for Workers, 1327 University Avenue, Madison, Wisconsin 53701.

See description under *Health Hazard in the Shop*.

Song of the Canary (1979, Manteca Films). Directed by Josh Hanig and Dave Davis. Colour, 16 mm., 58 minutes. Available from P.O. Box 315, Franklin Lakes, N.J. 17417. Rental $65, purchase $650.

Song of the Canary has been used successfully by many union and community groups to raise consciousness about occupational health and the long- and short-range effects of occupational illness. It is a prime example of the new generation of labour-oriented films that are being made, and that we hope will continue to be made.

The film-makers offer a humanist and personal view of chemical workers at California's Oxy-Chem pesticide plant stricken with fertility loss due to occupational chemical exposure, and of the older, longer-range effects of brown lung disease (byssinosis) from cotton dust on textile workers.

The film is emotional and terrifying, and emphasizes the need for cleaning up the industrial environment. The title reminds us of the once-common practice of coal miners to bring canaries into the mines to warn of otherwise undetected gases. The film makes it clear that the workers themselves have become the new "canaries."

Working For Your Life. Directed by Ken Light and Andrea Hricko. Colour, 16 mm., 55 minutes. Available from LHOP, 2521 Channing Way, Berkeley, Ca. 94720. Rental $65, purchase $475.

Working For Your Life, recently released, is a film about working women, their problems, and their struggles to correct workplace hazards. Filmed in over 40 workplaces, the vivid scenes and humanistic portrayal of women as part of the once male-dominated workforce make this film an important contribution to both occupational health materials and the filmed history of labour.

Working For Your Life interviews injured workers, from a woman who has asbestos-related disease to a woman who lost her finger in an industrial accident. Both sterilization of women workers and worker hysteria are discussed through interviews and filmed footage. This film is important because, unlike many of the other available health and safety films, it shows that people are beginning to deal with workplace hazards and points out that organization is one of the best ways to protect one's health.

Working Steel (1977, U.C.L.A. Institute of Industrial Relations). Directed by Ken Light and Charles West. Black and white, 16 mm., 20 minutes. Available from LOHP, 2521 Channing Way, Berkeley, Ca. 94720. Rental $30, purchase $175.

The glowing furnaces and steaming molten metal of America's foundries are the heart and lifeblood of the nation's heavy industry. Such is the vision of *Working Steel*, set in the context of the health and safety hazards within the foundry industry, one of the most hazardous in America.

Working Steel is one of the first of the new generation of occupational health films (released in 1976), and it still remains a film that is visually powerful. It is of interest to industrial workers, but has been shown to general audiences.

Working Steel is a useful tool, short enough to be shown at union meetings or to medical schools and community groups. The film follows the foundry process, discusses the hazards, and interviews injured workers. But the film does not directly lay blame for the treacherous conditions; thus it generally invites long discussion and usually leads viewers to discuss who is responsible for such unhealthful workplaces and what can be done to improve conditions.

Your Job or Your Life. Slide show with tape, 29 minutes. Available from Institute for Labor Education and Research, 853 Broadway, New York, N.Y. 10003.

Your Job or Your Life is a colourful and entertaining slide-tape show containing original cartoons, collages, and photographs discussing the political economy of health and safety. It points out how corporations attempt to force working people into choosing between their jobs and their lives. An excellent learning tool, it provides an introduction to the workers' health and safety issue and points out the connection between workplace and environmental pollution.

FRANCE

Sentenced to Success (1976, C.F.D.T. Union of Atomic Workers) Colour, 16 mm., 55 minutes. In French with English subtitles. Available from Development Education Centre, 121 Avenue Road, Toronto, Ontario, M5R 2G3.

Index